Stan Lee
PRESENTS

the AMAZING SPIDER-MAN

VOL. **3**

AMAZING SPIDER-MAN #44-65 & ANNUAL #4

the AMAZING SPIDER-MAN #64

WRITER: **STAN LEE**
PENCILERS: **JOHN ROMITA &
DON HECK**
INKER: **MIKE ESPOSITO**
LETTERER: **SAM ROSEN**

the AMAZING SPIDER-MAN #65

WRITER: **STAN LEE**
PENCILER: **JOHN ROMITA**
INKER: **JIM MOONEY**
LETTERER: **ART SIMEK**

REPRINT CREDITS

Marvel Essential Design:
John "JG" Roshell of Comicraft
Cover Art:
John Romita Sr.
Front Cover Colors:
Avalon's Ian Hannin
Collection Editor:
Mark D. Beazley
Assistant Editor:
Jennifer Grünwald
Senior Editor, Special Projects:
Jeff Youngquist
Masterworks Editor:
Cory Sedlmeier

Director of Sales:
David Gabriel
Production:
Jerron Quality Color
Book Designer:
Michael Short
Creative Director:
Tom Marvelli
Editor in Chief:
Joe Quesada
Publisher:
Dan Buckley

**Special Thanks To Ralph Macchio
& Tom Brevoort**

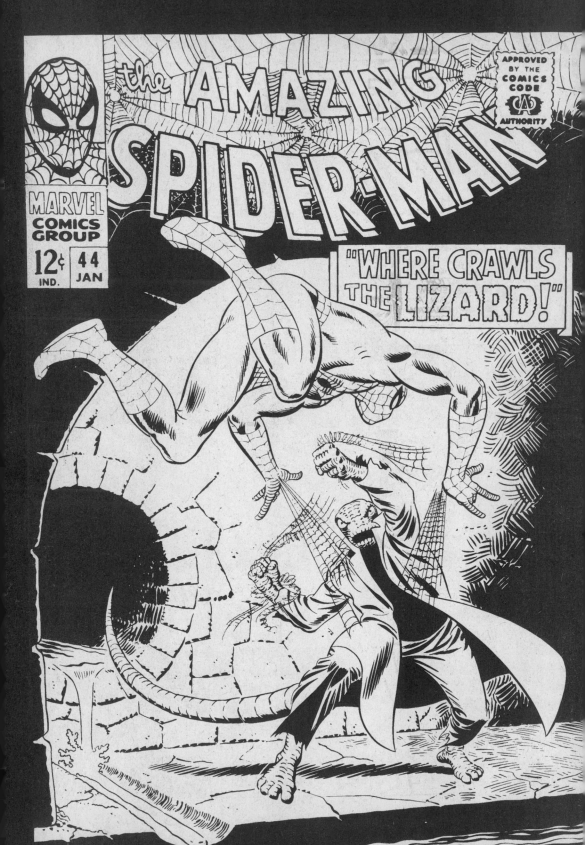

BUT THEN, SECONDS LATER...

IT'S *SUBSIDING* AGAIN... GETTING BACK TO *NORMAL!*

PERHAPS I JUST *IMAGINED* IT... IN THE EXCITEMENT OF WAITING FOR MARTHA AND BILLY!

AND YET... I'VE FELT *STRANGE...* EVER SINCE I HELPED *SPIDER-MAN* CREATE A POTION TO DEFEAT THE *RHINO!*

*JUST LAST ISH! IF YOU FORGOT, SHAME ON YOU! --STERN STAN.

THAT *POTION!* WHY DIDN'T I THINK OF IT *BEFORE?*

THE POTION WAS CREATED OF CERTAIN INGREDIENTS WHICH WERE *ALSO* USED IN THE FORMULA WHICH YEARS AGO TURNED ME INTO... THE *LIZARD!*

CAN IT BE THAT THE SIMPLE ACT OF *HANDLING* THE POTION... OF INHALING ITS *FUMES...* HAS ACTUALLY TRIGGERED THAT DREADFUL REACTION IN MY BODY *AGAIN?*

IF SO... IT MEANS THAT I MIGHT CHANGE BACK TO THE *LIZARD* AT ANY MOMENT... JUST AS *DANGEROUS...* JUST AS *DEADLY...* AS EVER BEFORE!

GOSH! I COULD HAVE *SWORN* I SAW *CURT CONNORS* BEHIND THAT PILLAR!

PETER, DEAR... ARE YOU *SURE* YOU'LL BE ALL RIGHT WITH ME *GONE?* WILL YOU GET TO BED EARLY AT NIGHT... AND EAT PLENTY OF *VEGETABLES?*

SURE, AUNT MAY! DON'T YOU WORRY ABOUT A *THING!* I'LL TAKE MY *VITAMIN PILLS* AND STAY OUT OF DRAFTS AND *EVERYTHING!*

AS FOR *YOU,* YOUNG LADY... REMEMBER.. NO *FOOTBALL* PRACTICE OR *KARATE LESSONS!* AT LEAST NOT FOR THE FIRST FEW DAYS!

OH, PETER! HERE I AM... *DESERTING* YOU... LEAVING YOU ALONE, WITH NO ONE TO LOOK *AFTER* YOU... AND YOU'RE TAKING IT WITHOUT A *WHIMPER!*

YOU'RE THE MOST *WONDERFUL* NEPHEW ANY WOMAN EVER HAD!

HONK!

MEANWHILE, AT A NEARBY TRACK, WE FIND...

GOLLY, MOM... DO YOU THINK *DAD'LL* TAKE ME TO SEE THE *JETS?*

I'M *SURE* HE WILL, BILLY! BUT... I WONDER WHERE HE *IS?* I WAS HOPING HE'D BE *WAITING* FOR US!

MAYBE HE'S *HIDING...* TO SURPRISE US... LIKE HE USED TO DO WHEN I WAS *LITTLE!*

CAN SOMETHING HAVE *HAPPENED* TO HIM?

I DON'T WANT TO WORRY BILLY, BUT CURT IS *NEVER* LATE... UNLESS..

NO! I WON'T EVEN *THINK* OF IT! IT *CAN'T* BE!

CK 5

AND, JUST A FEW FEET AWAY... CONCEALED BEHIND A SHADOWY ARCH...

I *WASN'T* IMAGINING IT! MY.. MY *RIGHT ARM* IS TINGLING... JUST AS IT DID... THE *LAST* TIME!

THAT'S HOW IT ALL *STARTED*--- I THOUGHT I COULD *RE-GROW* MY ARM... LIKE SOME OF THE LOWER ORDER *REPTILES* DO... BY DRINKING A *SERUM* EXTRACTED FROM EXPERIMENTAL *LIZARDS!*

BUT, I DIDN'T *REALIZE* THAT THE SAME SERUM THAT ENABLED ME TO GROW A NEW *ARM,* WOULD ALSO *CHANGE* ME.. INTO A HUMAN *LIZARD!*

*DON'T TAKE *OUR* WORD FOR IT! CHECK WITH ISH #6! --SCRUPULOUS STAN

IN FACT, IF SPIDER-MAN HADN'T SAVED ME BY GIVING ME THAT ANTIDOTE, I'D..OH..NO!!

MY HAND! IT'S TURNED SCALY AND GREEN AGAIN! BUT--THIS TIME...THERE'S NO DOUBT---

SO ALARMED... SO STRICKEN WITH SHOCK IS HE...THAT DR. CURTIS CONNORS MOMENTARILY FORGETS HIS EFFORT TO CONCEAL HIMSELF! HENCE, AT THAT MOMENT...

MOM...LOOK! IT'S HIM! IT'S DAD! OVER THERE! I SEE HIM!

OH, THANK HEAVEN! HE'S ALL RIGHT!

WHERE, BILLY? WHERE IS HE? SHOW ME--!

HE'S RIGHT OVER TH...MOM! HE'S RUNNING AWAY! HE'S DISAPPEARING INTO THE CROWD!

BILLY SAW ME!

I CAN'T FACE THEM LIKE THIS! I'VE GOT TO RUN... GOT TO HIDE! GOT TO GET AWAY..!

SAY! WATCH WHERE YOU'RE GOING!

IF I DON'T GET OUT OF HERE IN TIME... NOBODY WILL BE SAFE!

THAT MAN MUST BE MAD...!

---BULLING HIS WAY THROUGH A CROWD LIKE THAT!

LOOK OUT, MAC! WHAT DO YOU THINK YOU'RE DOING?!!

SOMEBODY STOP HIM! MAYBE HE'S A FUGITIVE... FLEEING THE LAW!

THE FOOLS! THEY DON'T REALIZE I'M TRYING TO SAVE THEIR LIVES! I'M TURNING INTO THE LIZARD FASTER THAN EVER NOW!

I'VE GOT TO REACH THE TRAIN TUNNEL... WHILE THERE'S STILL TIME!

CRASH!

SPIDER-MAN HELPED ME IN THE PAST! IF ONLY I KNEW WHERE TO FIND HIM AGAIN! BUT...I DON'T! NOBODY KNOWS WHERE HE IS...OR WHO HE IS!

THAT MAN... RUNNING INTO THE TUNNEL!

STOP! COME BACK! YOU CAN'T GO THERE! COME BACK!

SOMEBODY CALL THE POLICE!

THE CHANGE IS SPEEDING UP NOW! IT'S GETTING HARDER TO THINK CLEARLY! EVERYTHING GETTING HAZY... SHADOWY... CAN'T REMEMBER--- WHERE I'M RUNNING TO..!

MARTHA! BILLY! WANTED TO SEE THEM... HOLD THEM IN MY ARMS! BUT NOW...IT DOESN'T SEEM TO MATTER ---NOW...NOTHING MATTERS...!

NOTHING EXCEPT ESCAPE! NO ONE MUST FIND ME... NO ONE MUST GET ME! I MUST BE FREE!

WITH THE UNIMAGINABLE *POWER* I NOW POSSESS, I CAN DO *ANYTHING!*

NOTHING CAN STAND IN MY WAY! NOTHING CAN MATCH THE SUPREME POWER OF...THE *LIZARD!*

THROOM!

I'LL NEED A *LAIR* OF MY OWN...AND I'LL *FIND* ONE...BEHIND THIS TUNNEL WALL!

PERFECT! THE IDEAL PLACE FOR THE WORLD'S GREATEST *REPTILE*...A MAZE OF HIDDEN, UNDERGROUND *PIPES!*

IN SUCH AN ATMOSPHERE, WHAT PERFECT *PLANS* I CAN CREATE.. FOR THE DOWNFALL OF THE ENTIRE HUMAN RACE!

AND ESPECIALLY FOR THE DOWNFALL OF MY GREATEST ENEMY... THE MASKED *SPIDER-MAN!*

AND, SPEAKING OF SPIDEY...

REMEMBER, DEAR...IF YOU *NEED* ANYTHING, CALL MY FRIEND, *MRS. WATSON!* DRINK PLENTY OF MILK... DON'T NEGLECT YOUR STUDIES...AND BE SURE TO GET A *HAIRCUT!*

AND *YOU* BE SURE TO HAVE A GREAT TIME, AUNT MAY! *I'LL* BE OKAY, HERE, SO DON'T WORRY ABOUT A *THING!*

DON'T FORGET... THE DOCTOR SAID YOU'RE TO HAVE PLENTY OF *REST!* SO NO *PUSHUPS* FOR THE NEXT TWO WEEKS!

HONESTLY, PETER PARKER... YOU'RE SIMPLY A *CAUTION!*

NOW BE A REAL PUSSYWILLOW TILL I GET BACK!

AUNT MAY...FOR THE ZILLIONTH TIME...YOU MEAN *PUSSYCAT!*

AND DON'T FORGET TO WATER THE PLANTS...AND TURN OFF THE HALL LIGHT WHEN YOU GO TO SLEEP...

OH, DEAR! THE TRAIN IS *MOVING!*

GET LOTS OF *REST,* HEAR?

GO EASY ON THE *WATUSI!*

I'LL WRITE TO YOU EVERY DAY, PETER!

WHEW! I HAD TO KEEP *KIDDING* HER... OR SHE MIGHT HAVE CHANGED HER MIND ABOUT *GOING* AT THE LAST MINUTE!

DOC BROMWELL SAID SHE *HAD* TO HAVE THIS VACATION...BECAUSE SHE'S SO RUN-DOWN!

BUT IF ONLY I COULD CONVINCE HER NOT TO *WORRY* ABOUT ME SO! IF SHE ONLY *KNEW* THAT... *SAY!*

THAT'S *MRS. CONNORS...* THE *DOC'S* WIFE! THEN IT *WAS* HIM I SAW! BUT... SHE'S IN *TEARS!*

DON'T WORRY, BILLY! WE'LL FIND HIM... SOME-HOW...!

I DON'T KNOW WHAT'S *WRONG,* BUT SOMETHING TELLS ME I'D BETTER FIND *OUT!*

MOM...WHAT'LL WE *DO!* WHERE'LL WE GO?

5

SHE DOESN'T *KNOW* PETER PARKER.. BUT SHE MET ME AS *SPIDER-MAN* DURING MY BATTLE WITH THE LIZARD!

AND IT LOOKS TO ME AS THOUGH IT'S TIME FOR MRS. CONNORS TO MEET SPIDEY *AGAIN!*

THAT LADY CAN USE A *FRIEND!*

FINDING THE NEAREST PHONE BOOTH OCCUPIED, OUR HERO MAKES A QUICK CHANGE HIGH ABOVE THE RAFTERS ... AND THEN ...

WELCOME TO THE BIG TOWN, MRS. CONNORS!

LOOK! IT'S *SPIDER-MAN!*

THANK GOODNESS! HE'S THE ONLY ONE I CAN *TURN* TO!

I HAPPENED TO BE SWINGING BY AND RECOGNIZED YOU! YOU LOOK *UPSET*... IS THERE ANYTHING I CAN *DO?*

I DON'T *KNOW!* IT'S MY HUSBAND...CURTIS! HE WAS TO HAVE *MET* US HERE ON OUR ARRIVAL! BUT THERE'S NO *TRACE* OF HIM!

DO YOU *ALWAYS* SWING THROUGH PENN STATION LIKE THIS??

IT DEPENDS, BILLY! SOMETIMES I BUZZ THE *BUS TERMINAL* OR ZERO IN ON THE *AIRPORT!*

BILLY DEAR..GO GET SOME SODA POP WHILE I TALK TO SPIDER-MAN!

AWW, MOM! I WANNA TALK TO HIM..!

PLEASE, DEAR! IT'S IMPORTANT!

HE SURE HAS *GROWN* SINCE LAST TIME!

NOW, SUPPOSE YOU TELL ME WHAT THE *PROBLEM* IS, MRS. CONNORS! HAS IT ANYTHING TO DO WITH... YOUR *HUSBAND?*

I DON'T KNOW HOW TO *SAY* IT! BILLY AND I *SAW* HIM HERE! BUT, WHEN HE SAW *US*... HE TURNED IN PANIC, AND LOST HIMSELF IN THE CROWD!

STRANGE... I THOUGHT *I* HAD SEEN HIM EARLIER, TOO!

BUT, HE *LOVES* YOU... AND BILLY! WHY WOULD HE HAVE *RUN* FROM YOU?

I'VE BEEN ASKING MYSELF THE *SAME* QUESTION... AND I'M AFRAID TO EVEN *THINK* OF THE ANSWER!

FOR *YOU* KNOW...AS WELL AS *I*—...WHAT THE ONLY ANSWER CAN *BE!*

WHAT IF HE'S *CHANGING* AGAIN... BACK TO ... THE *LIZARD??*

YOU MANAGED TO SAVE HIM *ONCE*...BY A *MIRACLE!* BUT, IF IT HAPPENS *AGAIN*...HE'LL BE WISER...MORE CAUTIOUS...MORE DEADLY THAN *EVER!*

I HOPE OUR SUSPICIONS ARE *WRONG!* BUT... WE CAN'T AFFORD TO TAKE ANY CHANCES! WHICH WAY DID HE GO?

RIGHT *THERE!* HE SEEMED TO BE HEADING FOR THAT *TUNNEL!*

THAT'S ALL I WANTED TO KNOW!

"BUT THE MOST FRIGHTENING THING OF ALL WAS THE LIZARD'S INSANE MASTER PLAN...!"

HE INTENDS TO DROP HIS *SERUM* IN THE SWAMP WATER!!

BEFORE THE DAY IS OUT HE'LL CONTROL AN ARMY OF *MILLIONS* OF DEADLY, GIANT *LIZARDS!*

THERE ARE MORE *REPTILES* ON EARTH THAN *HUMANS!*

WHEN MY ARMY STARTS *MULTIPLYING,* MANKIND WON'T HAVE A *CHANCE!* THE *LIZARDS* WILL TAKE OVER THE *WORLD!*

"AND IT MIGHT HAVE *HAPPENED*... IF I HADN'T MANAGED TO FORCE HIM TO SWALLOW THE *ANTIDOTE* BEFORE HE COULD REACH THE SWAMP WATER!"

"THEN HE TURNED BACK TO DR. CONNORS... AND THE NIGHTMARE WAS ENDED FOREVER... OR SO WE *THOUGHT!*"

UH-OH! LOOKS LIKE THERE ISN'T MUCH *DOUBT* ABOUT IT NOW!

ONLY SOMEONE WITH THE *LIZARD'S STRENGTH* COULD HAVE POUNDED A HOLE LIKE *THIS* THROUGH A CEMENT *WALL!*

THERE ARE A *HUNDRED* OPENINGS AHEAD... NO WAY TO TRAIL HIM NOW!

I'LL RETURN TO MRS. CONNORS... BUT WHAT CAN I *TELL* HER?

A LITTLE WHITE LIE CAN'T DO ANY HARM AT THIS POINT!

I COULDN'T FIND A *THING!* WHY DON'T YOU JUST WAIT AT THE DOC'S *LAB?* MAYBE HE'LL CALL!

IF YOU *THINK* SO--!

MAYBE DAD'S WAITING FOR US *THERE!*

THAT'S *RIGHT,* BILLY! THERE'S ALWAYS A *CHANCE!*

IN THE MEANTIME, I'LL KEEP SEARCHING!

I'LL CONTACT YOU AS SOON AS I *LEARN* ANYTHING!

I'VE GOT TO *CATCH* HIM BEFORE THE CITY IS THROWN INTO A *PANIC.*

..OR BEFORE *HE*...OR SOMEONE *ELSE*...IS HURT..OR *WORSE!*

IT LOOKS AS THOUGH MY ONLY CHANCE TO RAISE THE *MONEY* I NEED IS AT *SPIDEY'S* EXPENSE! WHAT A *DEAL!*

SILVER SPOON

MIGHT AS WELL GET OUT OF THE RAIN WHILE I FIGURE MY NEXT MOVE!

OH..THERE'S *GWEN*...WITH *HARRY* AND *FLASH!*

HI, PETE! DIDN'T SEE YOU IN *CLASS* THIS MORNING!

I, EH, HAD SOME PER- SONAL THINGS TO TAKE CARE OF, HARRY!

SURE!..LIKE NOT GOIN' OUT IN THE *RAIN* BECAUSE LITTLE PUNY PARKER MIGHT MELT AWAY!

COME *OFF* IT, FLASH! YOU'RE AS FUNNY AS A *TOOTHACHE!*

IF YOU'D LIKE A *FILL-IN* ON WHAT YOU MISSED IN THE LAB TODAY, I'LL BE GLAD TO *REVIEW* IT WITH YOU, PETE!

THAT'LL BE *SWELL*, GWEN! I'D REALLY *APPRECIATE* IT!

SINCE WHEN DOES *HE* NEED HELP? I THOUGHT THAT EGGHEAD KNEW *EVERY-THING!*

I COULD KNOW *NOTHING* AND STILL BE SMARTER THAN *YOU*, BIG MOUTH!

LUCKY FOR *YOU*, I'VE MORE IMPORTANT THINGS ON MY MIND THAN MOPPING UP THE FLOOR WITH YOU!

FLASH REPORTS FOR HIS *DRAFT PHYSICAL* LATER TODAY, PETE!

HEY! DOESN'T THE BIG BRASS KNOW WE NEED YOU ON OUR *FOOT- BALL TEAM*, THOMPSON?

HAS ANYONE TOLD FLASH THE *NEWS*..?

WHAT NEWS?

THEY DON'T HAVE *CHEER-LEADERS* FOR YOU IN THE ARMY!

HEY, PARKER...MAYBE WE WON'T MISS THOMP-SON *AFTER ALL!* WE'LL JUST GET *YOU* TO TAKE HIS PLACE ON THE TEAM!

YEAH! THEY CAN ALWAYS USE A FEW *LAUGHS* DURING SCRIMMAGE!

GENTLEMEN.. WE'RE *TRYING* TO STUDY!

THAT'S REAL *EMOTIONAL!*

NOW THAT *FLASH* IS BEING DRAFTED, THEY OUGHTTA GRAB *WHITEY MULLINS* ALSO!

WHAT CHANCE'LL WE HAVE AGAINST *HIM* WHEN WE PLAY *METRO U.*?

UNLESS *PARKER* IS OUR NEW SECRET WEAPON!

AWW.. I WAS SAVING IT FOR A *SURPRISE!*

METRO'S STAR

WHITEY MULLINS

WOW! LOOK AT *THAT!*

WHERE'D *SHE* COME FROM?

I DUNNO... BUT HOW'D THEY EVER LET HER GET *AWAY?*

SHE MUST BE SOMEONE *NEW!* I'VE NEVER *SEEN* HER HERE BEFORE!

HI, MARY JANE!

PETE *KNOWS* HER?!!

THREE LIVING, BREATHING *MALES* TO ONLY ONE *GAL*, EH?

WHERE HAS THIS PLACE *BEEN* ALL MY LIFE?

SHE *WALKS!* SHE *TALKS!* AND I CAN TELL SHE'S BEEN *BUSTIN'* TO MEET OL' *FLASH!*

LET ME INTRODUCE YOU TO THE CROWD, M.J...!

IMAGINE SLY PETE KEEPING HER ALL TO *HIMSELF* TILL NOW!

CRASSHH!

ALL I NEED DO IS BREAK THROUGH THIS WINDOW...INTO THE WHOLESALE *JEWELRY* SHOWROOM INSIDE!

WITH LUCK, *SPIDER-MAN* HIMSELF WILL BE *ACCUSED* OF THIS ROBBERY...

IN WHICH CASE HE'LL BE TOO BUSY DODGING THE *LAW* TO BE ABLE TO GET IN MY WAY AGAIN!

OR ELSE HE'LL LEARN WHAT I'VE DONE AND COME *AFTER* ME, FAST...

GIVING ME A CHANCE TO *FINISH* HIM, ONCE AND FOR ALL!

EITHER WAY... THE *LIZARD* CAN'T LOSE!

SECONDS LATER...

LOOK, SAM! ON THAT BUILDING ABOVE...!

ONLY *SPIDER-MAN* CAN CLIMB A WALL LIKE THAT!

WE'D BETTER SEE WHAT THE SCORE IS!

THUS, IT'S ONLY A MATTER OF MINUTES BEFORE THE OFFICERS FIND...

THE PLACE WAS *CLEANED OUT!* MUST BE A *FORTUNE* IN GEMS MISSING!

GUESS THERE'S NOT MUCH DOUBT *WHO* DID IT!

YOU'D BETTER WAIT HERE WHILE I CONTACT HEADQUARTERS!

THEN, JUST AS DAWN IS BREAKING...

WHAT'S THAT?!! YOU PUT OUT A LATE EXTRA WHILE I WAS ASLEEP?

*SPIDER-MAN...*ACCUSED OF STEALING *GEMS?*

BUT, WHAT IF IT'S A *PHONY?...* LIKE ALL THOSE *OTHER* STORIES WE RAN! IF YOU MAKE ME A *LAUGHING STOCK* AGAIN...!!!

OF *COURSE* I WANT TO SEE HIM IN *JAIL!* BUT HE ALWAYS COMES OUT *LILY WHITE,* AND WE LOOK LIKE *FOOLS!*

HOLD EVERYTHING, BLAST IT! I'LL BE RIGHT THERE!

BUT BEFORE JOLLY JONAH CAN EVEN COMB HIS MOUSTACHE, THE SPECIAL EDITION IS ON THE STREETS

AND, WITHIN A VERY FEW MINUTES, *PETER PARKER* HIMSELF WILL BE REACTING ABOUT AS YOU'D EXPECT...

DAILY BUGLE

SPIDER-MAN ACCUSED IN DARING GEM THEFT!

SO LET'S REJOIN HIM AND SEE...

BOY! AN EVENING OUT WITH *MARY JANE* IS LIKE A DOZEN *HOLIDAYS* ROLLED INTO ONE! SHE'S THE MOST... *HEY!* WHAT'S *THIS?!!*

I WAS NOWHERE *NEAR* THERE LAST NIGHT!

THE *LIZARD!* IT HAD TO BE *HIM!*

I'D BETTER CALL *MRS. CONNORS* RIGHT AWAY!

YOU MEAN YOU DIDN'T HEAR A *THING?* HE DIDN'T CONTACT YOU AT *ALL?*

NO! AND, I JUST SAW THE MORNING PAPER! DO YOU THINK..??

DON'T WORRY, MRS. CONNORS! *I'LL* TAKE CARE OF IT!

NO, DON'T WORRY, MRS. CONNORS! LET *ME* WORRY! IT SEEMS TO BE WHAT I DO *BEST!*

THE LIZARD MUST HAVE *INTENDED* TO FRAME ME! BUT, WHAT DO I *DO* ABOUT IT? I'M STYMIED IF I CAN'T *FIND* HIM!

BUT I JUST *CAN'T* MISS ANOTHER DAY OF *CLASS!*

AND SO...

YOUNG MAN, IF YOU WON'T ANSWER TO *PARKER*, WHAT NAME WOULD YOU *LIKE* ME TO CALL YOU?

HE NEVER APPEARS IN *DAYLIGHT!* I'LL HAVE TO WAIT TILL *NIGHTFALL!*

IF I COULD JUST *FORGET* ABOUT HIM TILL THEN!

PETE! FOR GOODNESS SAKE... *WAKE UP!*

AND SO IT GOES FOR THE REST OF THE MORNING, UNTIL...

SAY, PETE..!

I TELL YOU SPIDEY'S *INNOCENT!* WHY WOULD *HE* WANNA STEAL ANY CRUMMY JEWELS?

GOOD OL' *FLASH*.. DEFENDING ME, AS USUAL! IF HE ONLY *KNEW..!*

THAT *MARY JANE* MUST BE *SOMETHING!* YOU WERE DAY-DREAMING ABOUT HER IN CLASS ALL MORNING!

AND WHO CAN *BLAME* YOU?

THEN, WHILE WAITING FOR *NIGHT* TO FALL...

IT'S NO USE! I CAN'T EVEN CONCENTRATE ON PAINTING MY CYCLE!

I'VE GOT TO CLEAR MYSELF WITH THE *LAW*... FIND THE *LIZARD*... AND RAISE SOME *MONEY* FOR AUNT *MAY!* THAT'S *ALL!*

BUT FINALLY, AS A SOFT BLANKET OF *DARKNESS* DESCENDS UPON THE CITY BELOW...

I'LL KEEP SEARCHING IF IT TAKES *ALL* NIGHT!

IF HE'S OUT TO *SHOW* HIMSELF SOONER OR LATER! AND I'M GONNA *BE* THERE WHEN HE *DOES!*

THEN, TRUE TO HIS WORD... SHORTLY AFTER MIDNIGHT...

IT'S *HIM!* AND HE DOESN'T *SEE* ME YET!

WITH LUCK, I'LL HAVE TIME TO SET UP MY *AUTOMATIC CAMERA* BEFORE I *TACKLE* HIM!

13.

THERE! IT'S ALL IN PLACE... WITH MY **WIDEST-ANGLE** LENS!

SO, THIS IS **IT!**

OKAY, LIZ... THIS IS THE **END OF THE LINE !!**

SPIDER-MAN! I **HOPED** YOU'D SHOW UP!

ONCE I PUT **YOU** OUT OF THE WAY, **NOTHING** CAN HALT MY MASTER PLAN FOR TAKING OVER THE **WORLD** WITH AN INVINCIBLE ARMY OF SUPER-STRONG, GIANT **LIZARDS!**

YOU BEAT ME ONCE BEFORE... BY **TRICKERY**---

BUT I'M **FAR WISER** NOW!

JUST AS I **FEARED!** HE'S LOST THE LAST VESTIGE OF **DR. CONNORS'** IDENTITY! HE'S TOTALLY **EVIL** NOW!

BUT I MANAGED TO TURN HIM BACK TO HIS NORMAL SELF ONCE BEFORE!! I'VE **GOT** TO FIND A WAY TO DO IT **AGAIN!**

AND IT MUST BE DONE WITHOUT **HARMING** HIM!

FOR WHATEVER HAPPENS TO THE **LIZARD** WILL ALSO HAPPEN TO **DR. CONNORS!**

I MIGHT AS WELL TRY A DIRECT, FRONTAL **ATTACK...!**

YOU'LL **NEVER** ESCAPE ME NOW!

ESCAPE YOU?

YOU'VE GOT THAT **BACKWARDS**, MISTER!

I'VE BEEN TRYING TO **FIND** YOU ALL NIGHT!

UNHHH! IT'S LIKE HITTING A **STONE WALL!**

BAH! YOU CAN'T HURT **ME!**

HE'S **RIGHT!** I FEEL LIKE I **FRACTURED** EVERY KNUCKLE!

BUT, I **CAN'T** GIVE UP **NOW!**

COME DOWN! LET'S GET IT **OVER** WITH!

RAKK!

14

THAT'S JUST WHAT I HAD IN MIND!

I DID IT! I GOT HIM OFF-BALANCE!

NOW, IF I CAN JUST KEEP HIM THAT WAY....

IF I CAN GRAB HIS TAIL...AND USE IT AS A WEAPON AGAINST HIM--!

THWOP!

LIZARD...LISTEN TO ME...YOU'VE GOT TO LISTEN!

I DON'T WANT TO HURT YOU...I WANT TO HELP YOU! YOU DON'T REALLY KNOW WHAT YOU'RE DOING!

YOU'RE NOT THE LIZARD! YOU'RE A SCIENTIST! YOUR NAME IS CURTIS CONNORS! HEAR? CONNORS! DOESN'T THAT NAME MEAN ANYTHING TO YOU? CAN'T YOU REMEMBER YOUR WIFE...YOUR SON?

YOU DON'T WANT TO HURT THEM, DO YOU? I KNOW YOU DON'T!

FTOK!

YOU FOOL! YOU THINK YOU CAN SAVE YOURSELF BY MAKING UP FAIRY TALES?!!

I CARE FOR NOBODY!! THE LIZARD HAS ONLY ONE GOAL...TO DESTROY THE ENTIRE HUMAN RACE!

IT'S NO USE! HE'S TOO FAR GONE!...CAN'T REASON WITH HIM!

:UHHH!: HIS TAIL! TOO POWERFUL! CAN'T HOLD IT BACK...:AGHH!:

ALMOST KNOCKED THE WIND OUT OF ME! I'LL PLAY POSSUM---PRETEND TO BE OUT! THEN, WHEN HE REACHES TOWARDS ME, I'LL GRAB HIM AGAIN!

I'VE WON! I'VE DEFEATED SPIDER-MAN AT LAST!

BY THE TIME HE COMES TO, I'LL BE SAFELY GONE! AND THE POLICE WILL PROBABLY HAVE FOUND HIM BY THEN!

IT DIDN'T WORK! THINKING HE'S BEATEN ME COMPLETELY, HE'S WILLING TO LEAVE ME FOR THE POLICE!

I MEAN NOTHING TO HIM PERSONALLY! HE FEELS SUPERIOR TO ALL HUMAN BEINGS!

BUT I DON'T DARE LET HIM GET AWAY! I'VE GOT TO GO AFTER HIM AGAIN!

I'LL FOLLOW THESE UNDERGROUND TUNNELS TILL I REACH THE EDGE OF TOWN! THEN..NO ONE WILL EVER BE ABLE TO FIND ME!

15.

THWIZZT!

He *SLICED* THROUGH MY WEBBING--- WITH ONE SWEEP OF HIS *TAIL!*

WHISST!

BUT IT TAKES MORE THAN *THAT* TO MAKE THIS A *SPIDEYLESS* WORLD..!

...SO LONG AS I CAN SHOOT A *WEB MATTRESS* OUT BENEATH ME IN TIME TO BREAK MY *FALL!*

FTUMM!

=UHH!= THE WEBBING *SAVED* ME...BUT I STILL HIT TOO *HARD!*

DIDN'T HAVE TIME TO TWIST MY BODY AROUND---TO BREAK THE FALL...!

IT'S *SPIDER-MAN!*

HOW'D HE EVER GET *UP* FROM A FALL LIKE *THAT?*

STAY WHERE YOU *ARE!* LET ME SEE THAT *ARM*...I'M A DOCTOR!

MY ARM...CAN'T *MOVE* IT! IT'S HURT... HURT REAL *BAD*..!

CAN'T GO DOWN THERE *NOW!* TOO MANY *PEOPLE* AROUND!

BUT, AT LEAST I PUT HIM *OUT OF ACTION!* HAH! HE'LL NEVER BE ABLE TO STOP ME *NOW!*

AND THEN, AS THE MURDEROUS, SUPER-POWERED MENACE SLITHERS AWAY INTO THE NIGHT...

YOU'RE MIGHTY *LUCKY!* IT'S ONLY A BAD *SPRAIN*...NO BONES BROKEN!

BUT YOU MUSTN'T *USE* IT TILL THE SWELLING GOES DOWN! I'LL *TAPE* IT SECURELY FOR YOU!

THEN I'LL TAKE YOU TO MY *OFFICE* WHERE I CAN GIVE YOU A *COMPLETE* PHYSICAL!

OH NO! TOO MUCH CHANCE OF A SMART MEDIC FIGUR- ING OUT MY *IDENTITY!*

I'LL HELP YOU *UP* NOW..!

18

I'M MUCH OBLIGED, DOC..!

BUT I CAN STILL MAKE IT ON MY OWN!

WAIT! THE POLICE WILL BE HERE SOON!

THEY'LL HAVE QUESTIONS..!

I'VE GOT TO MAKE SURE MRS. CONNORS IS OKAY!

CAN'T EVEN STOP FOR MY CAMERA NOW!

YOU ANSWER 'EM! I DON'T MIND!

SPIDER-MAN! YOUR ARM! DID.. DID YOU MEET--??

CAN'T KEEP IT FROM HER ANY LONGER!

IT'S HIM! NO DOUBT OF IT! HE'S THE LIZARD ONCE MORE!

BUT THERE'S STILL HOPE! FAR AS I KNOW, HE'S COMMITTED NO CRIME YET!

THERE MUST BE SOME WAY TO CHANGE HIM BACK TO NORMAL---

--AND I'LL NEVER REST UNTIL I FIND IT!

TRY TO HAVE FAITH IN ME, MRS. CONNORS! I WON'T FAIL YOU!

BUT HE'S TOO POWERFUL--- TOO MERCILESS! HE'LL NEVER BE BEATEN AGAIN...!

SHE'S TAKING IT AWFULLY HARD!

THERE WAS NOTHING I COULD SAY TO RE-ASSURE HER!

MIGHT AS WELL RETURN HOME... CAN'T BEAR TO SEE A WOMAN CRY...!

NEVER REALIZED HOW TOUGH IT IS TO DO THE SIMPLEST THINGS WITH ONLY ONE ARM!

I THOUGHT I'D NEVER GET MY CLOTHES ON!

GLAD THERE'S NO MOON TONIGHT... WOULDN'T WANT ANYONE TO GET A GOOD LOOK AT ME LIKE THIS!

FINALLY, THIRTY MINUTES LATER...

HOME AT LAST! NOW TO...

UH-OH! THE PHONE!

RRRING!

WHO CAN IT BE?

OH! AUNT MAY--!

IN THE EXCITEMENT I NEARLY FORGOT ABOUT HER!

YES, I REMEM-BER YOU SAID YOU'D CALL! HOW WAS YOUR TRIP? DO YOU FEEL OKAY?

IF ONLY MY ARM WOULD STOP ACHING!

19.

IT WAS A *LOVELY* TRIP, DEAR... AND EVERYTHING IS JUST *FINE!*

BUT YOUR VOICE SOUNDS SO *WEAK!* IS ANYTHING *WRONG?* ARE YOU GETTING ENOUGH *SLEEP?*

SURE! I'VE NEVER BEEN *BETTER!* WE MUST HAVE A BAD *CONNECTION!*

NOW ENJOY EVERY *MINUTE* OF IT, HEAR? THINGS ARE *GREAT* BACK HOME --- SO RELAX AND HAVE A GOOD *REST!*

I'LL TALK TO YOU *AGAIN* REAL SOON! SLEEP WELL NOW.. GOOD NIGHT, AUNT MAY!

CAN'T LET HER *WORRY* ABOUT ME.. NO MATTER *WHAT!*

IT'S LUCKY I GOT THROUGH *THAT* WITH... WHA? THE *PHONE* AGAIN!

I'VE *GOT* TO GET SOME REST! I JUS' WON'T *ANSWER* IT!

NO---IT MIGHT BE *IMPORTANT!*

R-R-RING!

YOU'RE IN *LUCK*, LOVER BOY! THIS IS M.J.! I'VE GOT AN *INVITE* FOR YOU!

I'M DANCING A *SOLO* AT PERFORMER'S SCHOOL TOMORROW NIGHT-- AND I CAN GET YOU A *TICKET* IF YOU PLAY YOUR CARDS RIGHT!

A TICKET-- TO -MORROW NIGHT-- TO SEE YOU DANCE--?

HOLD ON, PETEY-O! TRY TO *COOL IT*, DAD! YOUR *ENTHUSIASM* IS OVERWHELMING!

I KNOW YOU'RE *THERE*, TIGER... I CAN STILL HEAR *BREATHING!*

I'M *SORRY*, MARY JANE! ...I JUST CAN'T *MAKE* IT!

IT'S *YOUR* LOSS, DAD! SEE YOU AROUND! *CLICK!*

NOW THAT THE *PUBLIC* KNOWS *SPIDER-MAN* HAS AN INJURED ARM, I CAN'T LET *ANYONE* SEE ME LIKE THIS!

SHE *HUNG UP!*

WHAT HAPPENS *NEXT?*

I'M AFRAID TO BE *SEEN* WITH MY ARM THIS WAY-- BUT I CAN'T STAY HIDDEN IN THE *HOUSE* FOR DAYS!

MARY JANE MUST BE WRITING ME *OFF* BY NOW --- AND I LEFT MY CAMERA BEHIND, WHERE SOMEONE MAY *FIND* IT!

I'M FURTHER THAN *EVER* FROM THE EXTRA MONEY I NEED FOR *AUNT MAY*... OR FROM HELPING *DOC CONNORS* AND HIS FAMILY!

AND, TO TOP IT ALL OFF, THE *LIZARD* IS STILL AT LARGE... CAPABLE OF *ANYTHING*... WHILE I SIT HERE... *HELPLESS!*

WHAT'S *WRONG* WITH ME? WHY DO THINGS WORK *OUT* THIS WAY?

WHEN WILL I COME TO MY SENSES AND STOP BUCKING *FATE*... AND GIVE UP BEING *SPIDER-MAN* FOREVER?!!

DON'T DESPAIR SPIDEY-FAN--- "THERE'S *MORE* NEXT ISH! IT'S A *BOMB SHELL!*

2

the AMAZING SPIDER-MAN

APPROVED BY THE COMICS CODE AUTHORITY

MARVEL COMICS GROUP

12¢ IND. 45 FEB

ONE OF THE WILDEST OF ALL SPIDEY'S BATTLES!

"SPIDEY SMASHES OUT!"

I WAS *RIGHT!* THAT'S A REAL, OLD-FASHIONED *HI-JACKING* JOB IF EVER I SAW ONE!

THE TRUCK MUST BE CARRYING SOME VALUABLE *FURS* ... OR SOME SUCH!

WELL, HERE'S WHERE I FIND OUT IF THERE'S A *MARKET* FOR ONE-ARMED SPIDER-MEN NOWADAYS!

HEADS UP, GUYS! IT'S *PARTY TIME!*

CHEER UP, FELLAS... IT COULD BE *WORSE!*

AT LEAST I DON'T WEAR HOB-NAIL *BOOTS!*

THONK!

IT'S *SPI...UNHH!*

WOK!

LOOK AT 'IM! HE'S GOT A BUSTED *WING!* WE CAN TAKE 'IM! LET'S...

WPPFFF!

I'LL *GIT* 'IM BEFORE HE CAN TURN AROUND!

SPIDER-MAN! BEHIND YOU... *LOOK OUT!*

BRAK!

YOU DIDN'T *REALLY* THINK I'D *FORGET* ABOUT YOU, LITTLE FELLA?

THAT'S A RELIEF! MY WOUNDED ARM HARDLY SLOWED ME DOWN AT *ALL!*

RRRAD!

BUT THERE'S A BIG *DIFFERENCE* BETWEEN PUTTING TWO CHEAP *HOODS* ON ICE... AND TACKLING THE *LIZARD!*

HEY, SPIDEY... WE COULD *USE* YA IN THE *TEAMSTERS UNION!*

SORRY, PAL! THE WAY THINGS'VE BEEN GOIN' I COULDN'T EVEN AFFORD THE *DUES!*

I'D BETTER *CUT OUT* BEFORE THEY START PLAYING *HEARTS AND FLOWERS!*

2.

BETTER START SEARCHING FOR THE *LIZARD* AGAIN!

AND WITH ONE ARM OUT OF ACTION, IT'S EASIER TO USE A *WEB BRIDGE* THAN TO *SWING* AROUND TOWN!

NOW I KNOW HOW *DAREDEVIL* FEELS WHEN HE SKIPS ALONG THOSE *TELEPHONE WIRES!*

GLAD I REMEMBERED TO PICK UP MY *CAMERA* FROM WHERE I LEFT IT WHEN I *LAST* FOUGHT THE LIZARD!

MEANWHILE, ON THE OTHER SIDE OF TOWN, IN THE LABORATORY APARTMENT OF *DR. CURTIS CONNORS,* A SUDDEN *NOISE* AWAKENS HIS FITFULLY-SLEEPING *WIFE!*

THAT DULL SCRAPING SOUND! LIKE A *WINDOW* BEING FORCED OPEN!

CAN IT BE...*HIM*...AT LAST?

AND...IF IT *IS*...WHAT CAN HE POSSIBLY *WANT?*

THIS IS THE *LABORATORY*...WHERE CONNORS KEEPS ALL HIS *SERUMS* AND *CHEMICALS!**

I'LL FIND WHAT I *NEED*...IN *HERE!*

*WE TOLD YOU LAST ISH THAT THE *LIZARD* IS UNAWARE THAT HE ACTUALLY *IS* DR. CURT CONNORS..REMEMBER? ---STAN.

MY WORST FEARS HAVE COME *TRUE!* HE *IS* THE LIZARD ONCE AGAIN!

I KNOW HE WOULDN'T HARM BILLY..OR ME...BUT WHAT IS HE *LOOKING* FOR?

I PRAY HE ISN'T AFTER THAT SAME, DEADLY *LIZARD FORMULA* AGAIN!!

I'VE GOT TO FIND CONNORS' *NOTES!* THE FORMULA WHICH TRANSFORMED ME INTO A *HUMAN LIZARD* MUST BE HERE *SOMEWHERE!*

ONCE I *FIND* IT, I'LL BE ABLE TO DROP IT INTO *SWAMP WATERS* EVERY-WHERE...WATERS CONTAINING COUNTLESS *MILLIONS* OF CRAWLING REPTILES!

IN JUST A MATTER OF *HOURS,* I'LL HAVE A LIZARD *ARMY,* MIGHTY ENOUGH TO CONQUER ALL OF *MANKIND!*

BUT THEN, MOMENTS LATER...

IT'S *NO USE!* I CAN'T *UNDERSTAND* ANY OF THIS STUPID, SCIENTIFIC *GIBBERISH!*

THE PAGES CONTAIN NOTHING BUT CHEMICAL SYMBOLS... *NUMBERS...* EQUATIONS!! WHAT GOOD IS THAT TO *ME?!!*

I'LL FIND *ANOTHER* WAY! I'LL DO IT *WITHOUT* HIS NOTES! I'VE GOT THE *STRENGTH*---THE *POWER*..TO ACCOMPLISH *ANYTHING!*

THOP!

...ALL I HAVE TO DO IS *FIND* CONNORS, HIMSELF!

I'LL *FORCE* HIM TO GIVE ME THE FORMULA.. BEFORE I *DESTROY* HIM!

WHILE, BACK AT THE MOONLIT ROOM..

MOM! WHAT WAS THAT *NOISE?* SOMETHING WOKE ME UP!

IT WAS *NOTHING,* BILLY DEAR! THE, EH... THE *WIND* BLEW SOME OF YOUR FATHER'S *BEAKERS* OVER!

BUT I CLOSED THE WINDOWS... YOU'LL BE ABLE TO GO BACK TO *SLEEP* AGAIN!

I FEEL SO *ALONE*... SO *HELPLESS!* MY OWN DEAR, WONDERFUL HUSBAND... TRANSFORMED INTO A LIVING *MONSTER!*

WHOM CAN I *TURN* TO? WHAT CAN I *DO?* HOW CAN I PROTECT *BILLY* FROM KNOWING THE *TRUTH?*

IF ONLY I KNEW WHERE TO FIND *SPIDER-MAN!*

MOM..DID YOU..EVER FEEL *SCARED*... WITHOUT KNOWING *WHY..??*

4.

Panel 1: THE NEXT MORNING, AT THE OFFICE OF THE *DAILY BUGLE*, WE FIND---

THINGS ARE PRETTY *SLOW* RIGHT NOW...SO THIS IS MY CHANCE TO ASSUME THE IDENTITY OF *PATCH*, THE UNDERWORLD INFORMER, AND KEEP MY EYE ON *PETER PARKER!*

I'VE *GOT* TO LEARN HOW HE MANAGES TO GET SO MANY EXCLUSIVE PHOTOS OF *SPIDER-MAN!*

FOSWELL!

WHERE IN BLUE BLAZES DO YOU THINK *YOU'RE* GOING?

I'M NOT RUNNIN' A BLASTED *TRAVEL AGENCY* AROUND HERE!

Panel 2: I JUST THOUGHT I'D MOSEY AROUND TOWN, MR. JAMESON, AND SEE IF I COULD PICK UP SOME *LEADS* ON A NEW STORY!

FORGET IT, MISTER! THE *LIZARD* WAS SIGHTED LAST NIGHT! SEE WHAT YOU CAN DIG UP ABOUT *HIM!*

WELL, THAT TAKES CARE OF *THAT!* I'LL HAVE TO PUT OFF TAILING PARKER TILL SOME *OTHER* TIME!

DON'T JUST *STAND* THERE! GET *GOING!*

Panel 3: WHAT'S WITH *YOU* TWO, AGAIN?? HOW MANY TIMES DO I HAVETA *TELL* YOU TO MAKE YOUR *BLAMED WEDDING PLANS* ON YOUR *OWN* TIME??

SORRY, J.J....BUT IT WAS *BETTY'S* COFFEE *BREAK,* SO WE THOUGHT...

I'LL DO THE *THINKING* HERE! DOESN'T *ANYONE* DO A FULL DAY'S *WORK* ANY MORE?

BUT IT'S *NED'S* COFFEE BREAK, ALSO!

Panel 4: THAT *SINKS* IT! THE WHOLE *WORLD* IS AGAINST ME!

I WORK MY *FINGERS* TO THE BONE, KEEPING THIS NEWSPAPER TOGETHER... JUST TO PROVIDE *JOBS* FOR EVERY-ONE...AND *THAT'S* THE THANKS I GET FOR IT!

IT'S LIKE I ALWAYS *SAY*... EVERYONE TAKES *ADVANTAGE* OF ME BECAUSE I'M TOO *SOFT-HEARTED!*

THE OLD *HYPOCRITE!* HE MEANS *SOFT-HEADED!*

HUSH, DAR-LING! WE CAN'T AFFORD TO BE FIRED *NOW*--BEFORE OUR *WEDDING!*

NOW, BACK TO OUR LIST... WE'LL HAVE TO INVITE *PETER PARKER...*

Panel 5: BUT AT THIS PARTICULAR TIME, MISTER PARKER HAS *OTHER,* LESS ROMANTIC MATTERS TO CONCERN HIM---

I'VE PROVEN THAT I *CAN* HANDLE MYSELF IN A FIGHT...EVEN WITH *ONE* ARM...BUT NOW I'VE *ANOTHER* PROBLEM..

EVERYONE *KNOWS* THAT *SPIDER-MAN* HAS AN INJURED LEFT ARM...

SO WHAT'LL HAPPEN WHEN *PETER PARKER* IS SEEN AROUND TOWN *ALSO* SPORTING HIS WING IN A SLING?

MAYBE I CAN *FAKE* IT, BY KEEPING MY HAND IN MY *POCK...OWW!* NO..IT'S TOO *PAINFUL!*

Panel 6: THE *HECK* WITH IT! A FELLA HAS TO TAKE *SOME* CHANCES! I'LL JUST *BLUFF* MY WAY THROUGH!

WHY SHOULD ANYONE TRY TO CONNECT *ME* WITH SPIDEY? I COULD HAVE HURT *MY* ARM ON MY *CYCLE!*

THAT'S *IT!* THAT'S THE EXCUSE I'LL USE!

ANY-THING'S BETTER THAN HIDING INDOORS LIKE A *COWARD!*

Panel 7: I'LL HAVE TO GRAB A *BUS* THIS MORNING! CAN'T USE MY WHEELS WITH ONLY ONE HAND!

BOY, MARY JANE WILL *FLIP* WHEN SHE SEES HOW *ZINGY* IT LOOKS SINCE I PAINTED IT THAT ROLLICKIN' *RED!*

Panel 8: LATER, AT THE CAMPUS OF GOOD OL' E.S.U....

WILLYA LOOK AT *THAT,* HARRY! IT'S *PUNY PARKER,* WITH HIS ARM IN A SLING!

JUST MY LUCK! THE FIRST JOKER I RUN INTO HAS TO BE *FLASH THOMPSON!* OH WELL...

WHATCHA TRYIN' TO *DO,* USELESS...? MAKE US THINK YOU'RE *SPIDER-MAN?*

IF HE *IS,* HE'S SURE DOING IT THE *HARD WAY!*

Panel 9: *VER-RY FUNNY,* GROUP! ALMOST AS FUNNY AS *SPRAIN-ING* YOUR ARM WHILE DRIVING A *CYCLE!*

AWW, DON'T BE *ANGRY,* PETE! I *FIGURED* THAT MUST BE WHAT HAPPENED!

THAT'S WHAT YOU *GET* FOR RIDING THAT THING, SON! A CHARACTER LIKE *YOU* BELONGS ON A *TRICYCLE!*

WHEW! IT WENT EASIER THAN I EXPECTED! I SHOULD HAVE *KNOWN* THEY'D NEVER LINK ME WITH *SPIDEY!*

SEE YA AROUND, GUYS! I'M GONNA GRAB A CUP OF JAVA WITH GWEN!

SPEAKING OF GWEN, PETE.. SHE'S THROWING A PARTY FOR FLASH WHEN HE GETS HIS INDUCTION NOTICE! SHE ASKED ME TO INVITE YOU!

SURE, I'LL BE GLAD TO COME! FLASH ISN'T REALLY AS BAD AS HE SOUNDS!

BUT, TELL ME SOMETHING, HARRY..

HOW COME GWEN DIDN'T ASK ME HERSELF?

LET'S FACE IT, SON... YOU HAVEN'T BEEN AROUND THAT MUCH SINCE MARY JANE MADE THE SCENE!

OH...I--I GUESS YOU'RE RIGHT!

BUT IT'S NOT JUST MARY JANE'S FAULT...SENDING MY AUNT MAY AWAY FOR A VACATION TOOK ALL THE MONEY I HAD...AND I'VE BEEN KEEPING KIND'A BUSY TRYING TO SELL JAMESON SOME NEW PIX!

MEANING TO TALK TO YOU ABOUT THAT, PETE!

Y'KNOW MY DAD'S A CHEMIST, AND HE CAN USE A BRAINY SCIENCE MAJOR AS A PART-TIME HELPER!

THAT'S DARN NICE OF YOU, HARRY! I'LL REALLY THINK ABOUT IT!

NO RUSH, FELLA! WHENEVER YOU'RE READY, SAY THE WORD!

I'D SURE LIKE TO TAKE HARRY'S DAD UP ON THAT... BUT I'VE TOO MANY THINGS TO TAKE CARE OF FIRST!

I'LL BET I DON'T SEE MARY JANE NEARLY AS MUCH AS GWEN THINKS I DO!

IT'S FUNNY THE WAY I KEEP THINKING OF GWEN, EVEN THOUGH I'VE NEVER REALLY DATED HER! MARY JANE ALWAYS SEEMS TO POP UP BETWEEN US!

MEANWHILE, AT A QUIET SEASHORE RESORT, WE FIND THE OTHER FEMALE IN PETER PARKER'S LIFE, RECUPERATING FROM HER RECENT ILLNESS...

YOU'RE FROM NEW YORK CITY, AREN'T YOU, MRS. PARKER?

IT MUST BE TERRIBLE LIVING THERE WITH CREATURES LIKE THE LIZARD STILL AT LARGE!

OH DEAR! MY NEPHEW, PETER, IS THERE RIGHT NOW. HE'S A FRESHMAN AT E.S.U.!

DAILY BUGLE
LIZARD MENACES NEW YORK

BUT I DON'T HAVE TO WORRY ABOUT HIM! HE'S SUCH A QUIET, STUDIOUS LAD!

THANK HEAVEN HE'S NOT LIKE THOSE OTHER WILD TEEN-AGERS ONE IS ALWAYS READING ABOUT!

HE'S PROBABLY AT HOME RIGHT NOW, CURLED UP WITH A GOOD BOOK, AND A GLASS OF WARM MILK!

NO WONDER YOU'RE SO PROUD OF HIM, MY DEAR!

BUT, SOONER OR LATER, A FELLOW FINISHES HIS GOOD BOOK... AND A GLASS OF WARM MILK CAN'T LAST FOREVER! AND THEN, WITH A DEADLY SUPER-VILLAIN ON THE LOOSE, SOONER OR LATER IT GETS TO BE WEB-SWINGING TIME ONCE MORE...

IT'S LIKE LOOKING FOR A NEEDLE IN A HAYSTACK, BUT I CAN'T STOP SEARCHING!

SO LONG AS THE LIZARD IS STILL FREE, EVERY MAN, WOMAN AND CHILD IS IN DANGER!

6.

BUT THE *LIZARD* HAS NO SUCH SCRUPLES...AS HE STRIKES BACK WITH EVERY IOTA OF *POWER* HE POSSESSES...

YOUR SKIN IS NOTHING BUT WEAK, HUMAN *FLESH*... WHAT CHANCE CAN YOU HAVE AGAINST MY POUNDING *REPTILE* FISTS?!!

THOP!

EVERYTHING SPINNING 'ROUND.. CAN'T BREAK *FREE* IN TIME...!

THE *AMAZING SPIDER-MAN!* HAH!

TO ME, YOUR POWER IS A *JOKE!*

HAVE TO STAY *LIMP*...PREPARE FOR *IMPACT!*

MUSTN'T LAND ON WEAK *ARM*...!

BUT *YOU'LL* BE IN NO CONDITION TO *LAUGH!*

BTAM!

UNHHHH!

AT LEAST...I MANAGED TO *RELAX*.. LETTING MY *MUSCLES* CUSHION MOST OF THE SHOCK!

SO! YOU STILL *LIVE!*

BAH! NO NEED TO WASTE ANY MORE OF *MY* STRENGTH ON YOU!

NOT WHEN MY *COUNTLESS* POWERFUL *ALLIES* CAN DO THE JOB *FOR* ME!

THRAKK!

WHA... WHAT'S HE DOING... *NOW??*

10

THE CROC IS CLOSEST TO ME... I CAN TAKE CARE OF *HIM* BY WEBBING HIS JAWS SHUT!

BUT THERE'S NOT ENOUGH WEB FLUID IN THE *WORLD* TO STOP THEM *ALL!*

PHITTT

FASTER! ATTACK HIM *FASTER!*

OVERWHELM HIM BY SHEER FORCE OF *NUMBERS!* SPIDER-MAN MUST *DIE!*

BUT, SINCE OUR PRIME PURPOSE IS *ENTERTAINMENT*, LET'S TURN TO *PLEASANTER* MATTERS FOR JUST A BRIEF MOMENT OR TWO... AS WE VISIT THE HOME OF *MRS. ANNA WATSON*...

I'M GOING TO THE *FRENZY-VILLE À GO-GO*, AUNT ANNA! IF THE *BEATLES* CALL, TELL THEM I WON'T BE LONG!

OH! DO YOU *KNOW* THE *BEATLES*, DEAR?

OF *COURSE* NOT! BUT I BELIEVE IN *POSITIVE THINKING!*

BY THE WAY, I'M BRINGING A POT OF *VEGETABLE SOUP* OVER TO PETER PARKER!

WOULD YOU LIKE TO *WALK* ME THERE, MARY JANE?

SURE THING! I'M HEADED IN THAT DIRECTION, ANYWAY!

I'M *SO* GLAD YOU AND PETER ARE FRIENDS! HE'S THE *NICEST* BOY... AND MRS. PARKER IS MY DEAREST FRIEND!

HE'S JUST THE LEAST LITTLE BIT *SQUARE*.. BUT OUTSIDE OF *THAT*, HE REALLY TURNS ME ON!

I'LL BET HE'D BE A REAL *SWINGER* IF HE'D LET HIMSELF GO!

HOWEVER, A FEW MINUTES LATER...

THAT'S STRANGE! THERE'S NO ONE *HOME!* I DIDN'T THINK HE WAS THE *TYPE* TO GO OUT AT NIGHT!

WHY *NOT?* HE WALKS... HE *BREATHES*, DOESN'T HE?

WELL, I'VE GOTTA *DASH* NOW, AUNT ANNA!

IF I RUN *INTO* HIM AT THE DISCO, I'LL TELL HIM WHAT HE *MISSED!*

BUT THE WAY THINGS LOOK RIGHT NOW, PETER PARKER WOULD PROBABLY BE THE *LAST* ONE MARY JANE, OR ANYBODY, WOULD RUN INTO AT A DISCOTHEQUE...

THE *LIZARD* MUST REALLY BE *ENJOYING* THIS!

HE FIGURES THAT HE CAN'T *LOSE!* EVEN IF I MANAGE TO *ESCAPE* THE REPTILES, I'LL BE SO *EXHAUSTED* THAT HE CAN FINISH ME OFF IN A *BREEZE!*

BUT I *CAN'T* GIVE UP! THERE'S A LOT *MORE* AT STAKE THAN JUST THE LIFE OF ONE PART-TIME *WEBHEAD!*

MORE *CROCS* COMING! IF I CAN JUST DISLODGE THIS OVERGROWN EARTHWORM IN TIME..!

I'VE GOT TO KEEP HIM TOO BUSY TO *THINK!*

IF HE REALIZES WHERE HE *IS,* HE COULD ESCAPE BY SMASHING THROUGH THE WALL OF THE CAR!

BOK!

EVEN THOUGH I CAN'T REALLY *HURT* HIM, MY PUNCHES CAN *STILL* DRIVE HIM BACK... KEEP HIM *GROGGY!*

I NEED ONLY A FEW MORE MINUTES! FOR ONCE, *TIME* IS ON *MY* SIDE!

THRAK!

HE BROKE *AWAY* FROM ME! HE'S BRACING FOR AN *ATTACK!*

NEVER AGAIN WILL YOU STRIKE THE *LIZARD!* I'M GOING TO *DESTROY* YOU NOW!

IT WILL ONLY TAKE *ONE* SWEEP OF MY TAIL TO... TO... *WHA-??*

THAT WAS A MIGHTY *WEAK SWEEP,* LIZ! MAYBE YOU OUGHT TO USE A *BROOM!*

MY GAMBLE *PAID OFF!* HIS STRENGTH IS *EBBING*---AS I *KNEW* IT WOULD!

WHAT'S *HAPPENING* TO ME? I... I'M GROWING *WEAK*---

BUT, I'VE *STILL* GOT POWER ENOUGH... TO FINISH *YOU*...!

THINK SO?

I DON'T!

YOU FORGOT *ONE* LITTLE FACT... ONE FACT THAT MEANT THE DIFFERENCE BETWEEN VICTORY... OR *DEFEAT!*

LIZARDS FLOURISH IN *WARM* TEMPERATURES...

BUT, EXTREME *COLD,* SUCH AS YOU'LL FIND IN A *REFRIGERATOR CAR,* IS THE ONE THING THAT WILL *WEAKEN* A BIG, BAD, LACERTILIAN REPTILE!

TSK! I WISH YOU WOULDN'T FALL *ASLEEP* WHILE I'M LECTURING YOU!

16

I'VE DONE IT! I'VE BEATEN HIM! BUT, THE COLD MIGHT PROVE FATAL!

I'LL WRAP HIM IN A WEB-COCOON... IT'LL INSULATE HIM... KEEP HIM WARM ENOUGH TO SURVIVE!

BUT, I HAVEN'T ANY TIME TO WASTE! IF HE GETS TOO WARM, AND GETS FREE AGAIN, THAT'S THE BALL GAME!

FIRST THING TO DO IS STOP THE TRAIN!

I'VE GOT TO GET HIM BACK TO HIS LAB... WHILE I CAN STILL HANDLE HIM!

SKEEEEEEE

SECONDS LATER...

WE'LL HAVETA TAKE HIS WORD FOR IT, JOE! ONE THING'S FOR SURE... SPIDER-MAN'S NO ORDINARY BINDLESTIFF!

ALL I'M ASKING YOU TO DO IS FLAG DOWN A TRAIN HEADING BACK TO NEW YORK! A MAN'S LIFE DEPENDS ON MY REACHING THERE WITHIN THE HOUR!

OKAY, MISTER! WILL DO!

AND SO... SUBDUING HIM WAS ONLY HALF THE BATTLE!

NEXT, I'VE GOT TO FIND THE FORMULA THAT CAN TURN HIM INTO DR. CONNORS AGAIN!

LUCKY IT'S EVENING! I OUGHT TO BE ABLE TO BRING HIM BACK TO HIS LAB WITHOUT ANYONE TRYING TO STOP ME!

AFTER ALL, IF A FRIENDLY, NEIGHBORHOOD SPIDER-MAN CAN'T ACCOMPLISH A FEAT LIKE THIS... WHO CAN?

ALL'S WELL SO FAR!

NOW, IF HE'LL JUST STAY OUT LONG ENOUGH FOR ME TO FIND WHAT I'M AFTER...!

BOY! THIS PLACE LOOKS LIKE A HURRICANE HIT IT!

THIS IS WHAT I WANT!

I'LL BET THE LAB GOT WRECKED WHEN THE LIZARD LOOKED FOR THE SAME NOTES...

...ONLY TO REALIZE HE COULDN'T UNDERSTAND THEM, EVEN IF HE FOUND THEM!

-KNOCK, KNOCK!-

WHO'S IN THERE? OPEN UP..!

UH-OH! IT'S MRS. CONNORS! SHE HEARD ME!

IS THAT YOU, CURTIS? ARE YOU ALL RIGHT?? HAVE...HAVE YOU COME HOME AGAIN?

CURTIS, ANSWER ME! WHY WON'T YOU ANSWER?

THUD!

THUMP!

MAYBE IT ISN'T DAD! MAYBE IT'S SOMEONE ELSE!

IT'S SPIDER-MAN, MRS. CONNORS! DON'T TRY TO OPEN THE DOOR NOW! TRUST ME! I--I'M TRYING TO HELP!

DON'T WANT TO BUILD UP HER HOPES--- IN CASE THIS DOESN'T WORK!

ALSO, IT'S TOO DANGEROUS FOR HER HERE --- THE LIZARD MIGHT THAW OUT BEFORE I'M READY!

ANOTHER MIGHTY MARVEL FIRST! KNOWING HOW TITANICALLY TALENTED OUR RIOTOUS READERS ARE, WE'RE LEAVING THIS PANEL FOR YOU TO WRITE YOUR OWN DIALOGUE! IF YOU CAN GET SOMEONE TO PLAY HEARTS AND FLOWERS SOFTLY IN THE BACKGROUND, IT WON'T DO A BIT OF HARM, EITHER!

A SHORT TIME LATER, SPENT AN WEARY...ALMOST TO THE POINT OF EXHAUSTION.. A THOUGHTFUL YOUTH SLOWLY, LABORIOUSLY STRUGGLES INTO HIS STREET CLOTHES ONCE MORE, AND THE LISTLESSLY WENDS HIS WAY HOMEWARD...

I'M ALMOST SORRY IT'S ALL OVER NOW!

AT LEAST, WHILE I WAS FIGHTING THE LIZARD, I DIDN'T HAVE TIM TO THINK ABOUT MY OWN PERSONAL PROBLEMS.

MINUTES LATER...

HI THERE, PETE!

WOW! IS HE IN A WORLD OF HIS OWN! HE DOESN'T EVEN HEAR US!

LEAVE IT TO ME, HANDSOME HARRY! I'LL PUT HIM OUT OF HIS TREE!

HEADS UP, DAD! IN CASE YOU HAVEN'T HEARD, THE HUMAN RACE HAS ONE MORE OPENING ...IF YOU GET YOUR APPLICATION IN FAST!

HMM? OH-- HI, MARY JANE... AND HARRY! I, EH, MUST HAVE BEEN DAYDREAMING!

DAYDREAMING? TIGER, YOU WERE THE ORIGINAL ONE-MAN FOG! IF I DIDN'T KNOW YOU, I'D SAY YOU WERE STRICTLY OFF THE WALL...

CAN WE GIVE YOU A LIFT, PETE?

NO THANKS! I HAVEN'T FAR TO GO!

THEN REV'ER UP, HARRY BOY! SEE YA, PETEY... WE'RE WHEELIN' WHERE THE ACTION IS!

WHAT A PRIZE CHUMP I AM FOR WORRYING WHEN I HAVE TO BREAK A DATE WITH MARY JANE!

LOOKS LIKE SHE COULDN'T CARE LESS...LONG AS SHE'S GOT A JOE WHO'LL TAKE HER WHERE SHE WANTS TO GO!

NO DOUBT ABOUT IT... THAT CHICK'S AS PRETTY AS A PUMPKIN SEED... BUT JUST ABOUT AS SHALLOW!

AND I NEVER REALIZED HOW ICKY IT CAN BE... LISTENING TO A GAL WHO'S ON ALL THE TIME!

OR MAYBE IT'S MY FAULT! I'M JUST TRYING TO BLAME MY BLUE FUNK ON HER!

IT'S ALMOST TIME TO MAKE THE NEXT PAYMENT FOR AUNT MAY'S VACATION...AND I DIDN'T GET A SINGLE PICTURE OF THE LIZARD THAT I CAN SELL!

AS FOR THAT LAST BATCH OF PIX I SHOT... I NEVER DID DEVELOP THEM...AND THEY'RE ANCIENT HISTORY BY NOW, ANYWAY!

AND, JUST WAIT'LL AUNT MAY COMES HOME IN A FEW DAYS...AND SEES MY ARM IN A SLING! SHE'LL WORRY HERSELF SICK EVERY TIME I GET ON MY BIKE AGAIN!

ON TOP OF EVERYTHING ELSE, THERE'S MY STUDIES...!

I WAS SUPPOSED TO BE SPENDING THESE PAST DAYS BONING UP ON ALL THE WORK I'VE MISSED! HOW'LL I EVER CATCH UP NOW?

THEN, JUST AS THE BROODING YOUTH REACHES HIS FRONT DOOR...

PETER PARKER, YOU *NAUGHTY* BOY... COMING HOME SO LATE WHEN YOUR AUNT'S AWAY!

I BROUGHT YOU SOMETHING TO EAT... AND, IF YOU'VE ANY LAUNDRY YOU'D LIKE ME TO DO, I PROMISED MAY I'D DO IT FOR YOU!

MRS. WATSON! GEE, THAT'S SURE *NICE* OF YOU!

OH, *DEAR!* WHAT HAPPENED TO YOUR *ARM,* PETER? IS IT... ANYTHING *SERIOUS?* PERHAPS I SHOULD CALL YOUR *AUNT..?*

GOSH *NO,* MRS. WATSON! ..IT'S *NOTHING!* HONEST! I JUST SPRAINED IT ON MY CYCLE! I'VE GOT TO *REST* IT FOR A FEW DAYS... THAT'S ALL!

MY! THAT'S A RELIEF! YOU KNOW HOW YOUR AUNT WORRIES ABOUT YOU, DEAR!

YOU *SAID* IT, LADY! IF THERE'S *ANYTHING* I KNOW... THAT'S *IT!*

IF ONLY IT WOULD *HEAL* BEFORE AUNT MAY COMES HOME! BUT, THERE'S NOT A *CHANCE!*

I DON'T WANT HER WORRYING ABOUT MY SAKE, BUT WHAT ELSE COULD I HAVE SAID?

I COULD *HARDLY* ADMIT I GOT INJURED FIGHTING THE LIZARD IN MY SPIDER-MAN SUIT!

DRATS! I CAN'T EVEN FEEL LIKE EATING NOW!

EVERY PROBLEM I *HAVE* IS CAUSED BY MY BEING *SPIDER-MAN!*

IF I WERE JUST PLAIN *PETER PARKER,* I WOULDN'T HAVE TO BREAK DATES RIGHT AND LEFT!

I'D HAVE TIME FOR *STUDYING*... AND WOULDN'T HAVE TO FEEL *GUILTY* WHENEVER AUNT MAY *ASKS* ME SOMETHING!

I'D EVEN BE ABLE TO *TAKE* THAT JOB WITH HARRY'S DAD.. AND EARN A *STEADY* INCOME!

WHY DO I *DO* IT? WHY DO I CONTINUE RISKING MY *LIFE*... CAUSING A THOUSAND UNNECESSARY *PROBLEMS*... A THOUSAND HEARTACHES AND SLEEPLESS NIGHTS?

HAVE I AN INSANE LUST FOR *POWER*... A NEED TO FEEL MORE *IMPORTANT* THAN THOSE AROUND ME?

OR IS IT SOMETHING *DEEPER*... MORE *FRIGHTENING?*

HAS *SPIDER-MAN* BECOME SO MUCH A *PART* OF ME THAT I CAN NEVER LOSE HIM *AGAIN?*

AND, IN ANOTHER APARTMENT, IN ANOTHER SECTION OF THE CITY, THE MOOD IS SOMEWHAT *DIFFERENT*...

IF ONLY THERE WERE SOME WAY I COULD *REPAY* SPIDER-MAN FOR ALL HE'S *DONE* FOR US!

IF THERE WERE SOMETHING I COULD DO FOR *HIM* IN RETURN..!

I FEEL THE SAME WAY, CURT DEAR.. BUT IT'S SO *FUTILE*...

WOULDN'T *THAT* BE ONE FOR THE BOOKS, DAD? IMAGINE *US* DOIN' SOMETHIN' TO HELP *SPIDER-MAN!*

AFTER ALL, SPIDER-MAN IS SO *POWERFUL,* SO *SELF-SUFFICIENT!*

WHAT HELP COULD *HE* POSSIBLY NEED FROM ANYONE ELSE?

A PERSON LIKE *HIM* PROBABLY HAS EVERYTHING A MAN COULD WISH FOR!

NEXT: PETER PARKER'S PAD!

I'VE HEARD OF *PEOPLE* SHAKING WITH FRIGHT...

BUT A WHOLE *WALL* QUIVERING?

I'LL GET MY AUTO-MATIC *CAMERA* SET UP... POINTING TOWARD THAT WINDOW!

THEN I'LL JUST PAY A LITTLE *VISIT* INSIDE!

THERE'S SOMETHING ABOUT BEING SHOOK-UP BY A *WALL* THAT AFFECTS MY SPIDERY *CURIOSITY!*

WELL, WELL! LOOKS LIKE I'M JUST IN *TIME!*

DON'T YOU KNOW THAT SAFE-CRACKERS ARE *BAD GUYS...?*

AND BAD GUYS ALWAYS *LOSE!*

SPIDER-MAN!

WELL, I'M NOT HUBERT HUMPHREY!

I'LL RAM THOSE WISE GUY *WORD* RIGHT DOWN YOUR THROAT!

NOT FROM OVER *THERE* YOU WON'T--!

MY BLOW DOESN'T EVEN HAVE TO *REACH* YOU...!

UNLESS YOU CAN PUNCH CLEAR ACROSS A *ROOM!*

THIS IS WHY THEY CALL ME ...THE *SHOCKER!*

KLIK!

THAT'S HOW THE *WALL* SHOOK! HE'S GOT SOME GAD-GET ON HIS FIST... IT CAUSES VIOLENT *VIBRATIONS!*

IT MUST BE HOW HE OPENED THE *SAFE!*

NEXT TIME YOU'LL KNOW BETTER THAN TO CHALLENGE YOUR SUPERIORS!

MY VIBRO-BLAST POWER MAKES ME THE MOST INVINCIBLE HUMAN ON EARTH...AS YOU HAVE ALREADY LEARNED!

NO ONE CAN HURT ME WHEN I CAN DEFLECT ANY BLOW BY VIBRATING..

NO ONE...NOT EVEN THE SADDER BUT WISER SPIDER-MAN!

SECONDS LATER...

WOW-EEEE-- NOW I KNOW HOW BELL CLAPPER FEELS!

OF ALL THE GUYS TO TACKLE WITH A BAD ARM...I HADDA PICK HIM!

WELL, EVEN THOUGH HE GAVE ME MY LUMPS...AT LEAST I'LL HAVE SOME SHOTS OF HIM!

I'M GLAD I THOUGHT TO LEAVE MY CAMERA HERE...SET ON AUTOMATIC!

I GUESS THINGS COULD HAVE BEEN WORSE...

AT LEAST I'M LUCKY MY ARM WASN'T HURT WHILE I WAS ACTING LIKE A PART-TIME PUNCHING BAG!

HMM...IT'S HEALING PRETTY WELL NOW!

BUT I'D STILL BETTER KEEP IT IMMOBILE FOR A LITTLE WHILE LONGER!

THE NEXT TIME I MEET THE SHOCKER...I WANNA BE SURE I CAN USE IT!

WELL, I'D BETTER GET TO THE BUGLE AND SELL MY PIX TO JOLLY JONAH WHILE THEY'RE STILL NEWS!

ALTHOUGH, WHEN HE SAID I'D BE HELPLESS AGAINST HIM WITH EVEN TWO ARMS, I HAVE A FEELING HE MEANT IT!

WHATEVER ELSE HE MAY BE, THAT JOE IS GONNA BE NO PUSHOVER!

HI, THERE, PETE! CAN I GIVE YOU A LIFT?

YOU SURE CAN, HARRY...IF YOU'RE HEADING TOWARDS THE BUGLE!

IT'S A DEAL! HOP IN...THERE'S SOMETHING I'VE BEEN WANTING TO TALK TO YOU ABOUT, ANYWAY!

GREAT! AT LEAST IT'LL TAKE MY MIND OFF THE SHOCKER!

I'VE GOT AN OFFER TO MAKE YOU, SON!

AN OFFER?

5.

I FINALLY CONVINCED DAD THAT IT TAKES ME *TOO LONG* TO DRIVE TO AND FROM SCHOOL EACH DAY ALL THE WAY FROM OUR HOME IN WESTCHESTER!

DON'T TELL ME HE'S BUYING YOU A *WHIRLYBIRD*, HARR?

NOPE! EVEN *BETTER* THAN THAT, PETE!

HE GOT ME THE GREATEST LITTLE *APARTMENT*... JUST A COUPLE OF BLOCKS FROM CAMPUS!

YOUR OWN *PAD*, DAD? THAT'S *TERRIFIC*! BOY, WOULDN'T *I* GO FOR SOMETHING LIKE THAT!

THAT'S WHAT I *HOPED* YOU'D SAY..!

THIS NEW LITTLE INGLENOOK OF MINE HAS *TWO*--COUNT 'EM... *TWO* BEDROOMS...!

AND, IF YOU WANTED TO *SHARE* THE PLACE WITH ME, PETE, I'LL BET WE COULD HAVE A *BALL*!

GOSH, HARRY...IT WOULD BE THE *END*... BUT I DON'T KNOW IF I COULD *AFFORD* IT!

YOU DIDN'T *READ* ME, SON! I SAID DAD *GOT* ME THE PLACE... *HE'S* FOOTING THE RENT BILL!

SO WHAT'S THE *VERDICT*, MR. *P.*?

I'D LEAP AT IT IN A *SECOND*, HARRY....'CEPT FOR ONE THING.!

I'VE GOT TO FIND OUT HOW *AUNT MAY* WOULD TAKE IT!

YOU KNOW, I'M THE ONLY RELATIVE SHE'S GOT... AND SHE'S SORT OF *DEPENDENT* ON ME!

LET ME CHECK IT OUT WITH *HER* FIRST AS SOON AS SHE GETS BACK! AND THANKS A *MILLION*, FELLA!

SURE THING, PETE! I'LL WAIT TILL I *HEAR* FROM YOU!

IT'S FUNNY THE WAY HARRY AND I HAVE BECOME REAL GO FRIENDS...WITHOUT HIM EVER SUSPECTING WHO I REA AM... OR THAT I'M THE ONE WHO SAVED HIS *FATHER* WHEN HE WAS THE *GREEN GOBLIN* A WHILE BACK!

SEE YOU *LATER*, PE

BY THE WAY, NEXT TIM YOU SEE *MARY JAN* LEMME KNOW, AND I' CALL *GWEN*! THEY' MAKE A JAZZY *DOUBLE-DATE*!

YOU *KNOW* IT!

HE'S SURE BEEN SEEING A LOT OF *GWEN* LATELY...!

NOW WHY SHOULD *THAT* BOTHER ME? *I'VE* HARDLY GIVEN HER THE TIME OF DAY SINCE *M.J.* MADE THE SCENE!

HELLO, PARKER!

BOY! SOMETIMES I THINK THE HARDEST THING IN THE WORLD IS FOR A FELLA TO JUST KNOW HIS OWN *MIND*!

HE DIDN'T *HEAR* ME! PERHAPS IT'S JUST AS WELL! THIS IS MY CHANCE TO DO SOMETHING I'VE BEEN *WANTING* TO DO...!

I'VE ALWAYS *WONDERED* HOW HE MANAGES TO GET SO MANY EXCLUSIVE PHOTOS OF *SPIDER-MAN* IN ACTION!

I'M *POSITIVE* THERE'S SOME *CONNECTION* BETWEEN PARKER AND THAT WILY WEB-SLINGER...

AND *THIS* IS MY CHANCE TO DISGUISE MYSELF AS *PATCH* ONCE MORE, AND *TAIL* HIM TILL I LEARN HIS SECRET!

SOMETHING TELLS ME THERE'LL BE A GREAT STORY IN IT IF MY SUSPICIONS ARE CORRECT!

MR. JAMESON... MAY I *SEE* YOU FOR A MINUTE?

WASSAMATTE PARKER? YOU FORGOT WH I *LOOK* LIKE?

NOBODY COULD FORGET A THING LIKE *THAT*.. SIR!

AWRIGHT.. AWRIGHT! WHAT ON YOUR *MIND*?

WHAT'S ON MY *MIND* ISN'T FOR *SALE*, MR. J...

...BUT I'VE GOT SOME *PHOTOS* FOR YOU THAT *ARE*!

IT'S ABOUT *TIME*!

A NEW COSTUMED CREEP, EH? CALLS HIMSELF THE *SHOCKER*?

AND, AS FAR AS I KNOW... THESE ARE THE *ONLY* PHOTOS OF HIM *ANYWHERE!*

HE LOOKS LIKE A *NUT*... BUT HE'LL SURE SELL *NEWSPAPERS!*

THAT'S WHAT I *FIGURED!* SO HOW ABOUT SOME *BREAD?*

IF YOU'RE *HUNGRY*, GO TO THE DOWNSTAIRS *COMMISSARY*... AND CHARGE IT TO *ME!*

I WAS REFERRING TO *SCRATCH*... LONG GREEN... FOLDING STUFF... *MONEY*, TO YOU!

MONEY?? DON'T YOU *TRUST* ME, PARKER?

A QUESTION LIKE *THAT* CAN RUIN A GREAT RELATIONSHIP, JJ!

ALL RIGHT, YOU YOUNG *SHYLOCK!* I'LL HAVE BETTY BRANT GET YOU A CHECK!

MISS BRANT! WHERE IN BLAZES *IS* THAT GIRL?

ISN'T THIS *COFFEE BREAK* TIME UP HERE?

COFFEE BREAK! BIG DEAL! THE ONLY THING NO ONE TAKES IS A *WORK BREAK* IN THIS PLACE!

PAY NOW.. CRY LATER!

BLASTED GOLD-BRICKIN' LAZY NO-GOODS!

THUMP! BAM!

EVERYONE TAKES *ADVANTAGE* OF ME!

HERE... I'LL WRITE OUT YOUR BLASTED CHECK!

I'M *FLATTERED!* I KNOW THOSE THINGS SLIP THROUGH YOUR FINGERS LIKE *GLUE!*

VER-RY FUNNY! NOW *TAKE OFF* WHILE I GET 'EM TO STOP THE PRESSES!

GXXx$::!!! EVEN THE *PRESS ROOM* DOESN'T ANSWER!

HOW LONG DO COFFEE BREAKS *LAST* AROUND HERE, ANYWAY?

I OUGHT'A GIVE UP *PUBLISHING* AND START RAISIN' *COFFEE BEANS!*

THANKS FOR THE *DOUGH*, MR. JAMESON!

...KEEP *SMILIN'*, SWEETIE!

GOSH, I ALMOST *FORGOT!* AUNT MAY'S *TRAIN* WILL BE ARRIVING IN A FEW MINUTES!

I'VE GOT TO *MEET* HER AT THE STATION!

I CHANGED TO *PATCH* JUST IN TIME! PARKER'S LEAVING *NOW*...!

IF I CAN STAY WITH HIM *LONG* ENOUGH, HE'S GOT TO *LEAD* ME TO *SPIDER-MAN* SOONER OR LATER!

IT'S IMPOSSIBLE FOR ANYONE TO ALWAYS BE ON THE SPOT TO SNAP *PHOTOS* WHENEVER THAT WALL-CRAWLER IS AROUND... *UNLESS* THEY'RE WORKING *TOGETHER!*

AND IF THEY *ARE*... I'M BOUND TO GET *THE EVIDENCE* IF I DON'T LOSE SIGHT OF *PARKER!*

THERE'S JUST *TIME* FOR ME TO *WALK* TO THE STATION!

BUT PETER PARKER'S TIME MAY BE RUNNING *OUT*... FASTER THAN HE SUSPECTS! FOR AT THAT MOMENT, IN ANOTHER PART OF TOWN...

EVERYTHING WENT *PERFECTLY!*

NOBODY'LL THINK TO LOOK FOR ME *HERE* IN AN OLD, ABANDONED LOFT BUILDING!

AND IF THAT MEDDLESOME *SPIDER-MAN* BUTTS IN AGAIN, I'LL FINISH HIM FOR *GOOD* NEXT TIME!

IN FACT, IT MIGHT BE A *GOOD IDEA* TO DESTROY HIM... JUST TO SHOW THE *WORLD* HOW *POWERFUL* I AM!

7.

NOW IT'S TIME TO *COUNT* THE RESULTS OF MY DAY'S WORK... TO SEE IF MY *POWER* HAS *PAID OFF!*

AH! HUNDREDS AND HUNDREDS OF GREEN-BACKS! ALL *WON* BY THE MIGHT OF THE *SHOCKER!*

THIS IS WHAT I ALWAYS *DREAMED* OF... IN THE *OLD DAYS...*

"I REMEMBER HOW IT WAS *BEFORE* I GAINED MY GREAT *VIBRATING* POWER... I WAS JUST A TWO-BIT *SAFECRACKER* --- BUMBLING --- FRIGHTENED..."

I'M A TWO-TIME *LOSER!* CAN'T AFFORD TO GET NABBED *AGAIN!*

OH, *NO!* THERE WERE EXTRA GUARDS HERE TONIGHT! THEY *HEARD* THE NITRO!

I AIN'T GOT A *CHANCE!*

"SINCE I WAS GOOD WITH *TOOLS*, THEY PUT ME IN THE PRISON WORK-SHOP! BUT I HAD ONLY *ONE THING* ON MY MIND... DURING ALL THOSE LONG, ENDLESS MONTHS..."

IF I EVER GET *OUT*... I'LL DO THINGS *DIFFERENT!* THEY'LL NEVER CATCH ME *AGAIN!*

I'LL DESIGN A SET OF TOOLS THAT CAN OPEN *ANY* SAFE...SILENTLY --- IN *SECONDS!*

"BUT WHILE WORKING ON MY TOOLS... A ONE-IN-A-MILLION *INSPIRATION* HIT ME...!"

A GADGET THAT CAN *SHAKE* A SAFE DOOR LOOSE WOULD BE BETTER THAN ANYTHING *ELSE!*

IF I CAN JUST FIND A WAY TO *CONTROL* THE SHOCK OF THE *VIBRATIONS* ---!

LUCKILY, NO ONE HERE *SUSPECTS* WHAT I'M *REALLY* WORKING ON!

"THEN, MONTHS LATER... MY DEVICE WAS *READY!* IN THE DEAD OF NIGHT, WHEN MY CHANCES WERE THE GREATEST... I *USED* IT... AGAINST THE BRICK WALL, LEADING TO *FREEDOM..!*"

THIS IS *IT!* IT'S GOT TO WORK THE *FIRST* TIME... OR I'M *FINISHED!*

"IT *WORKED!* IT WORKED BETTER THAN I COULD HAVE *DREAMED!* THE WALL WAS *SHATTERED* WITHIN *SECONDS!* BUT I WAS ALMOST INJURED TOO BADLY TO MAKE A RUN FOR IT...!"

I DIDN'T REALIZE THAT THE *FEEDBACK* WOULD BE SO STRONG! LUCKY I WASN'T *KILLED!*

BUT I'LL WORRY ABOUT THAT *LATER*...ONCE I'M SAFELY *OUTTA* HERE!

"AND WORK ON IT I *DID!* HOUR AFTER HOUR...DAY AFTER DAY...WEEK AFTER WEEK...UNTIL FINALLY, JUST A SHORT TIME AGO..."

IT'S *FINISHED!*

THE FOAM-LINED FABRIC AND HEAVY BOOTS WILL *ABSORB* ANY FUTURE *SHOCKS!*

WHILE MY *BELT* WILL CONTAIN A LIFETIME *BATTERY* FOR A PERMANENT *POWER PACK!*

"BY LOCATING MY *VIBRA-SHOCK* UNITS WITHIN MY METAL *KNUCKLE PLATES*.. AND MAKING THEM *THUMB-OPERATED*...I KNEW I HAD MADE MYSELF *UN-BEATABLE!*"

AND, FROM THAT DAY ON, **THE SHOCKER** HAS PROVEN HIMSELF *SUPREME!*

NO ONE THAT LIVES CAN *STOP ME!*

MEANWHILE, AT THE NEWLY-CONSTRUCTED PENN STATION, MRS. MAY PARKER WAITS FOR HER BELOVED NEPHEW...

PETER SHOULD BE HERE AT ANY MINUTE!

OH DEAR.. I WONDER HOW HE'S GOING TO TAKE THE *NEWS* I HAVE FOR HIM...?

AUNT MAY!

THAT'S *HIM!*

PETER, DEAR, I'M SO GLAD TO... *OH!* YOUR *ARM!* WHAT *HAPPENED?*

NOTHING, AUNT MAY! JUST A LITTLE *SPRAIN!* IT'LL BE OKAY IN A DAY OR SO!

SAY! YOU LOOK *WONDER-FUL!* THE REST MUST HAVE BEEN *GOOD* FOR YOU!

HOW WILL I *EVER* BRING MY-SELF TO SAY IT--

YES, DEAR...I HAD A *WONDERFUL* TIME! BUT NOW---THERE'S SOME-THING I MUST *TELL* YOU---!

CAN IT *WAIT* JUST A SEC, AUNT MAY? I'VE GOT A REAL IMPORTANT MATTER TO DISCUSS WITH *YOU!*

GOSH! WHY THE *TEARS?* WHAT'S *WRONG?*

NOTHING, PETER! IT'S JUST THAT I'M *SO WORRIED* ABOUT YOU...!

WORRIED? WHY??

9

I KNOW HOW *DEPENDENT* YOU ARE UPON ME, DEAR, AND...OH, I'VE JUST *GOT* TO TELL YOU...!

MRS. WATSON IS SO LONELY SINCE *MARY JANE* MOVED AWAY...AND, SHE WANTS ME TO COME AND *STAY* WITH HER!

I'D *LOVE* TO DO IT... BUT IT WOULD MEAN LEAVING *YOU* ALL ALONE AT HOME...!

IF ONLY I HAD THE *NERVE* TO TELL HER THAT I WANT TO MOVE OUT---TO BE ON MY OWN...!

WAIT A MINUTE! *WHAT* DID SHE SAY..??

YOU WANT TO MOVE IN WITH *MRS. WATSON*? BUT...YOU'VE BEEN WORRIED ABOUT LEAVING *ME* ALONE?"

OH, PETER...I WAS *AFRAID* YOU'D TAKE IT THIS WAY! I...I DIDN'T WANT TO *UPSET* YOU!

UPSET ME? MRS. MAY PARKER, IT'S TIME YOU THOUGHT OF *YOURSELF* FOR A CHANGE!

STAYING WITH YOUR FRIEND, MRS. WATSON, WOULD BE JUST WHAT YOU *NEED*! YOU'D HAVE *COMPANY*... AND SOMEONE WHO'D ALWAYS BE THERE TO LOOK AFTER YOU WHEN YOU NEED IT MOST!

BUT WHAT ABOUT *YOU*, DEAR? WHAT WOULD *YOU* DO?

I'M NOT A *CHILD* ANY MORE, AUNT MAY...IT'S *TIME* I WAS GETTING OUT ON MY OWN! I'LL *SHARE* AN APARTMENT WITH *HARRY OSBORN*, ONE OF MY CLASSMATES!

I'M SO HAPPY... THAT YOU'RE *TAKING* THIS...

AND THAT MEANS YOU CAN *SELL* THE HOUSE...AND HAVE ENOUGH MONEY TO LIVE COMFORTABLY FOR THE NEXT FEW YEARS

THUS, A SHORT TIME LATER...

MAY, DEAR! HOW *WONDERFUL* YOU LOOK! COME IN AND TELL ME ALL ABOUT YOUR TRIP!

HELLO, MRS. WATSON! HI, MARY JANE! AUNT MAY HAS SOMETHING TO *TELL* YOU!

OH, ANNA DEAR... I'VE THE MOST *THRILLING* NEWS...!

IT'S ALL RIGHT WITH *PETER* IF I MOVE *IN* WITH YOU!

I *TOLD* YOU IT WOULD BE! YOU'VE *ALWAYS* WORRIED ABOUT THAT BOY MUCH TOO MUCH!

AS FOR *YOU*, YOUNG LADY, WHAT SAY WE SKIP OVER TO THE *SILVER SPOON* TO CELEBRATE?

CELEBRATIONS ARE MY FAVORITE PEOPLE, DAD! LET'S CUT OUT!

HI, MARY JANE! WHERE'D YA DIG UP THE SON OF FRANKENSTEIN?

BELA LUGOSI *RENTED* HIM TO ME! BUT DON'T GET HIM RILED TILL *AFTER* HE'S PAID FOR MY SODA, HEAR?

ANYWAY, WHAT'S *SHAKIN'*, TIGER?

NOTHING MUCH! WE WERE JUST GETTING SET TO SPIN A FEW PLATTERS!

C'MON IN! TH' STRAWS 'ON ME

WOW! WHO'S THAT *DOLL* DANCING OVER TH---HEY!

IT'S *GWEN*! I DIDN'T *RECOGNIZE* HER AT FIRST! LOOK AT HER *GO*!

HMM.. GWEN'S NOT *BAD*! NOT *GOOD*, MAYBE --BUT NOT BAD!

BUT WHY AM I SO *SURPRISED*? I NEVER *FIGURED* HER FOR THE WALL-FLOWER TYPE!

BEFORE I FORGET, I WANTED TO *TELL* YOU TWO...

FLASH'S *FAREWELL PARTY* IS JUST ABOUT ALL SET! WE'LL HOLD IT RIGHT *HERE*, AT THE SILVER SPOON, WHEN HE GETS HIS INDUCTION DATE!

WE WANT IT TO BE A REAL *BLAST*! HE'S THE FIRST ONE OF THE CROWD TO BE *DRAFTED*!

YEP! WE'VE GOTTA DO IT UP *RIGHT* FOR OL' FLASH!

MMM-MMM! THERE'S SOMETHIN' ABOUT A MA IN UNIFORM IT'S WOW CITY!

I WONDER HOW A *SPIDEY* COSTUME WOULD GRAB HER?

AND REMEMBER.. I GET 50% OF THE *MONEY* YOU RECEIVE FOR SELLING THE *PICTURES!*

DON'T WORRY! YOU'RE THE *ONE* GUY I'M NOT ABOUT TO START *CHEATING!*

LUCKY I CAN CHANGE THE TONE OF MY *VOICE* BY RAISING AND LOWERING MY *FACE MASK!*

NOW FOR A *QUICK CHANGE* WHILE I KEEP TALKING! GOOD OL' *SPIDER SPEED..* I COULDN'T *DO* THIS WITHOUT IT!

WHAT IF YOU CAN'T *BEAT* THE SHOCKER, SPIDEY?

YOU KIDDIN'? JUST TAKE THE *PIX*, PARKER... *I'LL* DO THE REST!

WHEW! IF I GET *AWAY* WITH THIS, IT'LL BE A *MIRACLE!*

HE'S STILL LISTENING, ON THE OTHER SIDE OF THE WALL!

JUST *STAY* THERE, PATCH... WHILE I RIG UP A *WEB-DUMMY* OF OL' *SPIDER-MAN!*

I'LL HANG IT BY IT'S OWN WEBBIN' AND GIVE IT A *SHOVE* TO STAR IT SWINGING.

YOU DIDN'T TELL ME WHERE YOU'RE *GOING*, SPIDEY?

NUTS! HE'S ALWAYS SWINGING OFF WITHOUT *ANSWERING!*

HOW *ABOUT* THAT! I WAS *DEAD WRONG!* PARKER IS STILL *STANDING* THERE WHILE THE WEB-HEAD SWINGS AWAY!

WELL, THAT'S IT! I'M NOT *BRANDO*, BUT I HOPE I ACTED GOOD ENOUGH TO FOOL MY ONE-MAN AUDIENCE!

I ALMOST MADE A KING-SIZED *JACKASS* OUT OF MYSELF! HOW COULD I HAVE THOUGHT A TEEN-AGED NOBODY LIKE *PARKER* COULD ACTUALLY BE *SPIDER-MAN!*

WELL, ANYWAY, I FOUND OUT HOW THE KID GETS THOSE EXCLUSIVE *PHOTOS!* HE'S GOT A *DEAL* COOKING WITH SPIDER-MAN! THE MASKED MAN *TIPS HIM OFF* WHEN HE'S GOING INTO ACTION... AND THEN PARKER SPLITS THE MONEY HE GETS FOR THE PIX WITH *SPIDEY!*

IT *STILL* DOESN'T SOUND KOSHER, THOUGH! YOU'D THINK A GUY LIKE *SPIDER-MAN* COULD MAKE ALL THE DOUGH HE *WANTS!*

BUT, WHY *FIGHT* IT? I *SAW* THEM... AND *HEARD 'EM* WITH MY OWN EARS!

OH, *BROTH-ER!* WAS *THAT* A CLOSE ONE!

FOR A *WHILE* THERE I COULD LIKE I COULD JUST KISS MY "SECRET IDENTITY BIT" BYE-BYE FOR *GOOD!*

WELL, NOW THAT *SHOW* TIME'S OVER...!

I'VE ABOUT *HAD* IT WITH THAT BLAMED *SLING!*

MY ARM'S *STILL* A LITTLE SORE, BUT WHAT THE HEY!

WHO EVER HEARD OF A SWINGIN' SUPER HERO *BABYING* HIMSELF?

THIS IS A MIGHTY BIG TOWN!

SO WHERE DO I START LOOKING FOR THE SHOCKER?

DOWN BELOW... A COP... RUSHING TO A CALL BOX! I'D BETTER GRAB A LISTEN...!

THAT'S RIGHT, SARGE! I GOT A REPORT OF TREMORS NEAR THE FEDERAL RESERVE BANK!

BETTER SEAL OFF THE SECTOR! IT MIGHT BE THE SHOCKER!

YOU CAN SAY THAT AGAIN!

BOY! IF IT HAD HAPPENED THAT EASY IN A MOVIE, I'D SAY IT WAS TOO PHONY!

BUT FOR ONCE IT'LL BE A PLEASURE NOT TO WASTE HALF THE NIGHT SEARCHING!

THE FED RESERVE IS ONLY A FEW BLOCKS FROM HERE!

WOW! THERE'S NO DOUBT ABOUT THESE TREMORS!

IT FEELS LIKE THE WHOLE BUILDING'S SHAKING ITSELF APART!

OKAY, SHOCKER... ROUND TWO COMIN' UP!

A VOICE! BEHIND ME! WHO...??

THANKS FOR LEAVING A HOLE FOR ME TO ENTER THROUGH, PAL!

SPIDER-MAN!

YOU WERE EXPECTING MAYBE THE MAN FROM U.N.C.L.E.?

13.

15.

AND NOW...THIS MAY NOT BE AS *COLORFUL* AS YOUR METHOD OF FIGHTING...

BUT THERE'S NOTHING LIKE A *FROLICSOME FULL-NELSON* TO MAKE A FELLA SEE THE ERROR OF HIS WAYS!

:UHHHH!:...BLAST IT... CAN'T *HOLD* 'IM!! HE'S *VIBRATING* HIMSELF OUT OF MY GRIP!

DON'T SAY I DIDN'T *WARN* YOU, SPIDER-MAN!

TO *ME*, YOU'RE NOTHING MORE THAN A *PETTY ANNOYANCE*...SOMETHING TO BE DEALT WITH QUICKLY, AND *DISPOSED* OF BEFORE YOU CAN BECOME TOO IRRITATING!

I WISH YOU HADN'T *SAID* THAT! IT MAKES ME FEEL LIKE ONE OF THOSE *AILMENTS* THEY'RE ALWAYS CURING WITH ASPIRIN ON TV COMMERCIALS!

NOW CRAWL OFF SOMEWHERE AND LICK YOUR WOUNDS...I'VE STILL GOT A *BANK* TO ROB!

SPIDER-SKILL... IF I EVER NEEDED YOU *BEFORE*, DON'T FAIL ME *NOW*!

THERE'S *GOT* TO BE A WAY TO *BEAT* THAT ROLLICKIN' RAT!

BUT I'LL NEVER *FIND* IT IF I SPEND ALL NIGHT GETTING MY *LUMPS* FROM THAT CHARACTER!

SO! YOU HAVEN'T *SENSE* ENOUGH TO LAND IN A *HEAP*.. AS I *HOPED* YOU WOULD!

UH-OH! HE'S *FIXIN'* TO TOSS ANOTHER *VIBRO-BLAST* MY WAY!

SO I'D BETTER MAKE SURE THERE'S *NOBODY HOME* WHEN IT ARRIVES!

IF YOU KEEP THAT *UP*, SHOCKER...I'M LIABLE TO DEVELOP AN *INSECURITY* COMPLEX!

AND, CONSIDERING WHAT *HEAD SHRINKERS* COST NOWADAYS, WE CAN'T LET *THAT* HAPPEN, CAN WE?

AND, THEN, FINALLY...

I KNOW HOW YOU FEEL, DEAR! IT WAS THE SAME WHEN MARY JANE MOVED AWAY FROM HOME!

THAT'S WHY I'M SO HAPPY YOU'RE COMING TO STAY WITH ME NOW!

HE'S ALL THE FAMILY I HAVE! I PRAY HE'LL BE ALL RIGHT...HE'LL BE HAPPY...ON HIS OWN!

BUT SHE COULDN'T HAVE BEEN SWEETER ...OR GENTLER... OR MORE WONDERFUL...THAN AUNT MAY!

I NEVER KNEW MY MOTHER..

THE WAY SHE ALWAYS WORRIED ABOUT EVERY LITTLE THING...!

THAT'S WHY I COULD NEVER... NEVER... LET HER LEARN THE TRUTH... ABOUT SPIDER-MAN!

A SHORT TIME LATER, IN A PLEASANT APARTMENT BUILDING JUST A STONE'S THROW AWAY FROM CAMPUS...

WELCOME TO THE PAD, LAD!

IT'S NOT THE TAJ MAHAL... BUT IT'S BETTER THAN A TENT!

YOU MEAN... ALL THIS IS OURS??

IT'S OUT OF SIGHT, HARR--!

--AND IN LIVING COLOR, TOO!

GLAD YOU LIKE IT, MR. PARKER!

I'VE GOTTA GO OUT FOR A WHILE... SO MAKE YOURSELF AT HOME!

SURE THING, PAL! THIS IS GONNA TAKE A LITTLE GETTING USED TO!

BUT HOW COME THERE'S NO BUTLER

SORRY ABOU' THAT! SEE YOU LATER, ROOM MATE!

BUT FOR LONG, LONELY SECONDS AFTER THE DOOR HAS CLOSED BEHIND THE EBULLIENT HARRY, PETER PARKER STANDS MOTIONLESS, SILENTLY CLOAKED IN HIS OWN SOMBER THOUGHTS...

I SHOULD BE CLICKING MY HEELS AND DOING CARTWHEELS RIGHT NOW! I'VE FINALLY GOTTEN WHAT I WANTED--

I'M ON MY OWN AT LAST...SHARING A PAD WITH A PAL!

SO WHY THIS LETDOWN FEELING? WHY THIS MOOD OF DEPRESSION THAT I CAN'T SEEM TO SHAKE?

IS IT JUST A NATURAL FEELING OF HOMESICKNESS? OR, IS IT SOMETHING DEEPER?

ON THAT FATEFUL DAY ...WHEN I BECAME SPIDER-MAN... PERHAPS MORE THAN A PHYSICAL CHANGE WAS WROUGHT

PERHAPS, IN SOME STRANGE, MYSTERIOUS WAY...WHEN I GAINED ANOTHER IDENTITY...I LOST THE CAPACITY... FOR HAPPINESS!

next:
MORE POWERFUL!
MORE DANGEROUS
MORE DEADLY
THAN EVER!
THE RETURN OF KRAVEN THE HUNTER!

THE AMAZING SPIDER-MAN!

WORRY NOT, FRANTIC ONE! IF THIS TANTALIZING TABLEAU MAKES YOU FEEL AS THOUGH YOU'VE JUST WALKED IN AT THE MIDDLE OF A MOVIE, THAT'S THE WHOLE IDEA!

IT'S SUPPOSED TO AROUSE YOUR INTEREST, EXCITE YOUR CURIOSITY, AND TITILLATE YOUR THIRST FOR THE UNEXPECTED!

HOWEVER, NOW THAT WE'D GOT YOU TO READ THIS FAR, WE'D BETTER ADMIT THAT IT'S A FLASHBACK SCENE, SHOWING AN INCIDENT THAT OCCURRED JUST A FEW MONTHS AGO! WHILE THE GREEN GOBLIN WAS STILL FLYIN' HIGH! SO LET'S JOIN THE PARTY, AND SEE WHAT'S SHAKIN', SWEETIE..!

HAH! SPIDER-MAN THINKS KRAVEN IS FIGHTING HIM JUST FOR THE SHEER LOVE OF BATTLE!

BUT, LITTLE DOES THE WEB-SLINGING FOOL REALIZE THAT THE GREEN GOBLIN HAS PROMISED TO PAY THE HUNTER TWENTY THOUSAND DOLLARS FOR THE DEATH OF SPIDER-MAN!

IF THAT'S THE BEST YOU CAN DO, MASKED MAN, THE VICTORY IS AS GOOD AS MINE!

"IN THE HANDS OF THE HUNTER!"

A SWINGIN' SUPER-SPECIAL SPIDEY SAGA, BY: **STAN LEE** and **JOHN ROMITA** ABETTED and LETTERED BY: SAM ROSEN

EVEN AS THEY *FOUGHT*, KRAVEN WAS SO OBSESSED WITH THE THOUGHT OF THE *$20,000* HE HAD BEEN PROMISED, THAT HE COULD BARELY CONCENTRATE ON THE MATTER AT *HAND...!*

HE'S BEEN *WATCHING!* HE *SEES* ME WINNING! THE MONEY'S AS GOOD AS *MINE!*

BUT NOW SPIDER-MAN IS RAISING HIMSELF *UP!*

I DIDN'T THINK HE HAD THE *STRENGTH!*

THEN, MOMENTS LATER...

I WAS TOO *CARELESS!* BY DIVERTING MY *ATTENTION*, HE MANAGED TO *ESCAPE* ME!

BUT I HAVE *PROVEN* THAT I AM HIS *MASTER!* THE *NEXT* ROUND WILL BE *MINE!*

AND WHEN THE GREEN GOBLIN'S *MESSENGER* MEETS ME TONIGHT, I'LL DEMAND THE FIRST HALF-PAYMENT OF MY *MONEY!*

AND SO...

THE GOBLIN *SAW* ME BATTLE SPIDER-MAN... HE SAW HOW MUCH *STRONGER* I WAS... HOW MUCH MORE *SKILLFUL!* NOW I WANT MY FIRST *PAYMENT!*

THERE WILL BE ONLY *ONE* PAYMENT... THE *FULL AMOUNT!*... BUT NOT UNTIL SPIDER-MAN HAS BEEN COMPLETELY *DESTROYED!*

THOSE ARE THE *GREEN GOBLIN'S* FINAL INSTRUCTIONS!

WHAT?!! DOES THE GOBLIN THINK HE CAN DICTATE TERMS TO *KRAVEN?*

LOOK... DON'T TAKE IT OUT ON *ME*, FELLA! I'M JUST HIS *GO-BETWEEN!*

IF YOU HAVE ANY *GRIPES*, TELL 'EM TO MY *BOSS!*

I'LL DO *MORE* THAN *TELL* HIM! AFTER *SPIDER-MAN* FALLS, THE GREEN GOBLIN WILL BY MY *NEXT* VICTIM!

YOU'RE LIVING IN A *FOOL'S PARADISE*, CHUM! *NOBODY* CAN BEAT THE *GOBLIN!*

GET OUT! TELL HIM TO PAY ME.. OR HE *DIES!*

BUT NO SOONER DID THE UNKNOWN EMISSARY *DEPART*, THAN...

HOW EASY FOR THE GREATEST HUNTER OF *ALL* TO SILENTLY *FOLLOW* THE GOBLIN'S HIRELING!

SOONER OR LATER HE'LL *CONTACT* THE GOBLIN... AND WHEN HE *DOES...!*

KRAVEN WILL HAVE HIS *MONEY.. AND HIS REVENGE!*

BUT, AS THE LONG UNEVENTFUL EVENING WORE ON...

NO SIGN OF THE GOBLIN! HE MUST NOT BE *MEETING* HIM TONIGHT!

BUT AT LEAST I LEARNED THAT HIS MOUTHPIECE IS *NORMAN OSBORN*, THE RICH CHEMICAL MANUFACTURER!

THE GOBLIN MUST BE BIGGER THAN I *THOUGHT* TO HAVE A MILLIONAIRE LIKE *HIM* SERVING AS HIS *FLUNKY!**

NEFARIOUS NOTE: IN CASE YOU DON'T *REMEMBER* THIS STIRRING SEQUENCE FROM ISH #15 OR #34 (KRAVEN'S LAST TWO APPEARANCES), IT'S BECAUSE WE DIDN'T *SHOW* IT! AFTER ALL, WE CAN'T BLOW THE WHOLE BIT IN *EVERY* YARN!
    --- SNEAKY STAN.

* TOO BAD *KRAVEN* NEVER READ ISH #40 LIKE *WE* DID, OR HE'D KNOW THAT OSBORN *HIMSELF* WAS THE GOBLIN.. RIGHT, TIGER?
    --YOU KNOW WHO!

2.

NO NEED TO TRAVEL ALL THE WAY TO WESTCHESTER TO HIS HOUSE...

OSBORN HAS AN *OFFICE*, RIGHT HERE IN THE *CITY* SOMEWHERE...

AND IT WON'T TAKE *KRAVEN THE HUNTER* LONG TO *FIND* IT!

KEEP YOUR CITY CLEA

BUT THE WEB OF FATE HAS *MANY* STRANDS! EVEN WHILE THE SUPER-POWERFUL JUNGLE-BRED *STALKER* NEARS HIS OBJECTIVE, WE TURN OUR ATTENTION TO *ANOTHER* SCENE...

IT'S SO *WONDERFUL* MOVING IN WITH YOU, ANNA!

THERE'LL BE SO MUCH FOR US TO *DO*, MAY DEAR! IT WAS SO *LONELY* FOR ME SINCE *MARY JANE* MOVED AWAY!

ESPECIALLY NOW THAT I KNOW *PETER* IS SETTLED IN HIS OWN NICE APARTMENT WITH THAT NICE *HARRY OSBORN* BOY!

SLAM

THAT WAS THE *FRONT* DOOR!

HI, PRETTY PEOPLE! I THOUGHT YOU MIGHT NEED A HAND WITH YOUR *UN*-PACKING...

IF *SO*, HAVE NO FEAR... *M.J.* IS HERE!

MARY JANE! HOW SWEET OF YOU TO DROP BY TO HELP!

IF ONLY MY *PETER* COULD BE SO HAPPY-GO-LUCKY!

DON'T WORRY ABOUT *PETEY*, MRS. PARKER! HE'S A REAL *SWINGER!*

...A REGULAR, FULL-TIME *PUSSYCAT!*

MARY JANE, YOU MIGHT HELP US BY STARTING TO MOVE THOSE... THOSE...*MARY JANE?*

SPEAKING OF PETER... I THINK I'LL PHONE AND SEE HOW HE *IS!*

OH WELL.. AT LEAST STAY OUT OF THE WAY SO WE DON'T *TRIP* OVER YOU!

TELL HIM NOT TO FORGET WE'RE *MAKIN' THE SCENE*, TONIGHT!

HOW *NICE!*

IT'S SO *RARE* TO FIND A YOUNG LADY WHO'S INTERESTED IN *HANDICRAFTS!*

SECONDS LATER, A BRIGHT-EYED AND BUSHY-TAILED *PETER PARKER* SAYS...

YOU SOUND *GREAT*, AUNT MAY! AND I HEAR SOME *ROCK'N'* ROLL IN THE BACKGROUND!

I HAD A *HUNCH* THAT YOU AND MRS. WATSON WERE REALLY *WITH* IT!

RINNG!

THE *DOOR-BELL!* I'LL GET IT, PETE!

WHAT'S THAT? THE MUSIC IS *MARY JANE'S?* OH, SHE'S PLAYING *RECORDS!* HUH? *WHAT* DID YOU SAY?

AUNT MAY---FOR THE *ZILLIONTH* TIME... THE WORD IS *PUSSYCAT*... NOT *PUSSYWILLOW!*

I'LL BET SHE'S PUTTING YOU *ON*, SON! YOUR AUNT'S PROBABLY *HIPPER* THAN *YOU!*

WHO *ISN'T*, DAD?

NO, NOT *YOU*, AUNT MAY! I WAS TALKING TO *HARRY!*

I'D BETTER SEE WHO'S AT THE *DOOR!* I'D HATE TO KEEP *SOPHIA LOREN* WAITING!

OR, WOULDJA BELIEVE *CAPTAIN KANGAROO?*

DAD! GOSH, WHAT A *SURPRISE!* YOU'RE A REAL *EARLY-BIRD!*

HELLO, SON! I CAME TO SEE HOW YOU AND YOUR NEW *ROOMMATE* ARE GETTING ALONG!

I'M *GLAD!* I'VE BEEN *WANTING* YOU TO MEET OL' *PETE!* COME ON *IN*--!

4.

WHO ARE YOU *KIDDING*, GWEN? YOU NEVER DUG FLASH IN THE *FIRST PLACE*!

WHY WON'T YOU *ADMIT* THAT *I'M* THE SECRET LOVE OF YOUR LIFE?

BECAUSE IT WOULDN'T BE A *SECRET* ANY LONGER IF I *DID*, HARRY! *TOUCHÉ*, MISS STACY! SAY, HAS ANYONE EVER TOLD YOU THAT YOU GET *PRETTIER* EVERY DAY?

ONLY MY *MIRROR*, MR. PARKER! WHOOPS... SORRY!

I'VE BEEN LISTENING TO *MARY JANE* TOO LONG!

OH, SPEAKING OF *MARY JANE*... IF YOU'D LIKE TO BRING HER TO THE *PARTY*, YOU MAY!

THINGS SHOULD REALLY BE *SWINGING* BY ABOUT EIGHT... ESPECIALLY WITH *HER* THERE!

THANKS, GWEN! I'M SURE M.J. WOULD GET A BIG *KICK* OUT OF IT!

GWEN DIDN'T EVEN GIVE ME A *CHANCE* TO ASK IF SHE'D... AWW, WHAT'S THE USE? TO *HER*, I'M JUST ANOTHER GUY NAMED PETE!

WILL *YOU* BE BRINGING A DATE, HARRY?

WITH *YOU* THERE, DOLL...?

...THAT WOULD BE LIKE BRINGING A *CHEVY* TO *GENERAL MOTORS*!

WELL, GENTLEMEN, IT'S BEEN A REAL *BALL*, BUT THE TIME HAS COME TO FILL MY LITTLE BLONDE HEAD WITH *LEARNING*!

YOU'RE *RIGHT*! WE'D BETTER *MOVE*! I'M DUE AT THE *LAB*!

SAY, GWEN... HOW ABOUT A *SODA* AFTER CLASS WHILE WE COMPARE SOME NOTES ON ENGLISH LIT? I'M AFRAID I'VE GOTTEN A LITTLE *RUSTY*!

OH, *BRO-THER*! HE WALKS AWAY WITH TOP HONORS IN EVERY CLASS... AND *HE'S* RUSTY!

SO WHAT DOES THAT MAKE A GUY LIKE *ME*?

COME TO *THINK* OF IT... DON'T *ANSWER* THAT!

WHAT DO YOU *SAY*, GWEN?

SORRY, PETE! I'LL BE BUSY GETTING THINGS READY FOR FLASH'S *PARTY*!

I'M SURE *MARY JANE* CAN HELP YOU BRUSH UP ON YOUR NOTES!

FACE IT, PARKER! YOU *DESERVED* THAT! WHEN GWEN *WANTED* TO BE FRIENDLY, I WAS NEVER AROUND!

YEAH, SURE, GWEN! NO SWEAT! SEE YOU LATER!

A FEW HOURS LATER, AS SOON AS CLASSES ARE THROUGH, A DRAMATIC FIGURE TURNS TO *WEB-SWINGING* AS HE ZOOMS ACROSS TOWN---

I ALMOST *FORGOT*... I HAVE TO REACH THE *BUGLE*...!

I STILL HAVE THOSE PHOTOS OF THE *SHOCKER* TO SELL*. AND I'D BETTER *DO* IT WHILE THEY'RE STILL *NEWS*!

*SEE? OLD VILLAINS NEVER DIE! WE ALWAYS MENTION 'EM IN THE FOLLOWING ISH! ... SENTIMENTAL STAN.

AND NOW THAT WE'VE PROVEN THAT JAZZY JOHNNY STILL REMEMBERS HOW TO DRAW SPIDEY...

THERE'S *NED* AND *BETTY*!

I'M GLAD I *CHANGED* UP ON THE ROOF *FAST* ENOUGH TO CATCH THEM BEFORE THEY LEAVE!

THEY MIGHT GET A CHARGE OUT OF COMING TO FLASH'S *PARTY*, ALSO!

WHERE ARE YOU TWO *GOING*?? YOU'RE SUPPOSED TO WORK TILL *NOON* AROUND HERE!

BUT IT *IS* NOON, MR. JAMESON!

BAH! I NEVER *COULD* STAND CLOCK-WATCHERS!

SOUNDS LIKE J.J.J. IS IN HIS USUAL MONDAY MORNING *MOOD*!

6.

SAY THERE, GROUP! HOLD IT *UP* A SECOND, HUH?

IT'S *PETER PARKER!* WHERE'VE YOU BEEN *KEEP-ING* YOURSELF THESE DAYS, FELLA?

HAVE YOU *FORGOTTEN*, NED? PETER IS ATTENDING E.S.U.!

HOW'VE YOU *BEEN*, PETER? HOW ARE *CLASSES?*

EVERYTHING *COPACETIC*, BETTY! DO YOU REMEMBER *FLASH THOMPSON?*

OF *COURSE* I DO! HE'S E.S.U.'S STAR *QUARTER-BACK!*

NOT ANY *MORE!* HE'S GOING INTO THE *ARMY*---AND WE'RE THROWING A *PARTY* FOR HIM TONIGHT!

SAY NO *MORE!*

WE WOULDN'T *MISS* IT FOR THE *WORLD!*

WELL, NOW THAT *THAT'S* OUT OF THE WAY---

HI, MR. JAMESON! I'VE GOT SOME GREAT *PIX* FOR YOU---!

SHADDUP!! CAN'TCHA SEE I'M ON THE *PHONE??*

NO! I'M NOT YELLING AT *YOU!* THAT PIN-HEADED *PETER PARKER*, JUST CAME IN--!

OKAY, THEN... THIS PINHEAD'LL SELL HIS PIX TO THE *GLOBE!* *WAIT! STAY HERE!* CAN'TCHA TAKE A *JOKE?!!*

LOOK, DAD... SOUNDS AS THOUGH YOU'RE *BUSY!* TELL PARKER "HELLO" FOR ME, AND I'LL TALK TO YOU LATER ON!

I JUST WANTED YOU TO KNOW THAT EVERYTHING'S *OKAY* HERE IN WASHINGTON, AND I'LL BE JOINING THE *SPACE TEAM* AGAIN SOON!

THAT'S MY BOY! REMEMBER, IF ANY OF THE *BRASS* GET IN YOUR *WAY*, TELL 'EM YOU'RE J. JONAH JAME-SON'S SON!

WE'RE HAVING ENOUGH TROUBLE *NOW*, DAD... WITHOUT STARTING *ANOTHER* WAR!

HEH HEH! YOU'RE A GREAT LITTLE *KIDDER*, JOHNNY BOY! BUT YOU'VE BEEN A *COLONEL* LONG ENOUGH! I WANT *MY* BOY TO BE A *GENERAL*, HEAR?

US JAMESONS ARE BORN *WINNERS!*

NOW! WADDAYA *MEAN* BARGIN' INTO MY OFFICE THAT WAY, AND...

I MEAN TO SELL YOU THESE PICTURES OF THE *SHOCKER* THAT'S WHAT!

YOU'VE GOT PIX OF THE *SHOCKER??* WHY DIDN'T YOU *SAY* SO? THAT'S *STOP THE PRESS-ES* STUFF! LEMME *HAVE* 'EM!

WHERE'S THE *MONEY?*

DO YOU THINK I'D *CHEAT* YOU??

EVERY CHANCE YOU'D *GET!*

BUT WHY DWELL ON HIGH FINANCE WHEN WE CAN SWITCH TO *KRAVEN THE HUNTER*--?

THERE'S OSBORN'S *MANSION!*

NOW I'LL SEE IF HE'S *REALLY* OUT OF TOWN... OR IF HE'S TRYING TO *HIDE* FROM ME!

I WANT OSBORN!! WHERE *IS* HE??!

K-RAK!

KRAVEN...THE HUNTER!

THE MASTER IS NOT *HERE*, SIR!--HE--HE IS ON A *BUSINESS TRIP*... OUT OF *TOWN*..!

DON'T TRY TO LIE TO ME!!

I CAN STOP A CHARGING *BULL ELEPHANT* IN HIS TRACKS WITH MY OWN *STRENGTH*!! I CAN DEFEAT A FULL-GROWN *LION* IN BARE-HANDED *COMBAT*!! NOBODY LIES TO KRAVEN!!

IT...IT IS THE *TRUTH*, SIR!! HE IS NOT HERE!! SEE FOR *YOUR-SELF*..!!

I DON'T *HAVE* TO SEE!! MY OWN *ANIMAL SENSE* TELLS ME YOU'RE TOO *FRIGHTENED* TO LIE!

HE'S GOT TO COME BACK *SOME* TIME, DOESN'T HE??

WHEN HE *DOES* RETURN... YOU GIVE HIM A *MESSAGE*..!

SKRI-SK!

YOU TELL HIM...

KRAVEN WAS HERE!

HE'S LIKE A WILD *BEAST*... BUT--MORE *POWERFUL* BY FAR!

I MUST CONTACT THE MASTER! MR. OSBORN MUST BE *WARNED*..!

JUST FORGIVE US THIS ONE ADDITIONAL INTERRUPTION! YOU SEE, PETER PARKER GOES TO SO *FEW* PARTIES, WE JUST DON'T WANNA MISS A *MINUTE* OF THIS ONE...

LET'S *FACE* IT, PETE! WE MUST BE DOING *SOME-THING* RIGHT!

BETWEEN MY *GWEN* AND YOUR *MARY JANE*, WE'VE REALLY GOT IT *MADE*!

IT *FIGGERS*, SON! WE'RE STRICTLY FROM *WOW* CITY!

WHAT'S *WITH* ME? WHY DO I GET ALL SHOOK-UP WHEN I HEAR HIM CALL HER *HIS* GWEN?!!

8.

ATTENTION SPIDO-PHILES: IN CASE YOU'RE WONDERING WHY WE'RE MAKING WITH ALL THE MOON-JUNE JAZZ WHEN WE'VE GOT A CAT LIKE KRAVEN JUST WAITING TO BE UNLEASHED... DON'T LOSE YOUR COOL...!

IT'S ALL GONNA DOVETAIL TOGETHER AND TURN INTO A SYMPHONY OF ACTION... OR ANYWAY, THAT'S THE WAY WE PLANNED IT! ...SMILEY!

GOOD THING YOU'VE GOT THIS BOAT, HARRY!

WE'D NEVER BE ABLE TO PICK UP BOTH GALS ON MY CYCLE!

ALTHOUGH...IT MIGHT BE FUN TO TRY!

I MAY HAVE TO TRADE THIS CAR IN SOON...IT NEEDS A WASH.

LOOK! THERE'S GWEN!

AHH, MY TWO GALLANT KNIGHTS ON THEIR SPEEDING STEED!

GWEN!! IF...IF I'D KNOWN YOU'D LOOK LIKE THAT.. I'D HAVE GOTTEN HERE SOONER!

WHAT DID YOU EXPECT ME TO LOOK LIKE? YOGI BEAR?

IF YOU...THINK IT'S TOO CHILLY.. WE CAN PUT THE TOP UP..?

BITE YOUR TONGUE, IMPETUOUS ONE! WE NIGHT PEOPLE THRIVE ON MOON BURNS!

IT'S THE SAME OLD STORY OF MY LIFE.. ALL OVER AGAIN!

WHEN I FIRST MET GWEN, AND SHE SORT'A TOOK A SHINE TO ME, I WAS TOO BUSY WALTZIN' AROUND WITH THE MOLTEN MAN, THE SCORPION, AND A DOZEN OTHER BADDIES TO GIVE HER THE TIME OF DAY!

BUT NOW....WITH EVERYTHING NICE AND PEACEFUL... AND WITH GWEN SENDING ME INTO ORBIT WHENEVER I LOOK AT HER..SHE SUDDENLY FORGOT MY NAME!

I CAN'T WAIT TO SEE FLASH'S FACE WHEN WE GIVE HIM HIS SENDOFF!

AND SPEAKING OF FACES... THERE'S M.J.--!

HI, MARY JANE! HOP IN---WE'RE ALL SET!

WHO NEEDS A CAR? WHEN THERE'S A PARTY TO GO TO, I CAN LIKE FLY ALL THE WAY!

SHE MAY NOT GRAB ME AS MUCH AS GWEN...BUT NOBODY CAN SAY THAT GAL ISN'T 100% DREAMSVILLE!

AND NOW, TO PROVE THIS REALLY ISN'T OUR VERSION OF PEYTON PLACE, WE'RE GONNA SKIP THE ENTIRE RIDE TO THE SODA PARLOR AND DELIVER YOU TO THE SCENE ONE-TWO-THREE...!

GWEN! YOU'RE TOO MUCH! DID YOU REALLY ARRANGE THE DECORATIONS? THEY'RE JUST OUT OF SIGHT!

THIS IS ONE NIGHT FLASH'LL REMEMBER!

I NEVER GOT A SENDOFF LIKE THIS WHEN I JOINED THE SCOUTS!

C'MON IN, KIDS! YOU'RE JUST IN TIME!

WELL, IT ISN'T THE COPACABANA, BUT IT BEATS DANCING ON THE SIDEWALK!

BUT WHERE'S THE GUEST OF HONOR! WHAT HAPPENED TO FLASH?

DON'T PANIC, PILGRIMS! THE NIGHT'S STILL YOUNG!

IT WAS SO NICE OF PETER TO INVITE US, NED!

I WONDER WHICH OF THOSE TWO GORGEOUS GIRLS HE'S MOST INTERESTED IN?

LOOKS LIKE THE GANG'S ALL HERE! NOW, ALL WE NEED IS FLASH!

WOULDN'T IT BE SOMETHING IF HE DOESN'T SHOW?!

KRAVEN'S STRONGER THAN A BULL ELEPHANT! I'VE GOT TO DO SOMETHING!

BUT I CAN'T GO INTO ACTION LIKE THIS...NOT AS PETER PARKER!

YOU'RE THE ONE I WANT!! I'D RECOGNIZE YOU ANYWHERE!

I KNEW OSBORN HAD A SON! AND IT WASN'T HARD FOR THE WORLD'S GREATEST HUNTER TO TRACK YOU HERE!

I DON'T KNOW YOU!! I--I NEVER SAW YOU! WHAT-- WHAT DO YOU WANT... WITH ME??

BACK OFF, MISTER!! NOBODY BREAKS UP MY PARTY THAT WAY!

SOMEBODY CALL THE POLICE! NO ONE HERE CAN HOPE TO STOP KRAVEN!

WHERE'S YOUR FATHER?? TALK...DO YOU HEAR?? TALK! NOBODY CAN DEFY ME!

HE'S OUT OF TOWN! I DON'T KNOW WHERE!

C'MON, YOU GUYS! WE CAN'T LET FLASH RUSH HIM ALONE!

NO MATTER WHO YOU ARE, YOU CAN'T FIGHT OFF ALL OF US!

BACK, YOU FOOL!

CAN A PACK OF RABBITS HOLD A LION AT BAY?

THWOP!

DON'T TRY TO STOP HIM!! IT'S HOPELESS! I'LL GO FOR THE POLICE!!

YOU HAD YOUR CHANCE! NOW I'LL TAKE YOU WITH ME!

IT'LL ALSO GIVE ME A CHANCE TO SWITCH TO SPIDEY! IF I MOVE FAST ENOUGH, I'LL CATCH HIM OUTSIDE!

KRAVEN MUST HAVE HAD DEALINGS WITH OSBORN WHEN HE WAS THE GREEN GOBLIN!

THE WISE HUNTER MAKES HIS PREY COME TO HIM!

ONCE OSBORN KNOWS THAT I HAVE HIS SON, HE'LL COME LOOKING FOR ME---TO HIS LASTING REGRET!

HE--LOOKS HUMAN--- BUT IT'S LIKE HITTING AN ELEPHANT'S HIDE!!

HE DOESN'T EVEN FEEL IT!

12

KRAVEN, YOU ALWAYS *WERE* A PARTY POOP!

ANYONE *ELSE* WOULD HAVE WAITED FOR THE REFRESHMENTS!

THAT *VOICE!* I'D KNOW IT *ANYWHERE!*

THE MIGHTY *KRAVEN*, TACKLING A *TEEN-AGER!*

NEXT THING WE KNOW, YOU'LL BE PROVING YOUR POWER BY WRESTLING A *PARAKEET!*

YOU!! THE ONE I'VE SWORN TO HAVE MY *VENGEANCE* UPON!

IT'S *WORKING!* HIS HATRED FOR ME IS SO GREAT THAT HE'S ALREADY FORGOTTEN *OSBORN!*

VENGEANCE INDEED! YOU OUGHTTA *THANK* ME FOR KEEPING YOU OUT OF *CIRCULATION* SO LONG!

EVERY TIME YOU MAKE THE SCENE YOU END UP IN JAIL!

ATTA-BOY! PUT HARRY *DOWN!* THAT'S A GOOD LI'L *KRAVEN!*

YOU'VE ALWAYS BEATEN ME BY *TRICKERY*... BUT *THIS* TIME I'M *WISE* TO ALL YOUR STUNTS!

YOU *ARE?* THEN HOW COME I CAN *STILL* OUTMANEUVER YOU BY A COUNTRY *MILE?*

THWIP!

THWIP!

FFTOK!

IN THE *JUNGLE* IT'S KNOWN... THE *FIRST* BLOW IS *MEANINGLESS!!* ONLY THE *FINAL* SMASHING ATTACK TELLS THE STORY!

THEN LET'S SKIP THE *PRELIMINARIES* AND GET TO THE *LAST* ACT!

I CAN'T WAIT TO TAKE MY *BOWS* AT CURTAIN TIME!

MR. JAMESON! IS--IS SOMETHING WRONG, SIR?

AND IF IT IS, WHAT ARE YOU GONNA DO ABOUT IT?

JUST PUT A REWRITE MAN ON THE LINE, AND HOLD THE PRESSES TILL I CALL!

AND, IF THAT PINHEAD PARKER CALLS IN, TELL HIM NOT TO SHOW HIS DUMB-LOOKIN' FACE AROUND HERE IF HE HASN'T ANY PHOTOS OF KRAVEN FOR ME!

OKAY.. THAT'S IT! GET BACK TO WORK! WE'VE GOT A PAPER TO PUT OUT!

NO, SIR! YES, SIR! NO, SIR!

AND DON'T ASK ANY MORE FOOL QUESTIONS!

WHERE IN BLAZES IS FOS-WELL?

RIGHT HERE, JJ!

WELL, DON'T JUST STAND THERE! LET'S GO!

MEAN-WHILE...

HE SEEMS TIRELESS! I CAN'T KEEP DODGING HIM FOREVER-- AND YET...

I'VE GOT TO FIND SOME WAY TO KNOCK THE WIND OUT OF HIS SAILS!

IF I CAN JUST MAKE HIM FALL-- FROM THIS HEIGHT--

IF YOU WANT ME, KRAVEY BABY.. COME 'N GET ME!

TSK-TSK! DIDN'T ANYONE EVER TELL YOU NOT TO END A SENTENCE WITH AN EXPLETIVE?

ONCE I GET MY HANDS ON YOU, I'LL..

UHHH!

I CAN TOLERATE YOUR NASTINESS BUT BAD GRAMMAR--- UNFORGIVABLE!

YOU THINK YOU OUT-SMARTED ME, EH?

NICE TRY, SPIDEY! TOO BAD IT WAS A WASTE OF TIME!

NO MERE FALL CAN PUT KRAVEN OUT OF ACTION!

NOT WHILE I HAVE THE AGILITY OF A JUNGLE CAT!

AT THAT VERY MOMENT, IN ANSWER TO HIS BUTLER'S URGENT SUMMONS, A PUZZLED NORMAN OSBORN HAILS A CAB AT KENNEDY AIRPORT---

I'LL DOUBLE YOUR FARE IF YOU CAN GET ME TO WESTCHESTER INSIDE OF AN HOUR!

HOP IN AND BUCKLE UP, MISTER! YOU GOT YOURSELF A DEAL!

IT'S LUCKY WE DON'T HAVETA PASS THROUGH MIDTOWN!

THE RADIO'S BEEN BLARIN' *BULLETINS* ABOUT *KRAVEN THE HUNTER,* TEARIN' *UP* THE PLACE!

KRAVEN?? IN MIDTOWN? FORGET ABOUT WESTCHESTER! GET ME AS *CLOSE* TO THE SITE AS YOU CAN!

THEY PROBABLY GOT *TRAFFIC* BACKED UP FOR *MILES* AROUND THERE!

IT MAY NOT BE *HEALTHY,* PAL!

'LL *TRIPLE* THE FARE!

THAT'S *HEALTHY* ENOUGH FOR *ME!*

AND, AS THE TAXI RACES ALONG THE GRAND CENTRAL PARKWAY...

I'VE DEFEATED *EVERY* FOE I'VE EVER *BATTLED!* I CAN'T LET *YOU* BE THE ONLY ONE TO MAR MY *RECORD!*

WELL, YOU WON'T CHANGE THE SCORE-BOARD *THAT* WAY, BIG MAN!

YOU'RE COMIN' IN TOO *LOW 'N' SLOW!*

GUESS *AGAIN,* YOU FOOL! I *PLANNED* IT THIS WAY!

ROK!

NOW YOU CAN FALL RIGHT INTO THE WAITING ARMS OF THE *BLUE-COATS* BELOW...

...AS THE WORLD REALIZES THAT KRAVEN HAS WON HIS *GREATEST* HUNT!

SEEMS A *SHAME* TO SPOIL SUCH A *DRAMATIC* SPEECH, PLAYMATE, BUT THAT'S *SHOW BIZ!*

IT'S REAL *OBLIGING* OF YOU TO WEAR THAT *LION'S MANE* GET-UP..!

IT MAY NOT BE *MOD*...BUT IT REALLY *GRABS* ME!--OR VICE-VERSA!

Y'KNOW, IF WE COULD *CHOREO-GRAPH* THIS ROUTINE, WE'D PROBABLY HAVE A *GREAT ACT* FOR ED SULLIVAN!

AND *NOW*.. THE *LONG-AWAITED FINISH!!*

MY *BRAIN* KNOWS WHAT TO DO.. BUT MY *BODY* WON'T.. OR *CAN'T*... RESPOND!

ALL IT WILL TAKE IS ONE *NERVE PUNCH*---THE SAME *BLOW* WITH WHICH I CAN PARALYZE A CHARGING *BENGAL TIGER!*

THERE! NOW I CAN *FINISH* YOU AT MY *LEISURE!* YOU'RE ALL SET UP FOR THE *KILL!*

POK!

*B*UT THEN....*SUDDENLY..THE SHARP EYES*---THE *JUNGLE-BRED SENSES* OF THE DEADLY HUNTER..PERCEIVE THE ARRIVAL OF *ANOTHER* FIGURE..

IN THE STREET BELOW... THAT *FIGURE*..*GETTING OUT OF THE CAR..!*

IT'S *HIM!!*

IT'S *OSBORN!!* I'VE FOUND HIM AT *LAST!*

HE WON'T *ESCAPE* ME *AGAIN!*

HARRY!! ARE YOU *ALL RIGHT*, SON? I HEARD WHAT *HAPPENED!* I CAME AS SOON AS I COULD!

DAD! SURE.. I'M *FINE*.. NOW!

THAT *KRAVEN*.. MUST BE A *MADMAN*...!

WHO IS HE?

YOU MEAN-- YOU DON'T *KNOW*, DAD?

OF *COURSE* NOT! I'VE NEVER EVEN *SEEN*---

WHAT..?!!

DAD!

THWUP!

DON'T STRUGGLE, OSBORN! IT WON'T *HELP* YOU!

EVEN THOUGH THE *GREEN GOBLIN* IS DEAD...I INTEND TO COLLECT MY *MONEY!*

GOBLIN? MONEY? WHAT ARE YOU *TALKING* ABOUT?

AND I'LL *COLLECT* IT FROM.. *YOU!*

STILL THINK YOU CAN *SAVE* YOURSELF BY ACTING *DUMB?*

WE'LL *SEE* ABOUT THAT!

18.

TWENTY THOUSAND DOESN'T MEAN THAT MUCH TO ME... AND I KNOW IT'S CHICKEN FEED TO A MAN LIKE YOU!

BUT IT'S THE PRINCIPLE OF THE THING..!

NOBODY BREAKS A PROMISE TO KRAVEN THE HUNTER!! NOBODY!

I DON'T KNOW WHAT YOU'RE TALKING ABOUT!!

I'VE NEVER PROMISED YOU ANYTHING-- NEVER SEEN YOU BEFORE!

DON'T MAKE ME BEAT IT OUT OF YOU!

MY JUNGLE INSTINCT CAN SENSE WHEN SOMEONE IS LYING! AND YOU... YOU!!

YOU DON'T REMEMBER! YOU DON'T KNOW ANYTHING ABOUT IT! YOU'RE TELLING THE TRUTH!

IT'S NOT POSSIBLE! I REMEMBER YOU... I SPOKE TO YOU... AND YET...

I DON'T KNOW HOW... BUT--YOU'RE THE WRONG ONE!

IT MUST HAVE BEEN SOME TRICK--- OF THE GREEN GOBLIN'S! HE DID IT TO CONFOUND ME!

AS FOR YOU... YOU'RE IN LUCK!

A JUNGLE BEAST DOES NOT ATTACK WITHOUT REASON--- AND KRAVEN NO LONGER HAS REASON!

BUT, HE'S DEAD NOW.. SO I'LL NEVER LEARN THE ANSWER!

THU-D!

THE PRIZE IS STILL MINE! KRAVEN HAS DEFEATED SPIDER-MAN!

≡WHEW...!≡ THAT RAY GIZMO IS FINALLY WEARING OFF...!

NOW... WITH THE PAST BEHIND ME...

KRAVEN CAN CARVE A MIGHTY FUTURE FOR HIMSELF!

HE'S RUNNING OFF... ESCAPING..!

I'VE GOT TO STOP HIM...!

BUT, BEFORE SPIDEY CAN MAKE ANOTHER MOVE---

OSBORN!!

TRYING TO GET TO HIS FEET, HE TOPPLED OFF THE GIRDER!

DAD! OH, NO! NOOOO!

LET YOURSELF GO *LIMP*... RELAX... YOU'LL BE OKAY!!

..'VE ..OT ..OU!

IN A WAY.. YOU SAVED *ME* AS MUCH AS *I* SAVED YOU!

SPIDER-MAN!

OSBORN IS OUT OF DANGER... NOW... BUT *KRAVEN'S* GONE!

I--I THOUGHT I WAS *DONE* FOR-- AND THEN--FROM OUT OF *NOWHERE*--

AND MAYBE IT'S JUST AS *WELL!*

EASY, DAD--- EASY NOW--!

DIDJA *SEE* HIM? DIDJA SEE OL' *SPIDEY* IN ACTION?!! HE'S THE *GREATEST!*

..SBORN! I SAW THE WHOLE *THING!* YOU COULD HAVE BEEN *KILLED!*

.PIDER-MAN .RIED TO *MURDER* YOU, DIDN'T HE? BUT THEN HE GOT *COLD FEET,* RIGHT?

.EN PRINT THE .RUTH, FOR ONCE! .PIDER-MAN SAVED .' *LIFE*...AND YOU .OW IT!

YOU CAN TELL *ME!* WE'RE FELLOW *CLUB MEMBERS!* I WANNA *HELP* YOU!

YOU'RE STILL IN A STATE OF *SHOCK*...YOU'RE NOT *THINKING* CLEARLY!

HE REALLY PUSHED YOU *OFF*...DIDN'T HE?

JAMESON, I DON'T KNOW THE *REASON* FOR YOUR PSYCHO-PATHIC *HATRED* OF SPIDER-MAN, BUT...

HATRED? WHO *HATES* HIM? I'M A *NEWSPAPER MAN!* I WANT THE *FACTS,* THAT'S ALL!

OF COURSE, I WOULDN'T WANT HIM FOR A *NEXT DOOR NEIGHBOR!*

C'MON, LET ME GIVE YOU A LIFT *HOME* WHILE I TELL YOU WHAT A *FINK* THAT WALL-CRAWLER IS!

WELL, WELL...LOOK WHO'S HERE...NOW THAT THE *ACTION'S* OVER! *PUNY PARKER* HIMSELF!

I DIDN'T HAVE MY *CAMERA* WITH ME...TRIED TO *RENT* ONE FAST BUT COULDN'T FIND A STORE IN TIME!

GUESS I MISSED THE WHOLE *THING,* HUH?

THAT OUGHTTA SOUND CONVINCING ENOUGH FOR *ANYONE!*

IT WAS A REAL *GASSER,* PETEY!

IT'LL CERTAINLY GIVE *FLASH* A SENDOFF TO REMEMBER!

.AT'S *RIGHT*...I ALMOST *FORGOT*...YOU *LEAVE* .MORROW...FOR THE *SERVICE!*

.WANNA WISH YOU ALL .E *BEST,* FLASH! SOME- .NG TELLS ME YOU'VE .T WHAT IT *TAKES* TO .COME OUT ON *TOP,* FELLA ...AND I'M BETTIN' YOU *DO!*

Y'KNOW SOME- THIN', PARKER? EVERY SO OFTEN I FIGGER YOU'RE NOT AS *SQUARE* AS I *THOUGHT!*

TAKE GOOD *CARE* OF THE *CHICKS* FOR OL' *FLASHEROO* WHILE I'M *GONE,* HEAR?

HOPE I'M NOT SQUEEZIN' YOUR *HAND* TOO HARD...'CAUSE A *SPIDER-MAN* YOU *AIN'T!*

FINALLY, THE BANTER DIES AWAY...THE CROWD THINS OUT... AND, A LONELY, THOUGHTFUL FIGURE SILENTLY TRUDGES HOMEWARD...

HE WAS PROBABLY MY GREATEST *FAN!*

IF ONLY I COULD HAVE *TOLD* HIM WHO I REALLY AM... JUST *ONCE!*

BUT WHY AM I THINKING OF HIM IN THE *PAST TENSE?!* HE'LL COME *BACK!* HE'LL *MAKE* IT...SOMEHOW!

THE GOOD GUYS *ALWAYS* WIN---

--*DON'T* THEY?

NEXT: THE WINGS OF THE **VULTURE!**

THE ONLY WAY TO BEAT THE COLD IS BY MOVING FAST!

AS SOON AS I START SLOWING DOWN, IT'S FREEZEVILLE!

THWIPP!

WITH THE PRICE OF WEBBING NOWADAYS, I'D BETTER START CONSERVING IT!

NO SENSE SWINGING OVER A ROOFTOP WHEN I CAN JUST AS EASILY LEAP IT!

BUT ALL I'M GETTING IS EXERCISE! IF KRAVEN IS ANYWHERE WITHIN MILES OF HERE, YOU CAN'T PROVE IT BY ME!

WOW! I'VE TRAVELED FURTHER THAN I THOUGHT!

I REACHED ALL THE WAY TO THE MUNICIPAL PRISON! ...AND I'M NOT GONNA SWING OVER THAT WALL!

WONDER HOW MANY NON-PAYING GUESTS IN THERE WOULD LIKE TO GET THEIR HANDS ON THIS OL' WEB-HEAD?

I'M PROBABLY THE BEST TALENT SCOUT THAT PLACE EVER HAD!

WELL, I LIKE WINTER SPORTS AS MUCH AS THE NEXT GUY-- BUT THIS IS GETTING RIDICULOUS!

KRAVEN'LL HAVE TO WAIT WHILE I GO HOME AND HIT THE SACK!

BUT, AS SPIDEY SWINGS AWAY, LITTLE DOES HE DREAM---

BEHIND THE GRIM, GREY WALLS OF THE PENITENTIARY, AN INMATE LIES NEAR DEATH BECAUSE OF AN UNEXPECTED MISHAP WHICH OCCURRED IN THE PRISON WORKSHOP---

HE'S SINKING FAST! I'M AFRAID HE CANNOT LAST MORE THAN AN HOUR, AT MOST!

I SUGGEST YOU GRANT HIM THAT REQUEST, WARDEN! IT CAN CERTAINLY DO NO HARM AT THIS STAGE OF THE GAME!

HE KNOWS IT, DOC! HE'S BEEN ASKING FOR ONE LAST REQUEST-- HE WANTS TO SEE HIS CELLMATE BEFORE HE CASHES IN!

HE'S COMING TO AGAIN PERHAPS FOR THE LAST TIME!

BLACKIE... I WANT--TO SEE--- BLACKIE...

ALL RIGHT WE'LL SEND FOR HIM...

IN THE MEANTIME DON'T TALK! TO SAVE YOUR STRENGTH

I'LL *SAVE* IT, ALL RIGHT! WON'T *CASH* IN...UNTIL I MAKE SURE...THAT BLACKIE..WILL *FINISH* THE JOB...I STARTED..!

MY *SENTENCE*...WOULD HAVE BEEN *UP*...IN ANOTHER MONTH! THAT'S WHY...I NEVER TRIED TO *ESCAPE!* I WAS...A *FOOL*...!

BUT...IT'S *NOT* TOO LATE! *BLACKIE* CAN CARRY ON.. WHERE..THE *VULTURE* LEFT OFF!

Minutes later, a scowling con reaches the quiet room under heavy guard...

YOU'VE GOT *FIVE MINUTES,* MISTER..SO MAKE THE *MOST* OF 'EM!

IT'S A *MIRACLE* HE'S MANAGED TO STAY ALIVE *THIS* LONG AFTER THAT ACCIDENT IN THE WORK-SHOP! HE'S HANGING ON BY A *THREAD!* YOU MAY GO IN *NOW!*

YEAH, SURE, DOC! I'LL *DO* THAT LITTLE THING!

WRIGHT, VULTURE...THIS *YOUR LAST* CHANCE! U GONNA TELL ME WHAT I ANNA *KNOW*...OR LET JUST DIE *WITH YA?*

YOU *WIN,* BLACKIE!...SOME-ONE *HAS* TO... CARRY ON FOR ME!

BEND *CLOSER* --NO-BODY MUST *HEAR* THIS..EXCEPT *YOU*..!

YOU'VE *HOUNDED* ME..FOR *MONTHS*..TO TELL YOU...WHERE I *BURIED*...MY LAST PAIR...OF VULTURE *WINGS*..!

I SWORE..YOU'D *NEVER* GET IT..OUT OF ME! BUT NOW...I *MUST* TELL YOU..!

FOR ONLY HE...WHO WEARS THE *VULTURE'S* WINGS.. WILL POSSESS THE POWER--TO DESTROY *SPIDER-MAN!*

AND, SPIDER-MAN MUST BE DE-STROYED!! HE *MUST*--!!! HE *MUST!*

'OP WASTIN' ME MAKIN' EECHES, ILLYA?

ONCE I GET THOSE *WINGS* OF YOURS, I'LL POLISH THAT WEB-HEAD OFF *EASY*...AND THE SAME FOR ANYONE *ELSE* WHO STANDS IN MY WAY!

THE *WINGS*...TOGETHER WITH *MAGNETIC PACK*...500 YARDS FROM NORTH GUN TOWER...NEAR BROKEN PINES--!

SO *TALK,* BLAME YA!! WHERE DID YOU *BURY* 'EM?! *HURRY*--WHILE YA CAN STILL *SAY* IT!!

I DID IT *MONTHS* AGO...SO I'D HAVE AN *EXTRA* PAIR...IN CASE POLICE JAILED ME--...

THEN, THEY'RE JUST OUTSIDE THE *WALLS!!* THAT'S ALL I GOTTA *KNOW!*

IT *WORKED!* I GOT WHAT I WANT...AT *LAST!*

NOTHIN' CAN STOP *BLACKIE DRAGO* NOW!

IT *WORKED??*..WHAT WORKED?...WHAT DO YOU *MEAN*--?

THAT WAS *NO ACCIDENT,* YOU OLD FOOL! *I* ARRANGED IT...TO GET YOU TO *TALK!*

BUT, NO ONE'LL EVER *KNOW* THAT...'CEPTIN' *YOU 'N ME!*

AND SOON... IT'LL JUST BE *ME*..BLACKIE DRAGO...THE NEW *VULTURE!!*

3.

A SHORT TIME LATER, *BLACKIE DRAGO* TAKES THE MOST DESPERATE GAMBLE OF HIS ENTIRE, SORDID CAREER...

IT TOOK ME *YEARS* TO GET TO BE A *TRUSTEE*--- TO BE ALLOWED TO MOVE AROUND INSIDE THE *GATES* LIKE THIS!

BUT STILL... I *GOTTA* DO IT!

IF I CAN GET *AWAY* WITH THIS, I'LL BE *UN-STOPPABLE!*

THOP!

THERE'S NO ONE *LIVIN'* WHO CAN STOP A MAN WITH *WINGS!*

SWEET DREAMS, MAC! I NEED THAT HEAP A LOT MORE THAN *YOU* DO!

SO FAR, SO GOOD!

ONCE I GET THROUGH THE *GATES,* ALL I HAVE TO DO IS DIG UP THE VULTURE'S *WINGS!*

MIGHT AS WELL GIVE 'ER THE *GUN!* IT DON'T MATTER IF THEY *HEAR* ME NOW OR *NOT!*

SCREEEEEE

IT WAS *BLACKIE DRAGO!!* I'D RECOGNIZE THAT COLD, RASPING VOICE *ANYWHERE!*

HE MUST BE OUT OF HIS *MIND* TO TRY A TRICK LIKE THAT--!

ONCE I REACH THAT *PHONE,* HE WON'T EVEN MAKE IT TO THE FIRST *MAIN ROAD!*

WHOOOOOOOOO

GO ON.... *HOOT!* GIT YOUR *MONEY'S WORTH* OUTTA THAT CRUMMY *SIREN,* FOR ALL THE *GOOD* IT'LL DO YA!

ALL I GOTTA DO IS GO *500 YARDS* FROM THE NORTH GUN TOWER--!

NOTHIN' CAN CATCH UP TO ME BEFORE I GRAB THE VULTURE'S *WINGS!*

AND ONCE I *DO...* THE WHOLE BLAMED *WORLD* WILL BE MINE.... JUST FOR THE *TAKING!*

5

MINUTES LATER...

HE ABANDONED HIS TRUCK IN THE SNOW BANK!

HE CAN'T GET FAR ON FOOT! WE'LL GET HIM NOW!

IT'LL BE A CINCH TO TRACK HIM IN THE SNOW!

HE MUSTA BEEN STIR-CRAZY TO TRY A BREAK ON A DAY LIKE THIS!

BUT, JUST A SHORT DISTANCE AHEAD, BLACKIE DRAGO SMIRKS WITH SINISTER, SAVAGE SATISFACTION...

I FOUND THEM... JUST WHERE HE SAID THEY'D BE!

THAT PLASTIC BAG KEPT 'EM IN PERFECT CONDITION HERE BEHIND THE BOULDERS!

NOW ALL I GOTTA DO IS SLIP INTO THEM AND TAKE OFF!

VOICES! THEY'LL BE REACHING ME SOON!

NO TIME TO PRACTICE! I GOTTA GET AIRBORNE, FAST!

THAT'S FUNNY.. THE TRACKS IN THE SNOW END OVER AT... HEY!

I THOUGHT I HEARD THE RUSTLE OF WINGS!

WINGS? WHAT ARE YOU TALKIN' ABOUT?

LOOK! UP THERE-- IT'S HIM!

STOP HIM!! HE MUSTA FOUND THE VULTURE'S WINGS!!

KRAK! KRAK!

BLAST IT.. IT'S HARDER THAN I THOUGHT!

I KEEP FLOUNDERING.. LOSING ALTITUDE!! CAN'T GET THE HANG OF IT!

BUT I'VE GOTTA DO IT! CAN'T FAIL NOW!

ALL THE THINGS THE VULTURE USED TO SAY... ABOUT AIR CURRENTS -- DOWN DRAFTS.. WIND VELOCITY...

IT'S COMIN' BACK TO ME.. I'M GETTING IT..!

HE'S GAINING ALTITUDE... SOARING OUT OF RANGE!

KRAK!

I GOT THE **FEEL** OF IT... JUST IN **TIME!**

I'M **FLYING!** I'M **SAFE!** **NOTHING** CAN TOUCH ME **NOW!**

HOLD YOUR **FIRE!** WE'VE **LOST** HIM...

HE'S TOO **HIGH...** AND GOING **HIGHER!**

BUT, EVEN AS THE NEW **VULTURE** SOARS OUT OF SIGHT, IT BEHOOVES US TO OBSERVE **ANOTHER** EVENT WHICH OCCURS NEXT MORNING...

'S A GOOD THING WE OT AN EARLY **START,** HARRY!

AFTER LAST NIGHT'S **SNOWSTORM,** HALF THE CITY IS STILL BLANKET-ED IN!

SPEAKING OF **BLANKETS,** PETE, ARE YOU SURE YOU SHOULDN'T HAVE STAYED IN BED TODAY?

FROM WHERE **I** SIT, YOU LOOK LIKE A TV AD FOR **HEADACHE PILLS!**

AW, I'M **OKAY,** HARR! I'M PROBABLY JUST COMING DOWN WITH A **COLD,** OR SOMETHING.

COMING **DOWN** WITH IT? SON, YOU LOOK AS THOUGH EVERY **VIRUS** IN TOWN IS HAVING A **CONVENTION** RIGHT IN YOUR NOGGIN!

JUST BETWEEN **US,** MR. OSBORN, I FEEL THAT WAY **TOO!**

WONDER HOW I'D LOOK SWINGING AROUND TOWN IN MY **SPIDEY** SUIT... ARMED WITH **ASPIRINS** AND A BOTTLE OF **NOSE DROPS!**

BOY! I'LL BET YOU COULD **INFECT** A WHOLE CITY... JUST BY **EXHALING** A FEW TIMES!

YOU BETTER **BELIEVE** IT!

EN, A FEW MINUTES LATER, AT GOOD '.E.S.U....

HI, GWEN! SAY... RE LOOK **GREAT** WEARING YOUR HAIR THAT WAY!

HY, **THANK YOU,** PETE!

S JUST A **CASUAL** LE STYLE... WHICH OK **ALL MORNING** TO ARRANGE!

OOOH BOY! UST MY **LUCK...!**

GWEN'S IN A **MELLOW** MOOD... AND I FEEL LIKE AN ACCIDENT LOOKING FOR A PLACE TO **HAPPEN!**

SAY! NO **WONDER** PETE LIKES YOUR HAIRDO, GWEN!

HARRY! HARRY! WHY MUST YOU HAVE SUCH A BIG FLAPPING MOUTH?

IT'S MORE LIKE THE WAY **MARY JANE'S** BEEN WEARING **HERS!**

OH, THAT'S **RIGHT!** I ...HADN'T **THOUGHT** OF THAT!

BUT, AS THE MORNING PROGRESSES, PETE FINDS IT INCREASINGLY DIFFI-CULT TO CONCENTRATE ON HIS **SUBJECTS,** LET ALONE GWEN STACY'S HAIR STYLE...

PARKER, YOUR FACE IS **FLUSHED,** AND YOU LOOK **FEVERISH** TO ME!

I GUESS YOU'RE **RIGHT,** MR. WARREN!

I SUGGEST YOU GO **HOME** AND GET YOUR-SELF SOME **REST!**

I DO FEEL KINDA **WOOZY...!**

7

AND SO, LATER THAT DAY OUR SOME-WHAT SICKLY SUPER-HERO TAKES HIS EASE IN FRONT OF HUMANITY'S ALL-PURPOSE PACIFIER, AS HE HEARS ---

..BEFORE BRINGING THIS NEWS PROGRAM TO A CLOSE, WE PRESENT AN *EDITORIAL* BY OUR SPONSOR, THE EMINENT PUBLISHER OF THE *DAILY BUGLE*... MR. J. JONAH JAMESON!

SHEEESH! AS IF I WASN'T SICK *ENOUGH!* WELL, I MIGHT AS WELL HEAR WHAT OL' *CHUCKLES* HAS TO SAY...!

ONCE AGAIN, EVENTS OF THE PAST WEEK HAVE PROVEN THAT *SPIDER-MAN* IS A DANGEROUS, DEADLY *MENACE* TO OUR FAIR CITY!

I MIGHT HAVE *KNOWN* IT! THE SAME OLD TIRED *WHEEZE* ALL OVER AGAIN!

FOR PROOF OF THE *HARM* WHICH THAT WEB-CRAWLING PUBLIC ENEMY CAN CAUSE, CONSIDER THE CASE OF *KRAVEN, THE HUNTER!*

HARM?!! I DARN WELL SAVED THE *LIFE* OF HARRY'S FATHER!*

JJ, YOU'RE JUST *TOO MUCH!*

*IT WAS ALL SPELLED OUT LAST ISH, RIGHT? YOU *KNOW* IT!
--- SMILEY!

IF SPIDER-MAN HAD NOT *INTERFERED,* THE *POLICE* WOULD HAVE *CAPTURED* KRAVEN BY NOW ---

INSTEAD, *ANOTHER* DANGEROUS KILLER NOW ROAMS OUR STREETS, THANKS TO THAT SCURRILOUS, SINISTER SUPER-HEEL!

THANK YOU, MR. JAMESON, FOR ANOTHER CANDID COMMENTARY IN YOUR FAMOUS, FEARLESS, OUTSPOKEN MANNER --!

THAT *DOES* IT! IF I EVER LISTEN TO THAT OLD *WINDBAG* AGAIN, I'LL...

SAY, *WAIT!* WHAT'S *THIS?*

AND NOW, FURTHER NEWS OF LAST NIGHT'S *JAILBREAK* AT MUNICIPAL PRISON!

A *JAIL-BREAK?!*

---MOMENTS AFTER *BLACKIE DRAGO* MADE GOOD HIS ESCAPE, A MAN WEARING THE *VULTURE'S* WINGS WAS SEEN FLYING ABOVE THE AREA ---

OH, NO!

IT'S NOT ENOUGH THAT *KRAVEN* IS STILL AT LARGE --!

NOW THERE'S A NEW *VULTURE* MAKING THE SCENE ... AND HE'S PROBABLY A LOT *YOUNGER* AND *STRONGER* THAN THE OLD ONE!

AND *NATURALLY,* IT ALL HAS TO HAPPEN WHEN I FEEL LIKE A REFUGEE FROM AN *OXYGEN TENT!*

IF YOU *SEE* THIS MAN, YOU ARE URGED TO CALL OUR SPECIAL POLICE NUMBER...

OHH! MY ACHIN' HEAD!

WONDER IF I SHOULD CALL THE *DOCTOR?*

BUT, LEST WE GET TOO *MEDICINAL* ABOUT THE WHOLE THING, LET'S SWITCH OUR SCENE ONCE AGAIN ---

THIS NEW *HELMET* I'M WHIPPIN' UP OUGHTTA GIVE MY *HEAD* SOME EXTRA PROTECTION...

...AND *ALSO,* IT'LL MAKE ME LOOK *SCARIER* THAN EVER ...

---WHICH IS A REAL BIG *PLUS* IN MY LINE OF WORK.

HEY! I'LL BET I COULD FIT A SMALL *SHORT WAVE RECEIVER* IN HERE, ALSO!

THUS, THE STARTLED CITY, WHICH HAD THOUGHT ITSELF *FREE* FROM THE SCOURGE OF THE *VULTURE*, SUDDENLY LEARNS THAT ONE OF THE MOST *DANGEROUS* OF ALL COSTUMED MENACES *FLIES* AGAIN...!

A *PAYROLL BAG!* JUST WHAT I *NEED!*

ANK

THE *VULTURE*.. SWOOPING DOWN FROM THE SKY...!

HE DIVED SO *FAST*... I DIDN'T HAVE *TIME*... TO DRAW MY GUN!

NOTHING CAN STOP A MAN WITH *WINGS!*

HOUR AFTER HOUR, THE *VULTURE* STRIKES LIKE A FLYING WRAITH! NO PERSON IS SAFE ... NO TARGET INVIOLATE ...!

GET ME THE *POLICE!* I'VE BEEN *ROBBED*... BY THE *VULTURE!*

HE DIDN'T TRY TO *HIDE*... DIDN'T WORRY ABOUT THE BURGLAR ALARM!

HE *KNOWS* THAT *NO ONE* CAN STOP HIM!

THE CITY... AND ALL ITS *WEALTH*...ARE *MINE!*

EVERYTHING I DESIRE ... IS MINE... JUST FOR THE *TAKING!*

EVEN *SPIDER-MAN* HASN'T DARED TO SHOW HIMSELF!

HE *KNOWS* I'M HIS *MASTER!*

AND SPEAKING OF OUR YOUTHFUL WALL-CRAWLER...

I'VE HAD JUST ABOUT ALL I CAN TAKE!

THE ONLY THING TO LISTEN TO ON THE RADIO IS *BULLETINS*.. ONE AFTER THE OTHER... ABOUT THE *VULTURE!*

THAT, HIGH-FLYIN' *HOOD* IS RUNNING *WILD!*

AND, HE'S *GOTTA* BE STOPPED!

I CAN'T LET A LITTLE *FEVER* KEEP ME..

OHHHH..MY *HEAD!*

I MUST BE EVEN WEAKER THAN I *THOUGHT!*

PARKER.. YOU BETTER HIT THE *SACK* AGAIN... *FAST!*

I HATE TO *DO* THIS---BUT MAYBE IF I CALL MATT *MURDOCK*.. HE'LL PUT *DAREDEVIL* ON HIS TRAIL!

IT'S THE *LEAST* HE CAN DO... AFTER ME FIG ING *STILT-MA* FOR HI

*IN DD #27...NOW ON SALE! BUT FINISH *THIS* YARN *FIRST!* ---SLEEPY STAN.

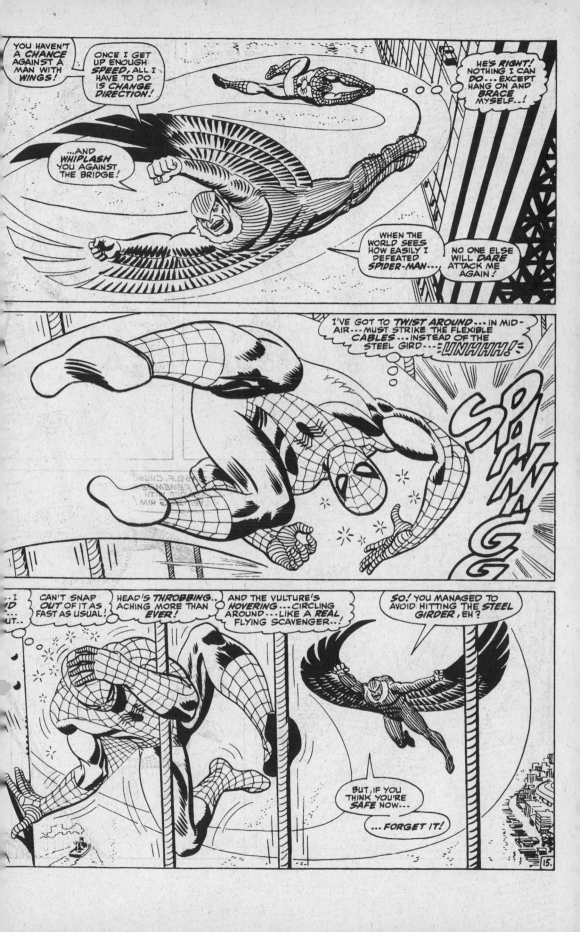

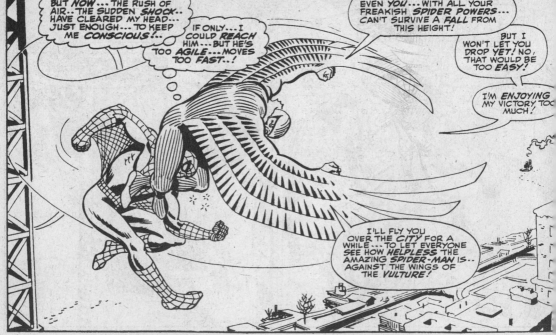

...AND, AT THAT VERY PRECISE, EXACT, SELF-SAME *INSTANT*... (NOT THAT OUR SPLIT-SECOND CHRONOLOGY IS *REALLY* ALL THAT IMPORTANT!)

NO NEED TO WORRY SO, MAY, DEAR!

I'M SURE PETER JUST HAS A SIMPLE COLD!

BUT WHEN I HEARD THEY SENT HIM HOME FROM *SCHOOL*, I FELT I SHOULD MAKE *CERTAIN*!

HERE'S HIS PAD *NOW*! AND NOT AN OXYGEN TENT IN SIGHT!

SURPRISE, HARRY BOY! WE BROUGHT GOODIES, GIGGLES, AND GRINS FOR YOUR GERM-RIDDLED ROOMIE!

HI, M.J.! OH, MRS. *PARKER*! GEE, PETE DIDN'T COME *HOME* AFTER CLASS---SO HE MUST HAVE FELT LOTS *BETTER*!

HE PROBABLY STOPPED AT THE *SILVER SPOON* FOR A SODA!

HEAR THAT, MAY? I *TOLD* YOU NOT TO WORRY SO!

THEN YOU DIDN'T *HAVE* TO CALL THE DOCTOR?

MY, I'M *SO* RELIEVED!

I *KNOW* I WORRY TOO MUCH, BUT PETER HAS ALWAYS BEEN SUCH A *FRAGILE* BOY--!

HEY THERE, HANDSOME! I JUST HAD AN ECONOMY-SIZED *BRAINSTORM*!

LET'S DRIVE MRS P. AND MY EVER-LOVIN' AUNTIE *HOME* IN YOUR CHARIOT---THEN WE CAN *JOIN* PETEY-O FOR A COKE! O.K. ?'

BEST OFFER I'VE HAD ALL DAY, M.J.!

YOU ONLY *SAID* THAT 'CAUSE IT'S *TRUE*!

AS YOU'VE PROBABLY *GUESSED*, WE JUST TOSSED IN THAT TITANICALLY TAME TABLEAU FOR THE BENEFIT OF *JAZZY JOHNNY*, WHO'D RATHER DRAW SLICK CHICKS THAN FLYING FIENDS!

BUT NOW, IT'S *FRENZY-TIME* AGAIN---

HAH! SO, YOU'VE STOPPED *STRUGGLING*, HAVE YOU? I *GUESSED* YOU'D SOON BE PETRIFIED WITH *FEAR*!

FEAR, SHMEAR! I'VE GOT TO PLAY POSSUM TILL MY HEAD CLEARS!

THAT *FLAGPOLE* BELOW! IT MIGHT BE MY ONE *CHANCE*..!

ARE YOU WONDERING WHEN I'LL *DROP* YOU?

WELL, IN CASE YOU'RE *INTERESTED*, I'LL --- UHH!!

TELL YOU *WHAT*, VULCH.. I'LL *END* THE SUSPENSE.. WITH A COUPLE OF *KARATE* CHOPS!

THAK!

THAK!

THOSE *HAVE* TO DO IT!! I'M --TOO *WEAK*--FOR ANOTHER TRY--!

17.

NOW..ALL I HAVE TO DO.. IS STAY IN THE *SHADOWS!*

AT THIS HOUR..THE STREETS ARE MOSTLY *DESERTED...*

THEN, AS THE LONG, TORTUROUS MINUTES DRONE ENDLESSLY ON —

JUST ANOTHER FEW BLOCKS... AND I'LL BE *THERE!*

THEN...IF I CAN JUST SNEAK IN...WITHOUT *HARRY* SEEING ME..!

MY LUCK'S HOLDING OUT..FOR ONCE!

HARRY ISN'T *IN!* MUS' BE ON A DATE...THE LUCKY STIFF..!

BUT THEN... OH *NO!*

HE'S AT THE DOOR *NOW!* ---MUSTN'T SEE ME..LIKE *THIS!*

CLICK!

PARKER... IF YOU EVER MOVED *FAST*... NOW'S THE TIME TO DO IT!

WOW, AM I *TIRED!*

HEY, ARE YOU *THERE*, PETEY BOY? CAN'T SEE A *THING* WITH THE LIGHT OUT!

OH, *SORRY!* I DIDN'T KNOW YOU WERE *ASLEEP!*

HOW'S YOUR *COLD*, PETE? ...FEELING *BETTER?*

SURE... MUCH BETTER! I GUESS I JUST NEEDED SOME *REST*..!

OKAY, MR. P.! SEE YOU IN THE A.M.!

BUT, JUST AS OUR AILING HERO GRATEFULLY SHUTS HIS EYES, *ANOTHER* MAN'S EYES ARE WIDE *OPEN*...AND FILLED WITH BESTIAL *RAGE*..!

SO! THE *VULTURE* IS NOW CONSIDERED THE CITY'S *DEADLIEST MENACE*, IS HE?

WELL... *KRAVEN THE HUNTER* WILL SEE ABOUT THAT!

XAK!

I'M THE ONE WHO FIRST BEAT SPIDER-MAN!

I'M THE ONE WITH THE STRENGTH...THE SPEED...THE STAMINA OF A JUNGLE MAN-KILLER!

NO WING-FLAPPING, FLYING FOOL CAN STEAL MY GLORY FROM ME!

NONE BUT KRAVEN CAN FIGHT THE MIGHTIEST CARNIVORE BAREHANDED!!

T-TIP!

COME, MY PET! IT'S TIME FOR YOUR MASTER TO TEST HIS METTLE ONCE AGAIN!

DEFEND YOURSELF, RAJAH! THE MOMENT BELONGS TO KRAVEN!

4.

HAH! IN THIS MANNER WILL I STRIKE AT THE HAPLESS VULTURE!

RRRRRRRR

ONCE AGAIN, I'VE PROVEN THAT KRAVEN IS AS POWERFUL AS SKILLFUL AS EVER!

NOW BACK, RAJAH... BACK TO YOUR CAGE! YOUR MASTER COMMANDS!!

EVEN THE TERROR OF THE JUNGLE IS HELPLESS BEFORE MY MIGHT!

NEXT, I SHALL CRUSH THE VULTURE...AND THEN...ALL OTHERS WHO TRY TO ROB ME OF MY GLORY!

FOR NO ONE'S KRAVEN'S EQUAL!

WHEREVER THE VULTURE MAY FLY... KRAVEN WILL BRING HIM DOWN!

SO LET THE HUNT BEGIN...!

ASK ANY COMIC STRIP WRITER...HE'LL TELL YOU THE MOST VALUABLE WORD IN CAPTION-WRITING IS... MEANWHILE...

MAY PARKER! YOU MUSTN'T ALLOW YOURSELF TO BECOME SO UP-SET!

YOUR NEPHEW JUST HAS A SIMPLE, EVERYDAY COLD!

I KNOW, ANNA, DEAR.. BUT HE'S SUCH A FRAIL BOY...

AND NOW, SINCE HE MOVED AWAY, THERE'S NO ONE TO LOOK AFTER HIM!

I JUST WANT TO BE SURE THAT HE DOESN'T NEED ANYTHING!

EVER NOTICE HOW THE SWEETEST, SHYEST LITTLE OLD LADY CAN OFTEN HAVE A WILL OF UNADULTERATED IRON?

HEADS UP, PETE! YOU'VE GOT GUESTS!

OH DEAR! MY LITTLE BOY IS STILL IN BED!

WITH HIS SPIDEY SUIT ON, NO LESS!

HI, AUNT MAY... AND MRS. WATSON! NICE OF YOU TO DROP BY!

I WAS JUST, EH, ABOUT TO TAKE A NAP!

IF ANYONE PULLS THIS COVER OFF, I'M DEAD!

I DO DECLARE! I THINK YOU'VE STILL GOT A FEVER!

I'M OKAY...HONEST! ALL I REALLY NEED IS A GOOD NIGHT'S SLEEP!

HOW SWEET! YOU DON'T WANT TO WORRY YOUR AUNTIE!

BUT WE'RE NOT GOING TO TAKE ANY CHANCES WITH THAT COLD, YOUNG MAN!

I'LL CALL DR. BROMWELL AND HAVE HIM COME OVER TO LOOK AT YOU!

OH, NO!! THE LAST THING IN THE WORLD I WANT IS AN EXAMINATION!

WAIT, AUNT MAY! THERE'S NO NEED TO CALL HIM...!

NONSENSE DEAR! YOU JUST STAY THERE AND REST!

BETTER DO AS YOUR AUNT SAYS, PETE! IT WON'T HURT TO HAVE THE DOC GIVE YOU A ONCE-OVER!

SO GET SOME SHUT-EYE, ROOM-MATE! I'LL GRAB THE PHONE IF IT RINGS!

WHAT'S THAT? HE'S IN SURGERY NOW? OH.. WELL, TELL HIM TO GET HERE AS SOON AS HE'S FINISHED! WE'LL WAIT FOR HIM!

HONESTLY! I'VE NEVER KNOWN A PERSON WHO WORRIED SO!

A BODY SIMPLY CAN'T BE TOO CAUTIOUS, ANNA!

6.

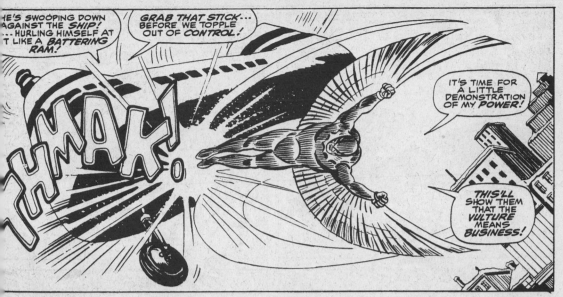

HE'S SWOOPING DOWN AGAINST THE *SHIP!* ...HURLING HIMSELF AT IT LIKE A *BATTERING RAM!*

GRAB THAT STICK... BEFORE WE TOPPLE OUT OF *CONTROL!*

THMAK!

IT'S TIME FOR A LITTLE DEMONSTRATION OF MY *POWER!*

THIS'LL SHOW THEM THAT THE *VULTURE* MEANS *BUSINESS!*

HAH! THEY JUST PULLED OUT OF THAT *DIVE* IN THE NICK OF TIME!

NOW THEY'LL DO *ANYTHING* I ORDER THEM TO...

...FOR THEY KNOW WHAT IT *MEANS* TO DEFY ME!

YOU MURDEROUS *MADMAN!* WHAT *IS* IT? WHAT DO YOU *WANT?*

THE *ATTACHE CASE* WHICH ONE OF THE *PASSENGERS* IS CARRYING! IT'S FILLED WITH UNCUT *DIAMONDS!*

...AND IT *OUT* TO ME--NOW.. OR YOU'LL NEVER REACH THE AIRPORT!

YOU'VE GOT *THIRTY SECONDS* BEFORE I SLAM INTO YOUR *SHIP* AGAIN!

HERE! THIS IS WHAT HE WANTS!

FOR THE LOVE OF HEAVEN-- GIVE IT TO HIM... BEFORE HE KILLS US *ALL!*

HURRY! HE'S GETTING READY FOR ANOTHER *POWER DIVE* AT US!

ONLY *FIVE SECONDS* LEFT! DON'T SAY I DIDN'T *WARN YOU...!*

8.

HERE!! TAKE IT, BLAST YOU... TAKE IT!

HAH! I KINDA THOUGHT YOU'D END UP SEEING THINGS MY WAY!

NO WONDER THE ORIGINAL VULTURE WAS WILLING TO GUARD HIS SECRET WITH HIS LIFE!

A MAN WITH WINGS!! CAN DO ANYTHING!! ANYTHING!!

AND NO ONE CAN EVER STOP ME!

BUT, THOUGH THE VULTURE IS AS YET UNAWARE OF IT, THERE IS ONE FUMIN' FOE WHO'S ANXIOUS TO TRY..!

I'VE FINALLY SEEN HIM IN THE FLESH!

HE'S FLYING OFF! I'VE REACHED THE SPOT TOO LATE! BUT IT DOESN'T MATTER NOW!

NOW THAT I HAVE THE SCENT, HE CANNOT ESCAPE ME!

AND THE BIRDLIKE BADDIE CAUSES CONSTERNATION AT THE DAILY BUGLE, AS WELL...

JJ, THE PUBLIC'S CLAMORING FOR MORE PHOTOS OF THE VULTURE!

SHADDUP, FOSWELL! DON'TCHA THINK I KNOW IT!

WHAT IN BLAZES HAPPENED TO OUR STAFF PHOTOGS? ARE THEY ALL ON VACATION??

MISS BRAN DON'T JUS STAND THER GET THAT CRE PARKER ON TH PHONE---

I MEAN NOW!!

WHAT? OH, SORRY.. PETE'S RESTING NOW.... CAN'T COME TO THE PHONE!

I DON'T CARE WHO WANTS HIM! JAMESON DOESN'T CUT ANY ICE WITH ME!

OH--IS IT THAT SWEET JONAH JAMESON?

TELL HIM THAT MAY PARKER SENDS HER REGARDS!

HE'S JUST THE DEAREST SOUL!

RINNG!

THE DOOR-BELL!

I'LL GET IT!

I DON'T SEE HOW THAT BOY CAN SLEEP THROUGH ALL OF THIS!

GWEN! M.J.! WOW... I FEEL LIKE I WON A RAFFLE!

YOU KNOW IT, SON! HI, AUNT ANNA! WE WERE PASSING BY AND THOUGHT PETEY COULD USE SOME CHEERING UP!

YOU KNOW OUR MOTTO: CHASE THE BLUES AWAY.. WITH GWEN AND M.J.!

OH! HO NICE T SEE YOU GIRL

WHEN PETE WAKES UP AN SEES WHAT HE MISSED, HE'LL KILL HIMSELF!

WELL, IF PETE IS *NAPPING*, WE'D BETTER FOLD OUR TENTS AND VANISH IN THE NIGHT!

YOU THINK I'D LET YOU SLIP AWAY THAT *EASY*?

HERE'S A *BEAT* THAT'LL BLAST 'IM OUT OF BED LIKE *GANG-BUSTERS*!

DON'T MAKE A *MOVE*, PUSSYCAT! HE CAN'T SLEEP *FOREVER*!

SIMMER DOWN, SWEET STUFF! THE POOR GUY *NEEDS* HIS REST-- HE'S BEEN RUNNING A FEVER!

CLICK!

YOU *KNOW* IT, *DAD*! BUT I THOUGHT IT WAS BECAUSE OF *ME*!

BUT, IT'S LIKE *TRAGIC* TO WASTE ALL THOSE DREAMY *DISCS*!

COME ALONG, LITTLE ONE! *GWEN* WILL BUY YOU A *MOVIE MAG* TO KEEP YOU CULTURAL TILL PETE'S ON HIS FEET AGAIN!

IF IT'S *MUSIC* YOU WANT, BUNNY.. WE CAN GRAB A *KAZOO* ON THE WAY!

HOLD IT! HOLD IT! I'LL WALK YOU GALS DOWN! NO *SACRIFICE* IS TOO GREAT FOR HEROIC HARRY!

IT'S LIKE I ALWAYS SAY-- THE BOY IS ALL *HEART*!

TELL PETER WE CAME BY, MRS. PARKER! AND CALL IF YOU *NEED* ANYTHING, HEAR?

THANK YOU, CHILD! YOU'VE BOTH BEEN SO VERY *KIND*!

SEE YA, AUNT ANNA!.. LIKE SUBSEQUENTLY!

BUT AS THE GLAMOR BRIGADE DEPARTS, WHAT OF OUR BROODING, BED-RIDDEN BUDDY..?

A *FINE* THING! I COULDN'T EVEN GO OUT TO SEE THE GALS!

THIS *DOUBLE IDENTITY* BIT SURE CAN BE A *DRAG* SOMETIMES!

ISN'T THE DOC *EVER* GONNA GET HERE?

WELL, I CAN ALWAYS KEEP BUSY THINKING OF THE *VULTURE*!

I WONDER WHAT THAT HIGH-FLYIN' HEEL IS *DOING*... RIGHT ABOUT *NOW*..?

AND SINCE HE *ASKED*...

IT FEELS SO *GREAT* TO BE UP HERE... WITH THE WHOLE *CITY* HELPLESS BELOW ME.. THAT I DON'T FEEL LIKE I'LL *EVER* COME DOWN!

YOU'LL COME *DOWN*, ALL RIGHT..!

THWIPP!

WHAT'S *THAT*?!!

10.

ALL RIGHT, WILD MAN...YOU ASKED FOR IT...!

HERE IN THE AIR I'M IN MY ELEMENT!

YOU TALK TOO MUCH! IN THE JUNGLE, BEASTS FIGHT SILENTLY! KRAVEN PREFERS IT THAT WAY!

YOU'LL NEVER HAVE A CHANCE TO TALK AGAIN, BECAUSE I'LL--!

HEY! CUT IT OUT!! HAVE YOU GONE MAD?!!

YOU'RE SHIFTING YOUR WEIGHT TOO FAST!

YOU'LL PULL US BOTH DOWN--INTO THAT SKYLIGHT BELOW!

CRASH!

OF COURSE! THIS IS EXACTLY WHAT I PLANNED!

NEEDLESS TO SAY, A BATTLE BETWEEN A FLYING PUBLIC ENEMY AND A SUPER-POWERED HUNTER ISN'T LIKELY TO GO UNNOTICED! THEREFORE, SECONDS LATER...

BULLETIN! AT THIS MOMENT, POLICE ARE ATTEMPTING TO CORDON OFF THE AREA AROUND THE CITY'S EXHIBITION HALL, WHERE THE VULTURE AND KRAVEN THE HUNTER HAVE CRASHED THROUGH THE SKYLIGHT INTO THE EXPLORERS' EXPOSITION!

THE VULTURE... BATTLING WITH KRAVEN!

IF THEY'RE NOT STOPPED, THEY'LL TEAR THE CITY APART!

AUNT MAY--- AND MRS. WATSON... THEY'RE BOTH DOZING!

I'VE JUST GOT TO TAKE A CHANCE AND SLIP OUT NOW! MAYBE I CAN RETURN BEFORE THEY AWAKE!

IF I RETURN AT ALL!

IT'S REALLY AMAZING! I FEEL AS THOUGH I'VE NEVER BEEN SICK!

I DON'T KNOW WHETHER IT'S MY OWN STAMINA, OR AUNT MAY'S CHICKEN BROTH...

BUT WHATEVER IT IS-- I'M RARIN' TO GO NOW!!

12.

AND SO, TO THE DELIGHT OF ZILLIONS OF *SPIDEYPHILES* EVERYWHERE, IT'S *WALL-CRAWLING TIME* ONCE MORE--!!

I *KNOW* HOW POWERFUL *KRAVEN* AND THE *VULTURE* ARE... BUT I *ALSO* KNOW I CAN TAKE 'EM *BOTH!*

I'VE GOT THE *SPEED*, AND THE *SKILL*, AND THE *STRENGTH* TO COME OUT ON TOP IN *ANY BALL GAME!*

I'VE HAD SOME *UNLUCKY* BREAKS BEFORE... BUT NOW MY LUCK'S *CHANGED* ... I CAN *FEEL* IT!

I *KNEW* IT WOULDN'T TAKE ME LONG TO REACH *EXHIBITION HALL!*

NO *WONDER* KRAVEN PICKED A SPOT LIKE THIS... IT'S ALL FITTED OUT FOR THE *EXPLORERS' EXHIBITION!*

HE'LL BE RIGHT IN HIS *ELEMENT*... IT'S LIKE A MINIATURE *JUNGLE* IN THERE!

PRETTY *CLEVER* THE WAY HE COVERED THIS SKYLIGHT WITH A *NET*, SO THE VULTURE CAN'T FLY *OUT* AGAIN!

WELL, I'D BETTER SET UP MY *CAMERA* AND JOIN THE PARTY WHILE IT'S STILL GOING STRONG...!

GREAT, FIGHT, FELLAS! I'M SURE GLAD I GOT ME A *RINGSIDE SEAT!*

SPIDER-MAN! HE DARED COME *HERE?!!*

YOU *FRAUD!* YOU CLAIMED TO HAVE *FINISHED* HIM... JUST AS *I* WILL FINISH *YOU!!*

13

16.

18.

Panel 1: AND NOW, AT *LAST*... THE ULTIMATE CONFRONTATION -- THE ULTIMATE *RECKONING!!*

LIKE THE MASTER *HUNTER* THAT I AM, I HAVE BROUGHT MY GREATEST QUARRY TO *BAY!* ALL THAT IS *LEFT* IS TO DELIVER THE LAST, SHATTERING *BLOW!!*

YOU *KNOW* IT, *GRUE-SOME!*

BUT THERE'S *ONE* THING YOU LEFT *OUT*--!

Panel 2: THAT LAST *BLOW* YOU MENTIONED WILL BE DELIVERED BY YOUR FRIENDLY NEIGHBORHOOD *SPIDER-MAN!*

WHUPPF!

AND NEVER LET IT BE SAID THAT TH[E] PROPORTIONAT[E] STRENGTH O[F] A HUMBLE *SPIDER* IS ANYTHING TO WHISTLE *DIXIE* AT, OL' BUDDY.

Panel 3: BECAUSE, IN CASE YOU DIDN'T *KNOW* IT, I JUST *WHUMMMPED* YOU WITH THE SAME KINDA *WHUMP* THAT ONCE STAGGERED THE *HULK!**

*DON'T TAKE *OUR* WORD FOR IT, TIGER! GET YOUR *SPIDEY* ANNUAL #3 OUT OF THE VAULT, AND SEE FOR YOURSELF! --SQUARE-SHOOTIN' STAN.

Panel 4: GET THE *MESSAGE*, JUNGLE MAN?

Panel 5: HE GOT THE MESSAGE!

THUMP!

THUS, A FEW SIMPLE, SOUL-SATISFYING SECONDS LATER...

JUST *HOLD THAT POSE*, GENTS! I WANNA HAVE A LITTLE *KEEP-SAKE* OF THE TWO OF YOU...

SOMETHING TO PUT IN MY *HOPE CHEST!*

HOW'S ABOUT SAYIN' *CHEESE* FOR A FELLA, KRAVEY?

OL' *JOLLY JONAH* OUGHTTA BE WILLING TO PAY THROUGH THE NOSE FOR A SHOT LIKE *THIS!*

CLICK!

OKAY, TRUE BELIEVERS... ON YOUR TOES!! IT'S *WRAP-UP* TIME AGAIN...

NOW *THAT'S* WHAT I CALL A REAL *FUN* EVENING!!

EXACTLY THREE MINUTES AND TWENTY-TWO SECONDS LATER---(AS IF IT MATTERS!)

PETER DEAR, DO YOU FEEL UP TO SEEING *DR. BROMWELL* NOW?

DON'T WORRY, SON...WE'LL HAVE YOU ON YOUR FEET IN *NO* TIME!

SURE, AUNT MAY! I, EH, I THINK I CAN *MAKE* IT!

MRS. PARKER, IT SEEMS THAT A DAY IN *BED* DID OUR PATIENT A WORLD OF *GOOD!*

FAR AS I CAN TELL, PETE, YOU'RE AS *FIT* AS THE PROVERBIAL FIDDLE!

I GUESS I JUST NEEDED SOME NICE, QUIET *REST!*

I STAYED OUT-SIDE, TO MAKE SURE HE WOULDN'T BE *DISTURBED!*

IT WAS PROBABLY JUST A 24-HOUR *VIRUS!* HE'S PERFECTLY *FINE* NOW!

I'M *SO* RELIEVED, DOCTOR! HE'S SUCH A *FRAGILE* BOY!

FRAGILE??! MY DEAR WOMAN, HE'S THE PICTURE OF ROBUST *HEALTH!*

MERCY, DOCTOR! IF I DIDN'T KNOW *BETTER*, I'D THINK YOU *MEANT* IT!

ISN'T THAT DR. BROMWELL THE *DEAREST* THING?

AS *YOU* WOULD SAY, PETER...HE'S A REGULAR *PUSSYWILLOW!*

NO, AUNT MAY! I KEEP *TELLING* YOU ...THE WORD IS *PUSSY-CAT!*

BUT I THINK PUSSYWILLOWS ARE MUCH *CUTER*, DEAR!

OKAY, PRETTY GIRL! IF *YOU* SAY SO, HE'S A *PUSSY-WILLOW!*

THE MORE MAY *SAYS* IT, THE MORE IT SOUNDS *RIGHT* TO ME!

TELL YOU WHAT! HOW ABOUT ME TAKING MY FAVORITE GALS TO A *MOVIE!*

THERE'S A WAY-OUT *WESTERN* AT THE BIJOU!

THAT WOULD BE *NICE*, PETER!

YOU'VE BEEN COOPED UP SO LONG, YOU CAN USE A LITTLE *EXCITEMENT!*

NEXT! "SPIDER-MAN NO MORE!"

20.

WELL, WHO CARES WHAT PEOPLE THINK, ANYWAY?

THAT'S JUST THE TROUBLE-- I CARE!

EVERYONE FLIPS OVER THE FF...

THEY THINK DAREDEVIL'S THE COOLEST..

CAPTAIN AMERICA TURNS 'EM ON---

BUT, JUST MENTION SPIDER-MAN...AND FREEZE-VILLE!

I'LL NEVER UNDER-STAND HOW IT HAPPENED!

I DON'T STEAL CANDY FROM BABIES, OR TIE TIN CANS ON PUPPY DOGS!

IT'S ALL JAMESON'S FAULT! HE'S G[OT] THE PUBLIC CONVINCED THAT NEXT [TO] ME, GENGHIS KHAN WAS [A] PIKER!

THE PUBLIC! THE MORE I HELP THEM--- THE MORE THEY HATE ME!

Minutes later, reaching his apartment, the brooding youth finds ANOTHER cause for concern...

MRS. WATSON CALLED EARLIER... IT'S YOUR AUNT... SHE'S ILL!

WANT ME TO DRIVE YOU THERE, PETE?

AUNT MAY! THAT MEANS.. SHE NEEDS ME!

I'LL TAKE MY BIKE, HARRY! IT'S FASTER!

I JUST PRAY I'M NOT.. TOO LATE.

AUNT MAY MUST HAVE HAD ANOTHER ATTACK! AND I WAS TOO BUSY PLAYING SUPER HERO TO BE THERE WHEN I SHOULD HAVE!

MRS. WATSON! I GOT HERE AS FAST AS I COULD! WHAT HAPPENED??

IT'S ALL RIGHT, PETER! SHE'S RESTING NOW! LUCKILY, THE DOCTOR WAS JUST PASSING BY! IF NOT FOR THAT..!

WHERE IS SHE? CAN I SEE HER?

SHE KEPT CALLING FOR YOU...WONDERING WHERE YOU WERE! SHE WAS SO WORRIED!

BUT THEN, DR. BROMWELL MANAGED TO GIVE HER A SEDATIVE!

IF I HAD BEEN AT HOME... LIKE ANY OTHER NORMAL GUY---THEY COULD HAVE REACHED ME FAST!

BUT NO....I WAS OUT.. FLEXING MY MUSCLES.. TRYING TO HELP THE VERY PEOPLE WHO FEAR ME!

WE'D BETTER LET HER SLEEP, PETER! I'LL TELL HER YOU WERE HERE!

...RY NOT TO BE ...OO FAR FROM ...HE PHONE ...LL YOUR ...UNT IS BACK ...N HER FEET, ...SON!

I WILL, MRS. WATSON!

AND THANKS.. FOR LOOKING AFTER HER!

IF..ANYTHING HAD *HAPPENED* ...BEFORE I COULD HAVE REACHED HER.. I'D NEVER *FORGIVE* MYSELF!

EVER SINCE I MOVED IN WITH HARRY, I'VE HARDLY EVEN *THOUGHT* ABOUT AUNT MAY!

AFTER ALL, WHY *SHOULD* I CARE ABOUT HER?

ALL SHE EVER *DID* IS SPEND A *LIFETIME* LOOKING AFTER ME.. TREATING ME LIKE HER OWN *SON!*

THAT'S... ALL...

SHE DEVOTED MOST OF HER LIFE..REPLACING THE *MOTHER*.. THAT I NEVER HAD!

AND, I SHOW MY *GRATITUDE*--BY NEVER *BEING* THERE...WHEN SHE *NEEDS* ME!

I'VE GOT A ROUGH *EXAM* TOMORROW.. BUT THERE'S NO USE TRYING TO *STUDY*...

I'D NEVER BE ABLE TO CONCENTRATE.. NOT *NOW!*

...HE NEXT DAY, AT THE CONCLUSION OF THE TEST...

...ANYTHING ...RONG, ...TE? I ...ARDLY ...AW YOU ...RITE A ...ING!

IF I *PASSED*, IT'LL BE A *MIRACLE!*

PARKER! WOULD YOU MIND *REMAINING* A FEW MINUTES AFTER CLASS?

I'D LIKE TO HAVE A WORD WITH YOU!

SURE, PROFESSOR WARREN!

JUST A FRIENDLY *WARNING*, SON! YOUR GRADES HAVE BEEN *DECLINING* STEADILY!

YOU CAME TO THIS CLASS WITH THE *FINEST RECORD* IN SCIENCE I'VE EVER SEEN! I HOPE YOU DON'T FEEL YOU CAN JUST *COAST ALONG* ON THAT!

NO, SIR! I'M GOING TO START *BUCK-LING* DOWN!

..., *PETER!* I'M HAVING ...LITTLE *GET-* ...GETHER AT ...ME TONIGHT!

I'D LOVE YOU TO *BE* THERE, IF YOU CAN!

I'VE BEEN *WAITING* FOR GWEN TO ASK ME! BUT WITH AUNT MAY SO ILL...AND MY GRADES SO LOW...

GEE, I'M *SORRY,* GWEN! WOULD YOU MIND IF I TAKE A *RAIN CHECK*, INSTEAD?

'COURSE NOT, PETER! THOUGH I *AM* DIS-APPOINTED!

EXIT

I'M PROBABLY THE *ONLY ONE* WHO'LL HAVE TO REFUSE HER INVITATION... ALL BECAUSE OF THE *COMPLICATIONS* SPIDER-MAN CREATES IN MY LIFE!

I HAVEN'T EVEN HAD TIME FOR DATING SCATTER-BRAINED, *MARY JANE* THESE DAYS!

OR, IS SHE *REALLY* SO SCATTER-BRAINED?

I'VE NEVER BEEN ABLE TO TAKE THE TIME TO FIND OUT FOR *SURE!*

SO LONG AS I HANG ONTO MY *SPIDER-MAN* IDENTITY I HAVEN'T TIME FOR *ANYTHING*---EXCEPT NEW *PROBLEMS!*

5.

ALL THE WAY HOME, THE TROUBLED YOUTH'S THOUGHTS KEEP TUMBLING TORTUOUSLY IN HIS BRAIN, UNTIL...

HARRY'S DAD OFFERED ME A JOB...WORKING IN HIS CHEMISTRY LAB...A JOB I'D GIVE MY EYE TEETH FOR!

BUT I'VE EVEN HAD TO TURN THAT DOWN, BECAUSE IT WOULD INVOLVE A LOT OF NIGHT WORK!

AND, I'VE GOT TO KEEP MY EVENINGS FREE.. IN CASE SPIDER-MAN HAS TO GO INTO ACTION!

SPIDER-MAN!! I'M BEGINNING TO HATE THE VERY SOUND OF THAT NAME!

BUT, HATE IT OR NOT, NO SOONER DOES HE TURN ON THE T.V., THAN THAT SOBRIQUET CONTINUES TO HAUNT THE BROODING ADVENTURER...

MAYBE IF I HEAR THE NEWS FOR A WHILE, I'LL--OH NO!

...AND MY NEWSPAPER CHALLENGES ANYONE TO PROVE THAT SPIDER-MAN ISN'T A PUBLIC ENEMY!

IT'S JAMESON AGAIN...USING THE SHOW HE SPONSORS TO STIR UP THE PEOPLE AGAINST ME!

SOME MISGUIDED FOOLS CALL HIM A SUPER HERO! BUT, WHY DOES HE OPERATE OUTSIDE THE LAW? WHY DOES HE CLOAK HIS IDENTITY BEHIND THAT UGLY FRIGHT MASK?! LET ME TELL YOU WHY...

BECAUSE HE'S REALLY AN EGOMANIAC...A NEUROTIC TROUBLE-MAKER, FLAUNTING HIS POWER BEFORE THE ORDINARY CITIZENS WHOM HE DESPISES!

FOR ALL WE KNOW, HE HIMSELF PROVOKES THE CRIMINALS WHOM HE LATER SEEMS TO DEFEAT!

DO WE WANT OUR YOUNGSTERS TO MAKE AN IDOL OF A MENTALLY-DISTURBED MENACE??

I SAY NO!! WE MUST FIND HIM... UNMASK HIM...AND THEN...DESTROY HIM!!

AS PUBLISHER OF THE DAILY BUGLE, I OFFER ONE THOUSAND DOLLARS FOR THE CAPTURE AND CONVICTION OF THAT WEB-SLINGING, WALL-CRAWLING MOCKERY OF A MAN...

A THOUSAND DOLLARS REWARD... JUST FOR ME?!

HE..HATES ME..FAR MORE THAN I THOUGHT..!

AGNAVOX

THE TIME HAS COME TO RID OURSELVES OF THAT FALSE-FACED FREAK WHO HIDES BY DAY AND TRIES TO TAKE LAW INTO HIS OWN HANDS UNDER COVER OF NIGHT!

THE TERRIBLE THING IS...HE MEANS IT! HE ACTUALLY BELIEVES WHAT HE SAYS! HE SINCERELY THINKS I AM A THREAT TO SOCIETY!

MENACE! EGOMANIAC! PUBLIC ENEMY! FRAUD! MENTALLY DISTURBED!

PERHAPS...ONLY A MADMAN WOULD DO WHAT I DO...TAKING THE RISKS...ACCEPTING THE DANGERS....AND...FOR WHAT??!

BUT...WHAT IF HE'S RIGHT?? HOW...CAN I HAVE BEEN SO BLIND...NEVER TO HAVE REALIZED..???

AFTER ALL THESE YEARS..IT'S SUDDENLY CLEAR...I MUST BE A GLORY-HUNGRY FOOL....OR WORSE!

LIKE A MAN IN A TRANCE, THE HEARTSICK YOUTH LEAVES HIS APARTMENT, TRUDGING LISTLESSLY THROUGH THE NIGHT...HIS THOUGHTS AS DARK AND STORMY AS THE SKIES ABOVE HIM...

IN ORDER TO SATISFY MY CRAVING FOR EXCITEMENT...I'VE JEOPARDIZED EVERYTHING THAT REALLY MATTERS..

BEING SPIDER-MAN HAS BROUGHT ME NOTHING...BUT UNHAPPINESS!

AUNT MAY...MY FRIENDS...THE GIRLS IN MY LIFE...

AND..FOR WHAT..??

CAN I BE SURE MY ONLY MOTIVE WAS THE CONQUEST OF CRIME?

OR WAS IT THE HEADY THRILL OF BATTLE...THE PRECIOUS TASTE OF TRIUMPH...THE PARANOIAC THIRST FOR POWER WHICH CAN NEVER BE QUENCHED??

MAY HEAVEN FORGIVE ME...THE MORE I THINK OF IT...THE MORE I FEEL THAT JAMESON WAS RIGHT!

IN WHICH CASE...FOR THE SAKE OF MY OWN SANITY...

..THERE'S ONLY ONE THING LEFT TO DO...

LOANS

7

NO...DESPITE WHAT YOU MAY THINK...OUR TALE IS NOT YET ENDED! FOR, THE VERY NEXT MORNING...

HOLD IT! STOP! YOU CAN'T GO IN THERE!

WAIT! THAT'S MR. JAMESON'S PRIVATE OFFICE!

MAINTAIN YOUR COOL, LADY!

WHEN HE SEES WHAT I'VE GOT HERE, HE'LL GIVE YA A MEDAL!

HEY, JAMESON... OPEN UP! THIS IS YOUR LUCKY DAY, MISTER!

MISS BRANT! SINCE WHEN DO YOU LET PUNK KIDS COME BARGING INTO MY OFFICE?!!

I-I'M SORRY! I COULDN'T STOP HIM! HE RACED RIGHT PAST ME...!

HOLD IT! BEFORE YOU BLOW A GASKET, LOOK WHAT I FOUND IN A TRASH CAN!

WHAT DO YOU THINK THIS IS... A GARBAGE-COLLECTION AGEN---HEY! WAIT! C'MERE!!

LET ME SEE THAT!! IT'S A COSTUME... IT'S THAT WALL-CRAWLING WEASEL'S COSTUME!

I'LL BE HANGED IF IT ISN'T! IT LOOKS LIKE THE REAL McCOY!

AND, IF YOU FOUND IT IN A TRASH CAN... IT CAN ONLY MEAN... ONE THING..!!

DON'T JUST STAND THERE, MISS BRANT! GET ME THE CITY DESK--AND I MEAN NOW!

YEAH! YEAH! YOU HEARD ME RIGHT! I'M HOLDING IT NOW!!

PUT OUT AN EXTRA! SPLASH IT ACROSS THE FRONT PAGE!!

YOU RATE A REWARD, KID! GRAB A FREE COPY OF THE BUGLE ON THE WAY OUT!

THAT'S A REWARD?

ALAS, WE WILL NEVER KNOW WHETHER OUR DISILLUSIONED YOUNGSTER EVER TOOK HIS FREE COPY OR NOT, FOR WE NOW LEAP AHEAD TO THE NEXT MORNING...

HOW ABOUT THAT? THEY FOUND HIS COSTUME IN A TRASH CAN!!

THAT WEB-SLINGIN' WONDER WOULDN'T EVER QUIT! SOMEONE MUST HAVE BEATEN HIM!

I'LL BELIEVE IT WHEN I SEE IT!

DON'T BET IT! MAYBE HE'S JUST BAG!

JAMESON WILL PRINT ANYTHING TO SELL HIS PAPER!

DAILY BUGLE
EXTRA | SPECIAL EDITION

IS SPIDER-MAN THRU?

EVERY COPY I PRINTED SOLD OUT! THIS IS THE SCOOP OF A LIFETIME!

AFTER ALL THESE YEARS, I FINALLY GOT SOME GOOD OUT OF THAT MASKED MISANTHROPE! EVERYTHING'S COMING UP ROSES!

BUT, IF SOMETHING HAPPENED TO SPIDER-MAN, WHY DIDN'T THE POLICE MAKE THE ANNOUNCEMENT?

WE DON'T KNOW ANY MORE ABOUT IT THAN YOU!

BUT WE'RE STARTING AN INVESTIGATION NOW!

IS IT TRUE, MOM? IS IT TRUE?

LET'S HOPE NOT, JOEY!

9.

NEEDLESS TO SAY, IT DOESN'T TAKE LONG FOR THE T.V. NETWORKS TO COVER THE BIGGEST HUMAN-INTEREST STORY OF THE YEAR--!

I'LL GIVE THE FOLKS A CLOSE-UP VIEW OF IT, JOHNNY!

LET'S NOT FORGET TO MENTION THAT IT WAS MY DAILY BUGLE THAT FIRST PUBLISHED THE NEWS! AS A PUBLIC SERVICE, OF COURSE!

WE'RE OFFERING A BARGAIN SUBSCRIPTION RATE RIGHT NOW!

SUPPOSE WE GET THE CONVERSATION BACK TO SPIDER-MAN, MR. JAMESON--!

NATURALLY! NATURALLY! YOU DON'T THINK I WAS TRYING FOR A FREE PLUG, DO YOU?

OH, PERISH FORBID!

IN FACT, ON JUST ABOUT EVERY MAJOR CHANNEL, THE SUBJECT IS THE SAME...

DO YOU FEEL THAT THE HUMAN ARACHNID'S PROCLIVITIES PRECLUDE THE POSSIBILITY OF THIS BEING MERELY A MONUMENTAL BIT OF CHICANERY?

WHAT DO YOU GENTLEMEN THINK IS THE ANSWER?

I'D RATHER NOT ANSWER THAT, DAVID!

MENACE!

BECAUSE OF ITS POSSIBLE IMPACT ON OUR VIEWERS?

NO-- BECAUSE I DON'T UNDERSTAND THE QUESTION!

IT'S OBVIOUS TO ME THAT THE UNDERWORLD HAS FINALLY DONE AWAY WITH HIM!

HERO?

SPEAKING AS A PSYCHIATRIST, I FEEL HE HAS SUFFERED A SCHIZOPHRENIC WITHDRAWAL FROM REALITY!

OR, TO COUCH IT IN LAYMAN TERMS, HE'S OUT OF HIS TREE!

AND, AMONGST THE HIGHEST ECHELONS OF THE UNDERWORLD, THE REACTION IS EQUALLY FAST AND FAR-REACHING..

THIS IS THE MOMENT WE'VE BEEN WAITING FOR!

WITH SPIDER-MAN GONE, MY PLANS CAN NOW REACH FRUITION!

TELL THE BOYS TO START SPREADING THE WORD...

I WANT EVERY MOB IN THE CITY TO KNOW... THE KINGPIN IS READY TO TAKE OVER!

WILL DO, KINGPIN!

WE'LL HAVE A SUMMIT MEETIN' THAT'LL MAKE APPALACHIN LOOK LIKE A TEA PARTY!

AS THE LONG, FATEFUL HOURS TICK BY, ONE MAN BECOMES INCREASINGLY AWARE OF A NEW MOOD AMONG THE CITY'S CRIMINAL ELEMENT...

SOMETHING'S IN THE AIR! I CAN SEE IT-- FEEL IT... I CAN ALMOST REACH OUT AND TOUCH IT!

MOBSTERS WHO WOULDN'T BE CAUGHT WITHIN MILES OF EACH OTHER-- DEADLY ENEMIES.. ARE MEETING---- AND WHISPERING --!

WHATEVER IT IS THAT'S IN THE WIND... ONE THING'S FOR SURE... IT'S SOMETHING BIG!

...ND IT WON'T BE LONG BEFORE PATCH, THE STOOL PIGEON, FINDS OUT WHAT'S GOING ON!

HOLD IT, PUNK! WHERE D'YA THINK YOU'RE GOIN'? THIS ISN'T YOUR TERRITORY... SO TAKE A POWDER!

HEY! WHAT GIVES, BLACKIE? YOU KNOW ME! IT'S OL' PATCH! I JUST WANT IN ON THE ACTION!

NOT THIS TIME, SMALL FRY! GO'WAN BACK TO PICKIN' POCKETS.. YER OUTTA YER LEAGUE HERE!

DON'T MAKE 'IM TELL YA TWICE, CREEP!

I WAS RIGHT! SOME OF THE BIGGEST MOBSTERS IN THE EAST ARE GETTING TOGETHER!

AND THEY'RE NOT DOING IT JUST BECAUSE THEY'RE LONELY!

I'D BETTER TAKE OFF AND MAKE MY OWN PLANS BEFORE THEY GET SUSPICIOUS OF ME!

...ND, AS THE THOUGHTFUL STOOLIE SLOWLY FADES INTO THE DEEPENING SHADOWS...

WITH SPIDER-MAN GONE, THE KINGPIN IS READY TO TAKE OVER AS HEAD MAN OF THE MOBS!

ANY QUESTIONS?

WHY DON'T HE TELL US HIMSELF? I DON'T DEAL WITH STOOGES!

RELAX, SHORTY! YOU KNOW THE KINGPIN LIKES TO STAY IN THE BACKGROUND.

IF ANYONE IS GONNA TAKE CONTROL AROUND HERE THE KINGPIN'S OUR BOY!

UP TO NOW, I ALWAYS BEEN MY OWN BOSS! I DON'T LIKE IT!

THEN START LIKIN' IT, MISTER! WHAT THE KINGPIN SAYS AROUND HERE.. GOES!

...HILE, IN A SMALL FURNISHED APARTMENT ON THE OTHER SIDE OF TOWN...

DON'T HAVE TO BE A GENIUS TO FIGURE OUT WHAT'S GOING ON!

SPIDER-MAN HELPED TO KEEP THE UNDERWORLD ON THE RUN! THEY WERE DISORGANIZED.. FEARFUL.. CAUTIOUS! BUT NOW, IT'S DIFFERENT!

WITH THE WEB-SLINGER OUT OF ACTION, THEY'RE READY TO POOL THEIR FORCES...

JUDGING BY THE ONES I'VE SEEN, IT COULD BE THE MOST POWERFUL ARMY OF CRIME EVER ASSEMBLED!

AND, SINCE SOMEBODY WILL HAVE TO LEAD THEM ... WHY COULDN'T IT BE --- THE MAN CALLED PATCH ?!!

NOT A MAN ALIVE KNOWS THAT I'M REALLY FREDRICK FOSWELL!

THE NEXT MORNING ...

AS FOSWELL, I'M JUST A TWO-BIT REPORTER---BUT, IF I COULD BECOME THE KING OF CRIME ONCE AGAIN...!*

HEY, FOSWELL! COME HERE... I WANNA SHOW YOU SOMETHING!

NOW THAT I'VE GONE STRAIGHT, EVERYONE TRUSTS ME! THEY'D NEVER SUSPECT!

YES, SIR, MR. JAMESON!

* REMEMBER WHEN JJJ GAVE FOSWELL A JOB AFTER HIS PAROLE? HE HAD BEEN KNOWN AS THE BIG MAN--TILL SPIDEY CAUGHT HIM! --- SUPER-MEMORY STAN.

11.

...OT LONG AFTERWARD, THE BROODING *KINGPIN* RECEIVES A ...PECIAL *REPORT*...!

...OST OF ...HE BOYS ...OT THEM- ...ELVES ...ABBED BY ...E COPS, ...OSS... ...T IT WAS ...ORTH ...T!

WE FOUND OUT WHAT YOU WANTED TO *KNOW*!.

IT LOOKS LIKE *SPIDER-MAN* REALLY *IS* OUT OF ACTION!

HE DIDN'T SHOW UP *NOWHERE*...AT NO TIME...*NOHOW!*

GOOD! IT WAS *WORTH* LOSING A FEW PETTY HOODS TO MAKE *CERTAIN!*

THIS MEANS THE TIME HAS COME TO PROCEED WITH MY *MASTER PLAN!*

INSTEAD OF *MANY* RIVAL GANGS OPERATING HAPHAZARDLY THROUGHOUT THE CITY...

INSTEAD OF COUNTLESS CROOKS ACTING *ALONE*... WITHOUT A *CHANCE* AGAINST THE POLICE ---

THE UNDERWORLD WILL NOW BE RUN LIKE A *BUSINESS*... AND THE *CHAIRMAN OF THE BOARD* WILL BE-- THE *KINGPIN!*

...HE NEXT DAY, AT GOOD OL' *E.S.U.* ---

...E *POLICE* SURE ...VE THEIR HANDS FULL LATELY!

I WONDER WHAT *REALLY* HAPPENED TO SPIDEY?

DO YOU THINK SOMEONE POLISHED HIM *OFF?*

HE'S IN *MOTH-BALLS,* WITH THE *OTHER* RELICS!

AND HE'S GONNA *STAY* THERE!

HI, GWEN! CAN I GIVE YOU A *LIFT?*

MOVE OVER, MR. P.! YOU FOUND YOUR-SELF A *PIGEON!*

JUST GOT A LETTER FROM OUR SWINGIN' SOLDIER BOY!

FEARLESS FLASH? LET'S SEE..!

...'S THE SAME OL' HOWLIN' HOT-SHOT! ...GIVES THE VEE-CEES 24 HOURS TO ...LEAR OUT WHEN HE GETS THERE!

...ANYONE *ELSE* ...CRIBBLED ...AT, WE'D ...LL HIM A ...REAT ...TLE ...DDER!

BUT, SINCE IT'S *FLASHEROO,* THEY'D BETTER START *PACKING!*

HE REALLY TURNS YOU ON, DOESN'T HE, GWEN?

FACE IT, CLASS-MATE...

HOW *MANY* BLUSHING BLONDES WOULD FIND A HIP, HANDSOME FOOT-BALL HERO TOTALLY *REPULSIVE?*

I'M SORRY I ASKED, PRETTY GIRL!

HOW WAS THE *PARTY?*

A DISASTER AREA... WITH-OUT *YOU!*

Y'KNOW... I KINDA WISH YOU *MEANT* THAT!

OH... YOU LOVABLE, BLIND *GOOF!!* CAN'T YOU SEE I *DO?!*

THANKS FOR THE *LIFT,* NEIGHBOR!

ANYTIME, PRINCESS!

MAN! IF ONLY I HAD A CHANCE IN *HER* LEAGUE!

A FELLA COULD SURE *SAIL* THROUGH LIFE WITH A GAL LIKE *THAT* TO COME HOME TO!

13.

...HANDICAPPED PEOPLE...OLD PEOPLE...HELPLESS INFANTS...WILL BE THE SUFFERERS!

AND THEY DON'T HAVE *BANK ACCOUNTS* TO FALL BACK ON WHILE WAITING FOR HELP!

THE POLICE MAY *ALREADY* HAVE PICKED UP THE TRAIL OF THE RATS WHO PULLED THAT JOB.. BUT, *JUST IN CASE*--

HEY! PARKER...HOLD IT! HOLD IT, YOU CHOWDER-HEAD!

YOU JUST TOOK THE *PLEDGE*, REMEMBER ? YOUR WEB-SLINGIN' DAYS ARE GONE *FOREVER!* SIMMER DOWN, SWEETIE!

YOU CAN READ ALL *ABOUT* IT.....IN THE *PAPER!*

AND, SIMMER DOWN HE *DOES*...THOUGH EVERY *INSTINCT* WITHIN HIM LONGS FOR THE THRILL OF *ADVENTURE* ONCE AGAIN! BUT THEN, THE NEXT MORNING...

SAY, PETE, DID YOU READ ABOUT THE WELFARE OFFICE *ROBBERY* LAST NIGHT?

GOTTA CHANGE THE SUBJECT-- KEEP MY MIND OFF *CRIME!*

OH, NO...I JUST HAD TIME FOR THE *SPORTS* PAGES!

HUH?

LOOKS LIKE WE'RE IN THE MIDDLE OF A FULL-FLEDGED UNDER-WORLD *INVASION!*

HOW'S YOUR *DAD*, HARRY? YOU HAVEN'T *MENTIONED* HIM LATELY!

...HAVEN'T *SEEN* HIM...HE'S BEEN OUT OF TOWN!

...AVE YOU THOUGHT ANY ...MORE ABOUT HIS *OFFER*...ABOUT WORKING PART-TIME IN HIS *LAB?*

...AS A MATTER OF ...ACT I *HAVE*, ...ARR...

I JUST HAVE TO *FINISH* SOME *PERSONAL* MATTERS FIRST!

SOON AS *AUNT MAY* IS ON HER FEET...AND MY *STUDIES* ARE UP TO SNUFF.. I'M GONNA *DO* IT!

THUS, AFTER ALL THESE YEARS, THINGS START *LOOKING UP* FOR OUR HARASSED HERO--OR, DO THEY...?

HOW ABOUT A SODA, SAND-WICH, AND SPIN AFTER CLASS, WOMAN?

LOVE IT, MAN..BUT I'VE A DATE WITH *HARRY* TONIGHT!

YOU TWO.. AREN'T.. *PINNED*, OR ANY-THING.. ARE YOU?

FIRST FLASH.. NOW *HARRY!* YOU'RE ALWAYS TRYING TO *PAIR* ME OFF!

HOW COME YOU HAVEN'T ASKED IF I'VE GOT A *MAAAAD* CRUSH ON A BASHFUL, BLACK-HAIRED *BIKE-RIDER?*

C'MON! WE *BOTH* KNOW NICE GUYS FINISH LAST!

FORGET IT, LADY!

YOU SAID IT, PETE...*I* DIDN'T!

...ONLY I THOUGHT THAT GWEN *MEANT*..

...ELLO, PETER DEAR! ...FEEL SO MUCH ...ETTER THAT ANNA ...D I ARE GOING ...O THE *MOVIES!*

OH! AUNT MAY AND MRS. WATSON ARE *LEAVING!*

GEE, THAT'S *GREAT!* HAVE A GOOD TIME, HEAR?

REMEMBER --NO FLIRT-ING WITH THE *USHERS!*

..PETER! ..U'RE SUCH ..CAUTION!

SO I GAVE UP BEING *SPIDER-MAN* TO HAVE MORE TIME FOR MY *FAMILY*... AND MY *FRIENDS*...

...ONLY TO FIND---THEY DON'T *NEED* ME!

I MIGHT AS WELL GO HOME AND BURY MYSELF IN A *BOOK!*

BUT, ON THE WAY BACK TO HIS PAD, PETE HEARS...

HELP!! SOMEBODY.. HELLLLP!

SOMETHING'S *WRONG* ....ATOP THAT WARE-HOUSE ROOF!

AND NO ONE ELSE *AROUND*... EXCEPT ME!

WAREHOUSE

5.

OF COURSE! NOW I KNOW!!

THAT'S WHY THE WATCHMAN SEEMED SO FAMILIAR...

UNCLE BEN!! HE REMINDED ME OF MY UNCLE BEN!!

HOW COULD I HAVE FORGOTTEN?? IT SEEMS LIKE ONLY YESTERDAY NOW...

AUNT MAY... AND UNCLE BEN... THE ONLY FAMILY THAT I EVER KNEW...!

THEY WERE THE GREATEST FOLKS THAT ANYONE COULD HAVE... KIND, LOVING, GENEROUS...

I'LL NEVER FORGET UNCLE BEN SAVING FOR MONTHS TO BUY ME MY FIRST MICROSCOPE...

THEN, WHEN I HAD THE LAB ACCIDENT WHICH GAVE ME MY SPIDER-MAN POWERS, I JUST BECAME A COSTUMED ADVENTURER FOR KICKS... AND THE MONEY I THOUGHT IT WOULD BRING!

I HOPED I'D BE ABLE TO PAY UNCLE BEN BACK AT LEAST A FRACTION OF WHAT I OWED HIM...!

AND WHEN IT CAME TO CHASING CRIMINALS, I WAS MORE THAN WILLING TO "LET GEORGE DO IT!"

EVEN WHEN I WAS YELLED AT OR NOT EVEN TRYING TO STOP A FLEEING BURGLAR, I SHRUGGED IT OFF! AFTER ALL, IT WASN'T ANY OF MY BUSINESS...

OR, SO I THOUGHT...

...UNTIL I LEARNED THAT THE BURGLAR HAD ACTUALLY COMMITTED A MURDER... AND HIS VICTIM HAD BEEN...

UNCLE BEN!!

THAT WAS THE TURNING POINT...

THAT'S WHEN I BECAME SPIDER-MAN --FOR REAL!!

17.

...VE GOT THE ...UTS...THE ...XPERIENCE.. ...ND THE, ...AVVY!

BUT, I'M NOT *GREEDY!* I'M WILLING TO *SHARE* THE *TAKE!* I CAN *USE* A MAN LIKE YOU.... AS ONE OF MY *LIEUTENANTS!*

WELL? WHAT DO YOU *SAY?*

YOU WITLESS *FOOL!!* YOU HAVE THE *TEMERITY* TO ADDRESS THE *KINGPIN* LIKE THAT?!!

YOU DARE OFFER *ME* THE POSITION OF YOUR *LIEUTENANT?!!*

I COULD *BUY AND SELL* YOU A HUNDRED TIMES A DAY!

THUMP!

HEY! TAKE IT *EASY,* KINGPIN... I DIDN'T WALK IN HERE *UNPREPARED!*

...ATURALLY! MY ...LECTRONIC ...CANNER INSTANTLY ...POTTED THE *GUN* ...OU HAVE HIDDEN ...N YOUR HAT...!

THE GUN WHICH I CAN EASILY *OBLITERATE...* ALONG WITH THE *HAT* ITSELF!

A *DISINTEGRATOR BEAM...* BUILT INTO YOUR *CANE!!* IF I HADN'T...LEAPED ASIDE..!!

ZZZZT!

...T MR. FOSWELL ON ...CE FOR A WHILE!

...E MAY PROVE ...SEFUL TO US ...ATER ON!

HOLD IT!! LISTEN TO ME!! YOU'RE MAKING A BIG *MISTAKE!*

THE *KINGPIN* DOES NOT *MAKE* MISTAKES!

AND, IN ANOTHER SECTION OF TOWN, A SILENT, SHADOWY FIGURE GRIMLY SCALES THE SHEER, STEEP WALL OF THE *DAILY BUGLE* BUILDING...

IT HAS TO STILL *BE* THERE! IT *HAS* TO!

19.

FOR *ONCE* I'M IN LUCK!

JAMESON'S OWN *HATRED* OF ME WOULDN'T LET HIM GIVE UP THAT COSTUME!

NOW, IF I CAN JUST MOVE *FAST* ENOUGH!!

THEN, NOT LONG AFTERWARDS...

HEY! HOW COME MY *DOOR'S* UNLOCKED?

I'LL SNAP ON THE *LIGHT*, AND... *YULLLP!*

YOU!

HI, CHUCKLES!

I THOUGHT YOU WERE *DEAD*... OR, AT LEAST *MORTALLY WOUNDED* SOMEWHERE...!!

RECRUIT-ING?!!

SORRY TO *DISAPPOINT* YOU! I WAS OUT RECRUITING...!

YOU *HEARD* ME! I'M SIGNING UP *VOLUNTEERS!* I'M GONNA FILL THE *WHOLE CITY* WITH SPIDER-MEN!

AWFULLY SORRY ABOUT THE *RETRACTIONS* YOU'LL HAVE TO PRINT IN YOUR PAPER!

BUT I GUESS YOU'RE *USED* TO THAT BY NOW!

HE'S *BACK!* HE'S STILL *ALIVE*... AND MORE *ROTTEN* THAN EVER

OH, NO! NO! NOOOO!

BY THE WAY, *NEXT* TIME I LEAVE MY COSTUME, THE *LEAST* YOU CAN DO IS HAVE IT *DRY CLEANED!*

WELL, SE YA AROUN FUN-FRIEND!

AND NOW, SPIDEY'S BACK IN ACTION!!

AND, AS FAR AS THE *WORLD'S* CONCERNED...

THEY BETTER *BELIEVE* IT!!

CONTINUED NEXT ISH

"AND HOW!"

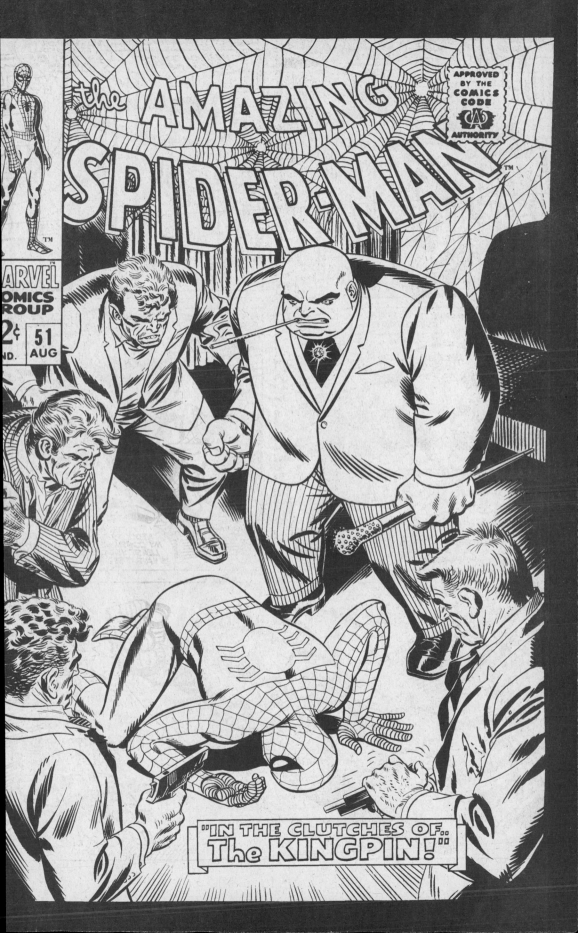

2.

SERVICE STATIONS?!! I THOUGHT WE WERE IN THE *BIG TIME!*

THIS IS JUST A *TEST!* I WANT TO SEE HOW YOU *OPERATE!* NOW *GET GOING!*

YOU GONNA LET 'IM TALK TO *US* LIKE THAT, *BIG TURK?*

YEAH!...AS LONG AS HE'S HOLDIN' THAT *DISINTEGRATOR CANE* OF HIS!

ANYWAY, WE DON'T HAVETA WORRY ABOUT *SPIDER-MAN* NO MORE!

---BUT THAT'S WHAT *THEY* THINK!

BOY, IT FEELS *GREAT* TO BE WEB-SWINGIN' AROUND TOWN AGAIN!

UH OH! WHAT'S *THAT...DOWN BELOW!*

LOOKS LIKE *TROUBLE* AT THAT *SERVICE STATION!*

THWIP!

OKAY, I GOT THE TAKE IN THIS *BRIEFCASE!* NOW LET'S---HEY!!

SOMETHIN' *PULLED IT..* OUTTA MY *HAND!*

IT'S A *HUNKA WEBBING!*

MUST BE.. *SPIDER-MAN!*

AWWW... ONE OF YOU MUSTA *PEEKED!*

CAN I *BORROW* THOSE *GUNS,* FELLAS?

THANKS A HEA...

DON'T JUST *STAND THERE,* YOU *LUNKHEADS!!* HE'S MAKIN' *MONKEYS* OUTTA YA!

NOT A *CHANCE,* CHUM! OL' MOTHER *NATURE* BEAT ME TO IT!

COME TO *POPPA,* LITTLE POP-GUNS!

RUSH 'IM! HE CAN'T FIGHT US *ALL!*

FIGHT YOU?? OH, *PERISH FORBID!!*

I THOUGHT THIS WAS A MEETING OF THE *SPIDER-MAN FAN CLUB* ---!

AND I JUST WANTED *IN!*

THOK!

WELL, THAT'S MY QUE TO DO A LITTLE WALL-CRAWLING!

THE *POLICE* WILL BE ABLE TO TAKE UP WHERE I LEFT OFF!

AS FOR *ME*, I'LL JUST COLLECT MY *AUTOMATIC CAMERA* AND SELL THE *SPIDEY PIX* TO JOLLY JONAH!

UH OH! I JUST *REMEMBERED*...!

WHEN I THOUGHT I WAS *FINISHED* WITH THE *SPIDER-MAN* BIT, I TOLD JAMESON WHERE TO GET *OFF!*

NOW I'VE GOTTA SWALLOW MY *PRIDE*, AND CONVINCE HIM I WAS...ULP...ONLY *KIDDING!*

...THERE IS THE MAN WHO CAN MOST *NEVER* HIS...! SUPPOSE I VISIT HIM AGAIN NOW...

I'LL SLIDE THE *DRAPES* BACK AND OBSERVE OUR CAPTIVE THROUGH THE HIDDEN *ONE-WAY MIRROR!*

SO, *FREDRICK FOSWELL* THOUGHT I WOULD LET *HIM* TAKE OVER OUR OPERATION, SIMPLY BECAUSE HE HAD ONCE BEEN THE *BIG MAN* BEFORE HE SUPPOSEDLY WENT *STRAIGHT!*

WHY DON'TCHA JUST POLISH HIM OFF *NOW*, KINGPIN? HE AIN'T DOIN' *ANYBODY* ANY GOOD IN *THERE!*

NO! I HAVE *OTHER* PLANS FOR *MR. FOSWELL!*

CLICK!

...MAN WITH HIS OTHER UNUSUAL EXPERIENCE MAY BE OF *SOME* USE TO ME!

AND A GOOD *GENERAL* NEVER LETS ANY MANPOWER GO TO *WASTE!*

BRING OUR GUEST *IN* HERE, FLINT! IT'S TIME WE HAD A LITTLE *TALK!*

AND SO...

I *THOUGHT* YOU'D REALIZE YOU *NEEDED* ME, KINGPIN!

INDEED? WHAT MADE YOU SO *SURE?*

BECAUSE NOBODY'S *EVER* BEEN ABLE TO TAKE OVER *ALL* THE MOBS BEFORE... EXCEPT *ME!*

I KNOW HOW *HARD* IT IS TO KEEP THEM ALL IN *LINE!*

YOU'D BE A *FOOL* TO PASS UP ANY HELP YOU CAN *GET!*

AND THERE IS ONE THING WE *BOTH* KNOW...

THE KINGPIN IS *NOT A FOOL!*

6

Panel 1:

LET'S QUIT *SPARRING* WITH EACH OTHER, KINGPIN!

IF WE'RE GONNA WORK *TOGETHER*, WHAT ARE YOUR *TERMS*?

BEFORE WE DISCUSS TERMS, I NOTICE YOU'RE REACHING INTO YOUR *POCKET*...

THEREFORE, LET ME EXTEND A SLIGHT *WARNING*...

THE *OBLITERATOR* BEAM WITHIN MY WALKING STICK CAN *ATOMIZE* YOU BEFORE YOU CAN MAKE ANOTHER MOVE!

RELAX, MISTER! I'M NO CHEAP *HOOD*, REACHING FOR A GUN!

Panel 2:

I DO MY FIGHTING WITH MY *BRAINS*!

FLINT! GIVE ME A *LIGHT*!

WHO DO YOU THINK YOU'RE *TALKIN'* TO, LITTLE MAN?

YOU *HEARD* THE MAN, FLINT! GIVE HIM A *LIGHT*!

OKAY! HERE...

WE'LL GET ALONG JUST *FINE*, FOSWELL!

I *LIKE* YOUR *STYLE*!

Panel 3:

SLAM!

THUMP!

SO! SPIDER-MAN'S OUT OF ACTION, HUH? WHAT WERE YA TRYIN' TO PULL, YA FINK!

WE JUST GOT AWAY BY THE SKIN OF OUR *TEETH*!

THEY.. SAW.. SPIDER-MAN??

BIG TURK!!

YOU DARE BREAK IN *HERE* ON THE *KINGPIN* LIKE THIS?

Panel 4:

THAT AIN'T ALL WE *DARE*! YOU'RE *FINISHED*, FATSO!

AND WE'RE GONNA TELL YA GOOD-BYE... *OUR* WAY!

LET'S *GET* 'IM, BIG TURK! NOBODY CAN MAKE FOOLS OF *US*, THE WAY THAT LYIN' FINK TRIED TO DO!

HOLD IT, YOU PUNKS! MAKE ANOTHER MOVE TOWARD THE KINGPIN, AND I'LL *VENTILATE* THE BOTH OF YA!

IT'S ALL RIGHT, FLINT! THERE'S NO NEED FOR *CONCERN*!

NOW I'LL SEE IF THE *KINGPIN* IS AS GOOD AS HE CLAIMS HE IS!

I'M NOT IN ANY *DANGER* AT ALL!

WE'RE MEREL[Y] FACED WITH A LITTLE *DISCIPLINAR*[Y] PROBLEM--A[ND] I'LL HANDLE IT MY *OWN* FOOL PROOF WAY.

YOU GENTLEMEN ARE ABOUT TO LEARN A LESSON YOU'LL *NEVER* FORGET..!

BIG TURK IS THE **STRONGEST**... THE **TOUGHEST** MOB LEADER IN THE EAST!

YET, THE **KINGPIN** TOSSED HIM LIKE A RAG DOLL!

LOOK AT HIM **STANDING** THERE... HE'S NOT EVEN **WINDED**!

HE'S FAR MORE **POWERFUL** ... MORE **DANGEROUS**... THAN I EVER SUSPECTED!

THE LESSON IS **ENDED**! ON YOUR **FEET**, YOU **CRINGING** CARRION!

WITH HIS **MONEY**...HIS **OBLITERATOR CANE**... AND HIS OWN **STRENGTH**... HE DOESN'T HAVE TO FEAR **ANYONE**!

SURE, KINGPIN... **SURE**! ANYTHING YOU SAY...!

GET BACK TO YOUR RAT-HOLES... **BOTH** OF YOU!

YOU WILL WAIT TILL I NEXT **SEND** FOR YOU ---AND, WHEN I DO... YOU'LL COME **RUNNING**!

NEVER, AS LONG AS YOU **LIVE**, WILL YOU FORGET THAT THE **KINGPIN** IS YOUR **MASTER**!

YOU CAN SAY **THAT** AGAIN!

NOW **GET OUT**! THE VERY **SIGHT** OF YOU IS **OFFENSIVE** TO ME!

C'MON, TUR-- DON'T MAK-- 'IM TELL US TWICE!

SO! SPIDER-MAN IS BACK IN **ACTION**, IS HE?

WELL, HE SHALL LIVE TO **REGRET** IT!

BUT **NOW**, I MUST FIND A USE FOR **YOU**, FOSWELL!

I **HAVE** IT! YOU'RE THE **MEANS** BY WHICH I'LL SILENCE **JONAH JAMESON**--FOREVER!

WHAT...DO YOU HAVE.. IN MIND?

AND, EVEN AS THE UNBELIEVABLY POWERFUL **KINGPIN** SPEAKS...

RUMORS! RUMORS! RUMORS! BUT NO BLASTED **NEWS**!!

THE CITY'S IN THE GRIP OF ITS **BIGGE**--CRIME WAVE, AND NO ONE CAN FIN--OUT WHO'S **BEHIND** IT!

AND WHERE IN **BLAZES** IS **FOSWELL** WHEN I **NEED** 'IM??

SUPPOSE WE **REPLACE** HIM WITH **NED LEEDS**?

YOU CAN REPLACE 'IM WITH **DONALD DUCK**, JUST SO **Y**--GET A **STORY**!!

SECONDS LATER...

I HEARD YOU **WANTED** ME, MR. JAMESON!

YOU'RE ROOTIN'-TOOTIN' **RIGHT** I WANT YOU! I WANT YOU TO GET THE **FACTS** BEHIND THE CRIME WAVE!

BUT, I'VE **BEEN** WORKING ON IT... NIGHT AND **DAY**... FOR THE PAST **WEEK**! THERE JUST AREN'T ANY **LEADS**!

THEN WORK ON IT NIGHT AND DAY FOR **ANOTHER** WEEK! I WANT **RESULTS**.. NOT **EXCUSES**!

AND FIND ME A **PHOTO-GRAPHER**--TO REPLACE THAT PUNK KID **PARKER**!

YOU DON'T HAVE TO **REPLACE** ME, MR. JAMESON..

I'M BACK!

YOU!

THE TEENAGE **TRAITOR** WHO WALKED OUT ON ME WHEN I **NEEDED** YOU **MOST**!

HE'LL PROBABLY BLOW A **GASKET**... BUT I'VE GOTTA **TAKE** IT!

WADDAYA MEAN YO-- **BACK**! WHO WANTS Y-- WHO MISS-- YOU? WHO NEEDS YO--

WE DO, MR YOU JUST S-- SO-- REMEMB--

SHUDDU-- LEEDS! NE-- MIND WH-- I SAID!

GET IN HER-- PARKER! I-- GOT SOM-- THIN' TO S-- TO YOU--

...WOULDN'T TAKE YOU BACK ON A *BET!*

YOU'VE BEEN A *THORN* IN MY SIDE SINCE THE DAY YOU FIRST *CAME HERE!*

NOW GOWAN-- GET OUT! GO PEDDLE YOUR PAPERS SOMEWHERE *ELSE!* YOU'RE *THROUGH* HERE!

I THINK YOU'RE TRYING TO *TELL* ME SOMETHING!

WELL, IN *THAT* CASE YOU WON'T WANT THESE LATEST *PICTURES* I TOOK...OF SPIDER-*MAN!*

WHA...? YOU'VE GOT *NEW* PICTURES OF THAT WALL-CRAWL-ING WEASEL ??!

THAT'S *RIGHT!* BUT DON'T WORRY ABOUT ME, J.J.!

I'M SURE I CAN SELL THEM SOMEWHERE *ELSE!*

HOLD IT, YOU SILLY BOY! CAN'TCHA TAKE A *JOKE?*

LET'S *SEE* THEM!

SAY! NOT *BAD!* NOT BAD AT *ALL!* SO HE *IS* BACK IN ACTION AGAIN, EH?

THIS IS YOUR *LUCKY DAY,* PARKER! I'VE DECIDED TO *FORGIVE* YOU AND TAKE YOU *BACK!*

NO WONDER THEY CALL YOU *SANTA!*

...T THAT DOESN'T MEAN THIS IS A HANGOUT FOR LOAFERS!!

LEEDS, GET TO WORK! *MISS BRANT,* FINISH YOUR FILING! AND *PARKER*...GET ME MORE *PICTURES!*

GLAD YOU'RE AS *LOVE-ABLE* AS EVER, JJ!

AND SOMEONE FIND *FOSWELL* FOR ME, BLAST IT!

SO FRED *FOSWELL'S* MISSING, EH?

HE'S JONAH'S *STAR REPORTER!* WONDER WHAT COULD HAVE *HAPPENED* TO HIM?

WELL, NO TIME TO WORRY ABOUT THAT NOW..I'VE STILL GOT TO LEARN MORE ABOUT THE *KINGPIN!*

BUT, WHERE DO I *BEGIN?*

I'M PRETTY DARN SURE HE WON'T BE LISTED IN THE *PHONE BOOK!*

LOOK! THERE'S PETER PARKER!

HE'S PASSING RIGHT BY---WITH-OUT EVEN LOOK-ING *IN!*

I'LL JUST KEEP RIDING AROUND...

I MAY GET *LUCKY* AND STUMBLE ONTO SOMETHING!

...AND JUST WHEN I COULD HAVE *USED* THOSE WAY-OUT WHEELS OF HIS FOR A LUSCIOUS LIFT *HOME!*

THAT'S THE *BREAKS,* MJ! BUT DON'T *DESPAIR...HARRY* AND I CAN DROP YOU OFF WHEN WE LEAVE!

I KNOW WHY *YOU'RE* SMILING, GWEN! IT *BUGS* YOU WHEN I'M ALONE WITH PETEY... *DOESN'T* IT?

IN CASE YOU HAVEN'T *NOTICED,* LADY---GWEN IS MY DATE!

SURE, BECAUSE MR. P. DIDN'T ASK HER *FIRST!*

GOOD OL' *MARY JANE!* ANYTHING FOR A *LAUGH,* EH?

DO YOU THINK I'M BEING FUNNY, GWENDOLYNE?

I THINK...PERHAPS IT'S TIME WE WERE GETTING *HOME!*

10.

AND, IT'S TIME WE WERE BRACING FOR NEW ACTION--!

WHY IS MY SPIDEY SENSE TINGLING? ALL I SEE ARE FOUR MEN, ENTERING THAT SWANKY PRIVATE CLUB--!

NOTHING SEEMS TO BE WRONG! AND YET...

BUT, I BETTER PARK MY BIKE AND GET INTO COSTUME... JUST IN CASE!

I CAN'T AFFORD TO TAKE ANY CHANCES! MY LITTLE BUILT-IN BUZZER HASN'T EVER FAILED ME YET!

UH OH! I WAS RIGHT!

WHILE NOBODY ELSE IS NOTICING, THOSE FOUR GOONS HAVE THE MANAGER OFF IN A CORNER...

AND I CAN TELL... EVEN FROM HERE... THAT THEY'RE ABOUT TO LEAN ON HIM!

ONE OF 'EM IS PULLING A GUN!

NO TIME TO FIND AN OPEN WINDOW-- I'VE GOTTA MOVE..!!

THE KINGPIN DON'T LIKE JOES WHO GIVE US ANY TROUBLE, SEE ??

THEN THE KINGPIN IS GONNA BE REAL ANNOYED AT YOUR FRIENDLY NEIGHBORHOOD SPIDER-MAN, GENTS!

HEADS UP, YOU GUYS! IT'S THE WALL-CRAWLER AGAIN !!

CRASH!

YOU OUGHTTA BE ASHAMED OF YOURSELVES!

NOT ONLY DO YOU TRY TO HIJACK ONE OF THE CLASSIEST PLACES IN TOWN...

--BUT YOU DIDN'T EVEN PHONE AHEAD TO MAKE A RESERVATION!

UHH!

OOOF!

≥ TSK TSK! ≤ HOW GAUCHE CAN YOU BE?

LOOK OUT!

THERE SHE GOES! ..I GUESS THEY JUST DON'T BUILD 'EM LIKE THEY USED TO!

WELL, IT COULDA BEEN WORSE! AT LEAST NO ONE WAS HURT!

NOW, ALL I'VE GOT TO DO IS PICK UP MY LITTLE TRACER'S TRAIL!

AND, UNLESS I'M WAY OFF BASE, IT'LL LEAD ME RIGHT TO COUSIN KINGPIN!

EVEN AS SPIDEY SWINGS THROUGH THE NIGHT, ANOTHER OF THE KINGPIN'S GUN-TOTING TASK FORCES APPROACHES THE DAILY BUGLE BUILDING...

THERE'S JAMESON NOW...AT HIS WINDOW!

HE'S WORKIN' LATE AGAIN!

OKAY! OKAY! THEN WHAT'RE WE WAITIN' FOR?

ON YOUR FEET, MISTER! YOU BEEN WORKIN' TOO HARD... SO WE'RE GIVIN' YOU A VACATION!

YEAH! WE'RE TAKIN' YA FOR A NICE LITTLE RIDE...TO VISIT THE KINGPIN!

THE KINGPIN! THEN...I WAS RIGHT! THERE IS SOMEONE BEHIND THE CRIME WAVE!

BUT...WHAT DOES HE WANT WITH ME??

RE YOU NICE AND OMFY, JAMESON?

THIS IS INSANE! NOBODY GETS TAKEN FOR RIDES ANY MORE...

--EXCEPT ON THE UNTOUCHABLES!

WHEN THE KINGPIN SAYS RIDE, BROTHER.. YOU RIDE!

WHO IN BLAZES IS THE KINGPIN??

HE'S OUR SCOUTMASTER! NOW SHUDDUP!

FINALLY...

WELL, WELL! IF IT ISN'T JONAH JAMESON! HOW NICE OF YOU TO DROP IN!

COME, COME, GENTLEMEN... DON'T KEEP OUR GUEST STANDING OUT IN THE HALL!

YOU HEARD THE KINGPIN!

WALK!!

14.

I KNOW WHAT A BUSY MAN YOU ARE, SO I'LL COME RIGHT TO THE POINT..

I WANT YOU TO STOP STEAMING UP THE PUBLIC ABOUT THE SO-CALLED CRIME WAVE HERE IN THE CITY!

IN A PIG'S EYE! NOBODY TELLS ME WHAT TO WRITE IN MY PAPER!

EXCELLENT! SPOKEN LIKE THE TRUE CRUSADER THAT YOU ARE!

I APPLAUD YOUR OBVIOUS COURAGE...

BUT ALAS...YOU WILL LIVE TO REGRET IT!

WHAT..DO YOU... MEAN? WHAT ARE YOU..GONNA DO?

ALL IN GOOD TIME, JAMESON!! BUT FIRST... WHAT IS THIS?

IT'S CHARLIE AND HIS BOYS, KINGPIN. THEY SAY THAT SPIDER-MAN KIBOSHED THE CAPER!

SPIDER-MAN.. AGAIN?!!

BUT THE WHOLE JOINT CAVED IN...AND HE WAS STILL INSIDE!

I FIGGER WE KISSED 'IM OFF AT LAST!

IN THAT CASE, YOUR MISSION SUCCEEDED..BEYOND MY FONDEST HOPES!

BUT NOW, I STILL HAVE ANOTHER MINOR MATTER TO DISPOSE OF..!

FOSWELL, WOULD YOU BE GOOD ENOUGH TO INFORM OUR GUEST THAT THE KINGPIN DOES NOT PLAY GAMES?

WHA--WHAT DID YOU MENTION MY NAME FOR ??

TO BE SURE YOU DO NOT TRY TO BETRAY ME!

ONCE IT IS KNOWN THAT YOU'VE RETURNED TO CRIME--- YOU CAN NEVER TURN BACK!

HE'S FAR CLEVERER, FAR MORE DEADLY..TH.. I THOUGHT.

IF JAMESON DOESN'T PLAY ALONG...IT'LL MEAN HIS LIFE!

FOSWELL! ARE YOU REALLY THERE?

IS IT TRUE THAT YOU'VE JOINED FORCES WITH THE KINGPIN??

NEVER MIND ABOUT ME, JAMESON!

I'M ADVISING YOU... DO WHAT THE KINGPIN TELLS YOU TO!

SO! I WAS WRONG TO EVER TRUST YOU!!

YOU'RE NO BETTER THAN...THAT SKUNK SPIDER-MAN!

AND, SPEAKING OF SPIDEY...

ACCORDING TO MY LITTLE TRACER, THE TRAIL ENDS IN THAT PENTHOUSE JUS' AHEAD!

THAT MAN MOUNTAIN.. BEHIND THE MARBLE DESK...

AND...IT LOOKS LIKE I'VE REALLY STUMBLED ONTO SOMETHING!

I MUST BE HIM..THE KING-PIN!

THEY'VE GOT JOLLY JONAH THERE...BLINDFOLDED!! HE MUST BE A PRISONER!

BUT, THAT'S NOT WHAT GRABS ME! BEHIND THE KINGPIN...IT'S FOSWELL!

HE'S TURNED CROOKED AGAIN! HE'S ONE OF THE MOB!

HEY... LOOK! WHAT'S THAT?!

IT'S THE SPIDER-MAN SIGNAL! ..COMIN' FROM THE WINDOW!

THE WALL-CRAWLER'S STILL ALIVE! HE FOUND US...HE'S ON THE TERRACE!

AFTER HIM !! QUICK!

ET'S GO! I'D RATHER FACE SPIDER-MAN THAN LET THE KINGPIN MAD AT US!

BUT...WHERE IS HE ?

LOOK ALIVE, YOU FOOLS! HE MUSTN'T GET AWAY!

FAN OUT! HE'S GOTTA BE HERE SOMEWHERE!

THERE AIN'T A SIGN OF HIM!

THANKS, BOYS! NICE OF YOU TO MAKE A FELLA FEEL WANTED!

THERE HE IS!

NOW YOU TELL US!

16

18

NEXT: "TO DIE A HERO!"

20.

the AMAZING SPIDER-MAN

APPROVED BY THE COMICS CODE AUTHORITY

MARVEL COMICS GROUP

12¢ IND. | 52 SEPT

"TO DIE A HERO!"

THEY'RE ALL SEALED IN, BOSS! THE WATER'S POURIN' IN *FULL FORCE!* IT SHOULDN'T TAKE MORE'N *FIVE MINUTES!*

SPARE ME THE BORING *DETAILS,* FLINT! JUST LET ME KNOW WHEN THE CHARADE IS COMPLETELY *ENDED!*

SPIDER-MAN!! FOR THE *LUVVA* -- *WHA*--?!!

HE'S *WAKING UP!* HE'S BEGINNING TO *STIR!* THE *GAS* MUST BE FINALLY WEARING *OFF!*

UHHH--!

IRON BANDS.. AROUND MY *WRISTS!*

WATER..GETTING *HIGHER* BY THE *SECOND!*

THAT MEANS... THE *KINGPIN*....IS TRYING TO..*FINISH* US!

WE DON'T NEED A BLASTED *HUNTLEY-BRINKLEY REPORT!!* NOW THAT YOU'RE *AWAKE*...GET US *OUT* OF HERE!

HOW ABOUT GIVING YOUR *GUMS* A REST WHILE I *TRY?*

THESE BANDS AREN'T *TOO STRONG!* THE KINGPIN MUST FIGURE THEY WON'T MAKE MUCH *DIFFERENCE!*

RIGHT! EVEN IF YOU DO GET FREE ... *THEN* WHAT?

EVEN *YOU* CAN'T BREATHE FOR LONG *UNDER WATER!*

IF YOU'LL *CLAM UP* FOR A FEW MINUTES, MAYBE NEITHER OF US WILL *HAVE* TO!

DON'T TRY TO KID ME, *WEB-HEAD!* WE'RE *DONE FOR..* AND YOU *KNOW* IT!

SNAP!

OF *ALL* THE PEOPLE TO SPEND MY LAST FEW MINUTES ON EARTH WITH.. IT HADDA BE ---*HEY!!*

I *DID* IT! MY HANDS ARE *FREE* NOW!

BIG DEAL! WHAT'RE YOU GONNA *DO*...BREATHE THROUGH YOUR *FINGERS?*

SNAP!

JAMESON, DID ANYONE EVER TELL YOU YOU'RE AN *ITCH!*

I KNEW IT! I KNEW IT! YOU FLIPPED YOUR *LID!*

WE'RE A FEW SECONDS AWAY FROM *DROWNING* ...AND YOU START SHOOTIN' THOSE NUTTY *WEBS* OF YOURS...INTO THE EMPTY *AIR!!*

I WAS ALWAYS *RIGHT* ABOUT YOU..! YOU'RE *BATTY* AS A *BEDBUG!*

MEANWHILE, AT THE OFFICE OF THE *DAILY BUGLE*, AT THAT VERY MOMENT...

NED! WHAT *HAPPENED?* WHY IS THE *DOOR BROKEN?* WHERE IS *MR. JAMESON?*

I DON'T *KNOW*, HONEY! I JUST *GOT* HERE!

BUT *SOMETHING* IS MIGHTY *WRONG!*

FIRST *FOSWELL* MISSING.. AND NOW THE *BOSS!*

I'LL CALL *ROBERTSON!* HE'S CITY EDITOR MAYBE *HE* CAN FILL US IN!

DON'T *BOTHER*, LEEDS! I'M RIGHT *HERE*..AND IT'S *GREEK* TO *ME!*

I JUST SENT FOR THE *POLICE!*

THERE MUST BE *SOMETHING* WRONG! JAMESON WOULD NEVER TAKE OFF WITHOUT *TELLING* US!

I FIGURE HE'S BEEN *ABDUCTED!* AND WE'VE GOTTA FIND OUT *WHY!* I'LL HOLD DOWN HIS DESK WHILE YOU SEE WHAT YOU CAN UNCOVER!

I'M ON MY WAY, ROBBIE! I'LL KEEP IN *TOUCH* WITH YOU!

LET'S GO, BOY! THERE'S NO TIME TO *WASTE!*

NED! WAIT..!

YOU'RE NOT A *CRIME REPORTER!* THAT WAS *FOSWELL'S* JOB!

WHAT IF--IT'S SOMETHING *DANGEROUS*..? I COULDN'T *BEAR* IT IF SOMETHING HAPPENED TO..!

DON'T *SAY* IT, BETTY!

I'VE A *JOB* TO DO...AND I'VE GOT TO *DO* IT..AS BEST I *CAN!*

Panel 1:

NOW STOP WORRYING, HONEY!

FIRST PETER PARKER, RISKING HIS LIFE TAKING CRIME PHOTOS...AND NOW NED, RUNNING HEADLONG INTO...WHAT?

AM I ALWAYS TO BE HAUNTED BY THE THREAT OF DANGER?

JUST FIGURE OUT WHERE YOU'LL PUT THE PULITZER PRIZE I'M GONNA GET...AFTER WE'RE MARRIED!

Panel 2:

AND, SPEAKING OF DANGER...LET'S RETURN TO THE WORLD'S GREATEST AUTHORITY ON THAT LITTLE SUBJECT...

KEEP YOUR FINGERS CROSSED, CHUCKLES!

EVERYTHING DEPENDS UPON MY HAVING ENOUGH WEB FLUID!

FOR WHAT? THE WATER'S UP TO MY TONSILS...AND YOU'RE PLAYIN' GAMES!

YOU'RE A NUT.. LIKE I ALWAYS SAID!

Panel 3:

I DO HAVE MY LITTLE IDIOSYNCRACIES...BUT, THAT'S PART OF MY CHARM!

A NUT!! I'M FINALLY GOING TO THAT OL' NEWSPAPER OFFICE IN THE SKY.. WITH A FULL-TIME, WEB-SLINGIN' NUT!

BEND YOUR HEAD BACK...CLOSER TO ME!

JAMESON!! DO AS I SAY!!

Panel 4:

WHY?? THE WATER'S UP TO MY CHIN!!

IN A FEW MINUTES.. IT'LL ALL.. BE OVER!

THEY CAN'T DO THIS TO ME!! I'M IN THE PRIME OF LIFE!!

AND IF YOU WANNA GET ANY OLDER..SHUDDUP AND HOLD YOUR BREATH!

GET THAT POINTY HEAD OF YOURS UNDER THIS WEBBING!!

Panel 5:

I..DON'T GET IT..!

WHAT ARE YOU.. TRYING TO DO??

I'VE MADE MY WEBBING TRIPLE-PLY THICK... DENSE ENOUGH TO HOLD THE OXYGEN WITHIN IT AGAINST THE PRESSURE OF THE WATER!

IT'LL BE LIKE BEING WITHIN A GIANT AIR BUBBLE!

THE ONLY PROBLEM IS.. HOW LONG CAN IT LAST?!!

WHILE, OUTSIDE THE SEALED CHAMBER...

IT'S ALL FILLED KINGPIN!

THEY'RE GONERS BY NOW!

NATURALLY! THAT WAS MY INTENTION!

WAIT ANOTHER THIRTY SECONDS.. TO BE SURE!

THEN, DRAIN THE ROOM AND DISPOSE OF THEM!

BE SURE YOU TIDY UP WHEN YOU'RE FINISHED! I DETEST SLOPPY WORK!

DON'T WORRY... YOU CAN COUNT ON US!

EXACTLY THIRTY SECONDS LATER...

FLINT SAID WE SHOULD... HEY!! WHAT'S THAT??

I DON'T GET IT!! ..LOOKS LIKE SOME KINDA BIG COCOON.. WITH SOMEONE INSIDE!

AWWW...YOU NOTICED!!

AND I WANTED IT TO BE A SURPRISE!

IT'S SPIDER-MAN!!
HOW DID HE--?!!

ARGGHH!

IT'S GETTING KINDA *CROWDED* UP THERE!

SO, IF YOU STALWARTS WILL *STEP ASIDE* FOR A MOMENT---

...I'LL TRY TO PROVIDE A LITTLE MORE *STANDING ROOM!*

ZOK!

JAMESON!! DON'T JUST *STAND* THERE, MISTER!! *TAKE OFF!!*

THIS IS YOUR CHANCE TO GET BACK TO THE *BUGLE* AND TELL EVERYONE WHAT A BIG, BRAVE *HERO* YOU ARE!!

DON'T WORRY.. THEY'LL *BELIEVE* YOU... SO LONG AS YOU KEEP PAYING THEIR *SALARIES!*

HE'S ALMOST PETRIFIED WITH *FRIGHT!* I'VE GOT TO *SHOCK* HIM INTO ESCAPING!

JAMESON!! I SAID *MOVE*-- OR YOU'LL BE MY *NEXT* TARGET!

KNEW IT!! YOU'RE *MAD--UNCONTROLLABLE!!*

OU'LL ATTACK *ANYONE*... JUST O PROVE YOUR *POWER!!*

YOU'RE EVEN *MORE* OF A MENACE THAN I *SAID* YOU WERE!

WELL, I HADDA DO IT THE *HARD* WAY...

BUT, AT LEAST I GOT HIM TO *RUN!*

HOWEVER, UNBEKNOWNST TO THE BATTLING WEB-SLINGER, JOLLY JONAH'S ESCAPE IS SUDDENLY *CUT SHORT*...

THUNNGG!

...AS HE RACES INTO A LOW-HANGING *PIPE* IN THE GLOOMY SUB-CELLAR..!

AND SO WE LEAVE THE BUGLE'S PEERLESS PUBLISHER FOR NOW.. AS HE SLUMPS IN THE SHADOWS IN A SOMEWHAT *UNUSUAL* CONDITION.. COMPLETELY *SILENT*..!

WHILE, JUST AROUND THE CORNER, SPIDEY HEADS FOR A *DIFFERENT* DESTINATION...

JAMESON'S PROBABLY HALF-WAY TO HIS *OFFICE* BY NOW..

SO, SINCE THE *PRELIMINARIES* ARE OVER...

IT'S TIME FOR THE *MAIN EVENT!*

WHEREVER THE *KINGPIN* IS.. I'M GONNA *FIND* HIM !!

AND, SPEAKING OF THAT ESTIMABLE EVIL-DOER...

SPIDER-MAN.. AND JAMESON..BOTH DEAD??

I..I DON'T *BELIEVE* IT!!

THE *KINGPIN* DOES NOT LIE!

BUT, WHY DO YOU SEEM SO *NERVOUS*.. SO *SHAKY*??

CAN IT BE THAT MY NEWS IS *UNWELCOME* TO YOU ?

CAN IT BE THAT I WAS *WRONG* TO TRUST YOU?

HOLD IT, MISTER! *NOBODY* TALKS TO FRED FOSWELL THAT WAY!

I'LL GO ALONG WITH *ANYTHING* THAT'LL MAKE US A BUCK...

BUT COLD-BLOODED *MURDER* JUST ISN'T MY *STYLE!!*

SPIDER-MAN! HE'S STILL ALIVE! BUT.... HOW??

SO! IT SEEMS I UNDERESTIMATED YOU ONCE MORE!

BUT THE KINGPIN NEVER MAKES THE SAME MISTAKE *TWICE!*

STAND ASIDE, FOSWELL! I'LL DEAL WITH *YOU* LATER!

YOU'LL DO ANY OF *YOUR* FUTURE DEALING FROM BEHIND *BARS*, MISTER!

BUT, KNOWING HOW YOU *WORRY* ABOUT SPIDEY IN MOMENTS LIKE THIS, LET'S BREAK THE TENSION FOR A FEW SECONDS AS WE SWITCH OUR SCENE TO THE DOORWAY OF THE *SILVER SPOON*, WHERE AN UNEXPECTED *VISITOR* IS JUST ENTERING ---

HI, CIVILIANS!

FLASH!! YOU'RE *BACK!*

HEY! HOW *ABOUT* THAT? WHO'S MINDIN' THE WAR FOR YOU, *SOLDIER?*

WESTMORELAND PROMISED TO KEEP AN *EYE* ON THINGS WHILE I'M GONE!

GOOD TO *SEE* YOU AGAIN, FLASHEROO!

YEAH... BUT GORGEOUS *GWENDOLYNE* IS OVER *HERE!*

HEY... I'M STANDIN' OVER *HERE!*

HOW DO I *LOOK*, DREAM STUFF?

IF YOU LOOKED ANY *BETTER*, YOU'D BE *OFF-LIMITS*

BUT WE THOUGHT YOU'D BE A *COLONEL* BY NOW!

SHHH! DON'T BREATHE A *WORD* OF IT! I'M REALLY A THREE-STAR *GENERAL* ... BUT I DRESS THIS WAY 'CAUSE I'M *MODEST!*

IT'S THOSE *SHY-NESS* LESSONS YOU TOOK FROM *MARY JANE!*

SAY! SPEAKING OF M.J., WHERE'S SHE *HIDING?* AND WHAT ABOUT OL' HARRY'S ROLLICKIN' *ROOMMATE?*

US *CONQUERING HEROES* EXPECT A *FULL TURNOUT* WHEN WE COME *WALTZIN'* HOME ON FURLOUGH!

WE HAVEN'T *SEEN* PETE FOR A WHILE!

MAYBE HE'S OUT WITH M.J.!

SHE'S STILL *DATIN'* PUNY PARKER?

I DIDN'T KNOW THINGS WERE *THAT* DESPERATE ON THE HOME FRONT!

C'MON FLASH... CLUE US IN ON *ARMY LIFE!*

WOW!! HE BOUNCED RIGHT BACK UP LIKE A BASKET BALL!!

ONLY A FOOL CONTINUES TO FIGHT WHEN IT'S WISER TO FLEE AND FORMULATE A NEW SET OF PLANS!

AND THE KING-PIN IS NO FOOL!

THERE'S SOME SORT OF HIDDEN ESCAPE HATCH BEHIND THAT CURTAIN!

BUT... WHY WOULD HE RUN... BEFORE HE'S BEATEN?

NO MATTER WHAT ELSE I MAY THINK OF HIM...THAT BOZO IS NO COWARD!

SO THAT'S HIS ACE IN THE HOLE...A MAN-SIZED PNEUMATIC TUBE...FOR INSTANT ESCAPES!

HE'S HEADING STRAIGHT DOWN, TOWARDS...

OF COURSE!! THAT'S IT! THAT'S THE ANSWER!

HE SUDDENLY REALIZED IF I FREED MYSELF FROM THE DUNGEO JAMESON MIGH BE FREE, TOO!

AND WITH JOLL JONAH ON THE LOOSE... HE CAN'T AFFORD TO WAIT AROUND FOR THE POLICE!

BUT...HOW CAN I BE SURE JAMESON DID ESCAPE??

WHAT IF HE'S STILL DOWN THERE...AND THE KINGPIN FINDS HIM??

ONLY ONE WAY TO FIND OUT!

I'VE GOTTA FORCE THIS THING OPEN, AND CRAWL DOWN THE TUBE AFTER HIM!

BUT THEN, SUDDENLY...

SHOOSH!

UNHHH!

LOOKS LIKE THE KINGPIN THOUG OF EVERYTHING!

THE TUBE WA BOOBY-TRAPPE

IF NOT FOR MY SPIDER-STRENGTH, THAT GAS-BLAST MIGHT HAVE FINISHED ME!

BUT I CAN'T JUST SIT HERE AND SULK!! I'VE GOTTA DO SOMETHING!

YEAH... LIKE WHAT?!!

...IF I CAN'T USE THE ...RE, THERE ARE *OTHER* ...S TO REACH THE *CELLAR!*

I'LL JUST HAVE TO TAKE THE *SCENIC* ROUTE, THROUGH THE *CORRIDORS!*

AND, RUNNING ALONG THE SIDE OF THE *WALLS* OUGHTTA *BY-PASS* ANY *OTHER* BOOBY-TRAPS THE *KINGPIN* MAY HAVE PLANTED!

WHILE, MOVING SOMEWHAT *SLOWER,* A SHORT DISTANCE AHEAD---

I THOUGHT I HEARD A *GROAN...* FROM AROUND THAT CORNER!

IF IT'S *JAMESON..* IT MEANS HE'S STILL *ALIVE!*

PLINK!
-UNK!
PLINK..!

OHHHH... MY *HEAD..!*

WHERE *AM I ?* ...WHAT *HAPPENED!!*

WHO'S *POUNDING* ON ME... WITH A *SLEDGE HAMMER--?*

I *REMEMBER* NOW!! THE *KINGPIN...* HE TRIED TO *KILL* ME!!

AND THEN... *SPIDER-MAN* THREATENED ME!!

EVEN *FOSWELL* TURNED AGAINST.. *WAIT!!*

WHAT'S THIS..ON MY *HEAD*..?

IT'S *WET!!*

IT MUST BE *BLOOD!!*

I'M *WOUNDED!!* I'M *DYING!!*

HELP!! SOMEONE *HELLLP!*

...K! IT'S ...ESON!

WE'RE IN *LUCK!* LET'S GET 'IM---!

THE KINGPIN'S GUNMEN!! *NOOOO!*

HE SOUNDS *SCARED!*

IT *FIGGERS!*

THEY'VE GOT *GUNS!*

WHERE CAN I *RUN ??* WHAT CAN I.. *HUH ?!!*

ANOTHER ONE !!

IT'S *FOSWELL!*

JAMESON!! TURN THIS CORNER.. *QUICK!!*

YOU'RE THE *ONLY* ONE WHO EVER *HELPED* ME-- OR GAVE ME A SECOND CHANCE..!

I DIDN'T WANT *YOU* TO BE HURT!

I'LL HOLD 'EM OFF FOR YOU---*SOMEHOW!*

HURRY, MAN--- *HURRY!*

YOU FOOL! YOU SHOT FOSWELL!

SO WHAT? HE WAS TRYIN' TO PROTECT JAMESON, WUZN'T HE?

GIT BACK BEHIND THE WALL!

AS LONG AS HE'S HOLDIN' THAT GUN, HE'S DANGEROUS!

≡UNHHHH!.!≡

CRACK!

YOU--TOOK THE SHOT-- THAT WAS INTENDED-- FOR ME!!

I DON'T UNDERSTAND

I DON'T GET... ANY OF THIS

BUT--YOU'RE HURT!!..HURT BAD!

WHAT DO WE DO NOW?!!

HOWEVER, BEFORE JONAH JAMESON HAS A CHANCE TO DO ANYTHING...

THAT WAS A SHOT I HEARD!!

IT CAME FROM THE END OF THIS CORRIDOR--!

I'M NOT SURE WHAT'S GOING ON--- BUT I'VE A FEELING I'M GONNA BE NEEDED--

..AND FAST!

OTHERWISE, SPIDEY SEN WOULDN'T TINGLING THIS WAY

FOSWELL!! YER HURT! YA NEED A SAWBONES!

TOSS DOWN YER GUN AND MAYBE WE'LL LETCHA LIVE!

NO! ..YOU'RE NOT... GETTING JAMESON-- NOT WHILE--I CAN HELP IT--!

YOU AIN'T GONNA HELP IT MUCH LONGER, MISTER!

WHAT'S HOLDING 'IM UP? WHY DON'T HE FALL?

LOOKS LIKE I DIDN'T ARRIVE A MINUTE TOO SOON!

EPILOGUE...

STILL NO SIGN OF THE *KINGPIN!*

HE MUST HAVE MADE GOOD HIS *ESCAPE*.. FOR *NOW!*

THERE'S *NED LEEDS,* REACHING THE SCENE AHEAD OF THE OTHER NEWSMEN!

HE'LL PROBABLY MAKE A GOOD *REPLACEMENT* FOR POOR FOSWELL!

OF *COURSE* I'M OKAY!

I FOUND OUT WHO'S BEHIND THE CITY'S NEW *CRIME WAVE!*

IT'S AN OVERSIZED *ODDBALL* CALLED THE *KINGPIN!*

BUT, WHO'S *THAT...* ON THE *STRETCH...*

IT'S FOSWELL! HE WAS *MURDERED* TRYING TO SAVE *ME!*

I WANT YOU TO DO A *FRONT PAGE STORY* ABOUT HIM, LEEDS! GIVE HIM ALL THE *FAME*...ALL THE *GLORY* HE NEVER *HAD* WHILE HE LIVED!

AND *THEN...*I'LL WRITE ANOTHER BLAST AGAINST *SPIDER-MAN!!*

HE'S MORE OF A *MENACE* THAN EVER!

--BECAUSE YOU NEVER KNOW *WHAT SIDE* HE'S ON!

THAT SINKS IT!

I WOULDN'T LIFT A *FINGER* NEXT TIME TO HELP THAT MISANTHROPIC MEAT-HEAD..NO MATTER *WHAT!*

I'M *THROUGH* BEIN' A FALL *GUY* FOR EVERYONE ELSE!

I'VE HAD IT... IN *SPADES!*

AWWW--WHO AM I *KIDDIN'?*

I'D DO THE SAME THING ALL *OVER* AGAIN IF I HAD TO... AND I *KNOW* IT!

IN MY OWN WAY, I'M PROBABLY A LOT LIKE *JAMESON!*

HE'S A COMPULSIVE *CRANK*...AND I'M A COMPULSIVE *DO-GOODER!*

THE ONLY THING IS... *HE* MAKES A LOT MORE *DOUGH* AT IT THAN *I* DO!

THERE'S PROBABLY A *MORAL* HIDDEN AWAY IN ALL THIS...BUT I'M TOO POOPED TO *WORRY* ABOUT IT!

I'M GONNA HEAD BACK TO MY PAD AND *SLEEP* FOR A WEEK!

But ALAS, THERE'S NOT MUCH SLUMBER IN SPIDEY'S FUTURE... AND YOU'LL KNOW THE REASON W... AS SOON AS WE TELL YOU THAT NEXT BOMBSHELL ISSUE FEATUR... THE INCREDIBLE VILLAINY OF...

DOCTO... OCTOPU...

--NUFF SAID?

KING-SIZE SPECIAL!
APPROVED BY THE COMICS CODE CA AUTHORITY
the AMAZING SPIDER-MAN™
ALL
EW!
NOT
A
NGLE
EPRINT!
ARVEL
OMICS
ROUP
4
NOV
AN ALL-NEW 41-PAGE EPIC BATTLE... STARRING SPIDEY and the TORCH!
PLUS: FEATURES! SURPRISES! AND TWO GREAT MYSTERIOUS GUEST VILLAINS!
"THE WEB AND THE FLAME!"

BUT THEN, SUDDENLY--- HOLD IT! HOLD IT!

HUH? NOW WHAT--?

WHO'RE YOU??

DON'T STOP US NOW, MR. BELLINI!

NOT TILL I PULVERIZE 'IM!

NO! NO! NO! YOU'RE MY STAR! I CAN'T HAVE YOU ENGAGING IN A COMMON BRAWL!!

STAR?? BELLINI--THE FAMOUS DIRECTOR!!?

SAY! WHAT'S GOIN' ON HERE?

AND NOW, YOU MASKED MEDDLER, YOU'VE JUST RUINED AN ENTIRE SCENE IN MY LATEST MOVIE--"THE TORCH GOES WILD!"

A COUPLE OF MINUTES AGO, THAT PIN-HEADED PYGMY WAS MELTING ARMORED CARS!

MOVIE?!! YOU--YOU MEAN--? HOOO BOY!!

ONLY A FULL-TIME CREEP LIKE YOU WOULDA MESSED THINGS UP WITHOUT ASKIN' SOMEONE FIRST!

IT'S YOUR OWN FAULT, USELESS!

YOU'RE JUST TOO GOOD AN ACTOR!

THEY OUGHTTA LOCK UP A NUT LIKE HIM!

WELL, THAT'S SHOW BIZ!

AN DON COM BAC

ALL RIGHT--PLACES, EVERYBODY!

IF THE HULK SHOWS UP NEXT --I QUIT!

BRO-THER! I SURE BLEW IT THAT TIME!

I HATE TO THINK OF HOW THIS'LL READ AFTER THE DAILY BUGLE GETS WIND OF IT!

AND, SPEAKING OF THE BUGLE, LET'S VISIT THE OFF OF ITS PEERLESS PUBLISHER, JOCULAR J. JONAH JAMESON, THE NEXT A.M.--

WHAT LUCK! NOT ONLY DID THAT WEB-HEADED WEASEL MAKE A BLITHERING JACKASS OF HIM-SELF, BUT SOME OF THE TOP MOVIE CAMERAMEN IN THE BUSINESS GOT PHOTOS OF THE WHOLE BLAMED BUSINESS!

OF COURSE, I'D NEV PRINT THESE PIX AND EMBARRAS MY OLD PAL, SPIDER-MAN

NOT MUC I WOULDN'

Panel 1:
THUS, WHEN THE NEXT EDITION HITS THE STREETS--

IT'S LIKE I ALWAYS *SAID!* THAT WEB-HEAD IS A PUBLIC *MENACE!* HE SHOULD BE DRIVEN OUT OF TOWN!

BUT, HE'S DONE SO MANY *HELPFUL* THINGS, TOO! I JUST CAN'T *BELIEVE* THIS!

THEY'RE TALKING ABOUT *SPIDER-MAN!* I'D BETTER GET A *NEWSPAPER!*

AND YET--THERE ARE THE *PHOTOS!*

I FIGURE *ANYONE* CAN PULL A BONER!

Panel 2:
SO! THE ACCURSED *HUMAN TORCH* IS FILMING A *MOVIE*--AND THAT FOOL *WEB-SLINGER* BLUNDERED IN AND ALMOST RUINED EVERYTHING!

WELL WELL!! HOW VERY *INTERESTING!*

THAT GIVES ME A MOST *DANGEROUS* IDEA--!!

DANGEROUS FOR *THEM*, THAT IS!

Panel 3:
BUT, IT'S TOO NICE A DAY TO WORRY ABOUT NASTY, MYSTERIOUS *VILLAINS*--JUST *YET!*

SO, LET'S TURN TO THE EVER-POPULAR *PETER PARKER*, AS HE LISTENS TO A TV NEWS REPORT--

IT'S JUST BEEN ANNOUNCED THAT *PARAGON PRODUCTIONS*, IN *HOLLYWOOD*, IS ANXIOUS TO MAKE A NEW FILM--STARRING *SPIDER-MAN* AND THE *HUMAN TORCH!*

THIS IS THE RESULT OF THE *PUBLIC INTEREST* THAT'S BEEN AROUSED BY RECENT *NEWSPAPER PHOTOS*--.

THEY WANT *ME*--FOR A FILM?!!

Panel 4:
PARAGON FEELS THAT ANY FILM FEATURING A *BATTLE* BETWEEN THE *TORCH* AND *SPIDER-MAN* WOULD BE THE YEAR'S BIGGEST *SMASH HIT!*

THE TORCH HAS *ALREADY* CONSENTED--AND A NATIONWIDE *SEARCH* IS IN PROGRESS--TO FIND *SPIDER-MAN!*

HMM...A CHANCE FOR SOME *REAL* MONEY--AT *LAST!*

THEY WON'T HAVE TO SEARCH MUCH *LONGER!*

Panel 5:
I NEVER *HEARD* OF PARAGON PRODUCTIONS BEFORE--IT MUST BE A *NEW* STUDIO!

WHEN *AUNT MAY* GETS BACK FROM HER VACATION, WON'T SHE BE SURPRISED WHEN I GREET HER WITH A FISTFUL OF *MONEY?!!*

BUT, NEW OR OLD--WHO CARES?--AS LONG AS THEY PAY *HOLLYWOOD* SALARIES!

AND IT'LL BE GREAT BEING ABLE TO DO THE TOWN WITH *GWEN*, WITHOUT HAVING TO WORRY HOW *EXPENSIVE* ANY RESTAURANT IS!

Panel 6:
AND SO, A SHORT TIME LATER, A ROARING *JET* WINGS SWIFTLY WESTWARD--CARRYING A YOUTHFUL PASSENGER TO FAR MORE *ADVENTURE* THAN HE SUSPECTS--!

IT'LL BE A *BLAST* IF I GET AN *OSCAR*-- AND THE TORCH *DOESN'T!!*

THEN, SIX HOURS LATER --

HOLLYWOOD AT LAST!

WITH SOME OF THE KOOKS THEY'VE GOT OUT HERE, I COULD PROBABLY WALK AROUND IN MY SPIDEY SUIT AND NOT EVEN BE NOTICED!

ANYWAY, I'D BETTER MAKE A SUCCESS OF THIS LITTLE PROJECT --

BECAUSE IT TOOK EVERY LAST NICKEL I'VE MANAGED TO SAVE ALL YEAR TO PAY FOR THE PLANE FARE!

FINALLY, A SHORT TIME AFTER TOUCHDOWN --

HOW DO I KNOW YOU'RE THE REAL SPIDER-MAN?

WELL, I CAN PROVE IT BY CARRYING YOU UP A STEEP WALL SOMEWHERE!

--OR SWING YOU ACROSS A COUPLE OF ROOFTOPS ON MY WEBBING!

I'LL TAKE YOUR WORD FOR IT!

I KINDA THOUGHT YOU WOULD!

AND SO...

NO, I DON'T HAVE AN APPOINTMENT!

BUT, I'M THE ONE THE BIG BRASS HAS BEEN LOOKING FOR!

I HOPE

VERY WELL, SIR! I'LL MAKE AN APPOINTMENT FOR YOU FOR 9:00 TOMORROW MORNING!

GOOD DEAL! YOUR FRIENDLY NEIGHBOR-HOOD SPIDER-MAN WILL BE HERE RIGHT ON THE BUTTON!

IT WORKED! HE SNAPPED AT THE BAIT--JUST AS I KNEW HE WOULD!

BY THE TIME HE REALIZES HE IS THE VICTIM OF A FANTASTIC, DEADLY PLOT-- IT WILL BE TOO LATE -- TOO LATE FOR ANYTHING, EXCEPT HIS FINAL DEFEAT!

HOW DID IT GO? DID HE SUSPECT ANYTHING?

NO! NOT A THING! THIS WILL BE OUR GREATEST TRIUMPH!

BEFORE WE ARE DONE, WE WILL HAVE BROUGHT ABOUT THE DESTRUCTION OF BOTH THE MASKED WEB-SPINNER-- AND THE HUMAN TORCH!

LOOK-- WE'RE BOTH GONNA BE IN THE SAME PICTURE--

SO, WHY DON'T WE GROW UP AND CALL IT A TRUCE!

OKAY, WEB-HEAD-- I'M GAME IF YOU ARE!

BUT IF YOU TRY TO UPSTAGE ME-- OR ASK FOR YOUR NAME TO BE LETTERED BIGGER THAN MINE--ALL BETS ARE OFF!

REMEMBER, THIS TRUCE DOESN'T MEAN I HAVE TO LIKE YOU!

DON'T WORRY, SMALL FRY--

I'VE GOT ENEMI WHO I'D RATHER FRIENDS WITH!

THUS, A FEW SECONDS LATER, THE TORCH AND SPIDEY HEAD FOR PARAGON STUDIOS IN A SOMEWHAT SPECTACULARLY UNORTHODOX MANNER--

DON'T MAKE YOUR FLAME TOO HOT! THIS ASBESTOS WEBBING COSTS MONEY!

WHAT DOESN'T NOWADAYS

THEN, AT LAST, THE GREAT MOMENT BEGINS--

SO, IT'S ABOUT ALIENS WHO LAND IN CENTRAL PARK, EH?

WHAT AM I SUPPOSED TO DO WHEN I SPOT THEIR SPACESHIP?

YOU TRY TO STOP THE PUE FROM PANICKI

OKAY--LET'S GET THINGS ROLLIN'! WHERE'S THE 'ORCH?

THE PLOT SOUNDS KINDA CORNY TO ME--

BUT I SHOULD WORRY!

--JUST SO LONG AS THEY PAY ME!

LOOK ALIVE, WEB-HEAD! WE'RE IN THE BIG-TIME NOW!

ALL OF A SUDDEN MY SPIDER-SENSE IS TINGLING!

BUT-- WHY??!

SO THERE YOU ARE!

FLY TO POSITION A AND WAIT FOR YOUR CUE!

QUIIIET ON THE SET!

PLACES, EVERYBODY!

THIS IS SCENE ONE-- TAKE ONE--THE CENTRAL PARK SCENE--WHERE THE ALIEN SPACE SHIP LANDS!

OK, CHARLIE--

ROLL 'EM!

A FLYING SAUCER-- FROM OUTER SPACE!!

RUN! RUN! IT'S LANDING RIGHT HERE --IN THE PARK!

IT'S AN INVASION!! WE'RE BEING ATTACKED!! THEY'RE OUT TO DESTROY US!

AND, AS MYSTERIO AND THE *WIZARD* TURN TOWARDS THEIR PREVIOUSLY-PREPARED ELECTRONIC *VIEWER*, WE CAN BEAT THEM TO THE SCENE MERELY BY GLANCING AT THE TINTINNABULATING TABLEAU WE SEE BEFORE US--!

I DON'T KNOW WHAT YOUR CRUMMY *GAME* IS, TORCH--

BUT, I'LL MAKE YOU PRETTY DARN *SORRY* YOU EVER TRIED IT ON *ME!*

WHAT'S THE *MATTER* WITH ME?? EVEN THOUGH HE TRIED TO *PARBOIL* ME BEFORE--

HERE I AM PULLING MY *PUNCH* SO I WON'T *HURT* HIM WHILE HE'S NOT IN *FLAME!*

I ALWAYS *THOUGHT* YOU WERE A *FRUITCAKE,* FELLA--

AND NOW I *KNOW* IT!

DON'T TRY TO PLAY THE *INJURED INNOCENT* WITH ME, SQUIRT!

THAT'S IT! GET YOUR *FLAME* GOING--SO I CAN STOP HOLDING MYSELF *BACK!*

BOY! YOU'RE REALLY *GONE,* KIDDO!

I'LL FIGHT YOU *ANY TIME*-- AND ANY *PLACE*--!

BUT, HOW ABOUT TELLING ME *WHY??*

OKAY! IF THIS IS WHAT YOU *WANT*--

IT'S ALL *YOURS!!*

BIG DEAL!! I CAN DODGE *THOSE* THINGS WHILE RECITING *McLUHAN*-- BACKWARDS!

BUT, THIS STUFFY *DRESSING ROOM* IS CRAMPING MY *STYLE!*

C'MON *OUTSIDE,* HOT-HEAD, WHERE I CAN MOP UP THE WHOLE *LANDSCAPE* WITH YOU!

IT'LL BE A *PLEASURE,* LOUDMOUTH!

YOU'VE GOT ABOUT AS MUCH CHANCE AGAINST MY *FLAME* AS *WOODY ALLEN* WOULD HAVE AGAINST THE *HULK!*

DON'T *BET* ON IT! OL' *GREEN SKIN* WOULD PROBABLY *LAUGH* HIMSELF TO DEATH!

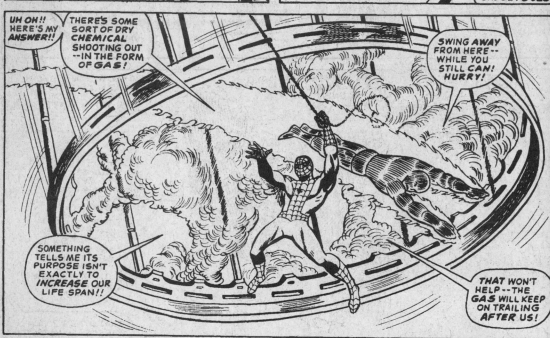

THE TORCH IS COMING AROUND NOW!

HE'LL BE GOOD AS NEW IN A FEW MINUTES!

BUT, I'D BETTER USE THOSE FEW MINUTES TO GET BACK TO THAT CONTROL CENTER AND SEARCH FOR SOMETHING!

THIS IS WHAT I WANT! I THOUGHT I NOTICED SOME MAGNETICALLY-ACTIVATED FLUID USED TO OPERATE THE GEAR DRIVE!

I'VE A HUNCH THIS MAY COME IN MIGHTY HANDY WHEN WE HAVE TO TACKLE OUR TWO FRANTIC FRIENDS AGAIN!

SO, I'LL JUST FILL A FEW CARTRIDGES AND LOAD THEM INTO MY WRIST CONTAINER!

THEN, A FEW MINUTES LATER, AFTER THE HUMAN TORCH HAS FULLY RECOVERED--

THEY HAVE MORE LIVES THAN A PAIR OF CATS-- BUT, WE'LL GET THEM YET!

WITH THE WEB-SLINGER'S ACCURSED SPIDER SENSE, IT WON'T BE LONG BEFORE THEY FIND US HERE --

--WHICH IS EXACTLY WHAT WE WANT THEM TO DO!

FORGET IT, HOT-HEAD!

LOOKS LIKE I'M SORT-OF IN YOUR DEBT, SPIDEY!

I JUST DID WHAT ANY RED-BLOODED, CLEAN-CUT, SELF-SACRIFICING SUPER-HERO WOULDA DONE!

THERE'S OUR OBJECTIVE -- RIGHT AHEAD OF US--OBSERVATION SLIT AND ALL!

BUT, WE'D BETTER APPROACH IT CAREFULLY IT'S PROBABLY CRAWLIN WITH BOOBY TRAPS!

HANDS OFF THAT GUN, WIZ--

--UNLESS YOU'RE COLLECTING *BLISTERS!*

DON'T WORRY, TORCHY--

I'LL KEEP 'EM OUT OF TROUBLE WITH SOME NICE COZY *WEBBING!*

DEFEATED AGAIN!! OH *NOOO*-- NOT *AGAIN!!* NOT *AGAIN!!*

HOW?!! HOW DID IT *HAPPEN?!!*

I PLANNED EVERYTHING TO *PERFECTION!* WE SET A DOZEN *TRAPS!* WE *COULDN'T FAIL*--!!

WWW, SHUT UP, YOU CREEPS!

YOU THINK *YOU'VE* GOT TROUBLES?

WHAT ABOUT THE MONEY I WAS COUNTING ON FROM YOUR *PHONY MOVIE?*

WELL, LOOKY *HERE!* NOW MYSTERIO AND THE WIZARD WON'T HAVE TO WORRY ABOUT BEING *LONELY!*

HI, MEN! WE'VE GOT 'EM ALL *GIFT-WRAPPED* AND READY FOR *DELIVERY!*

MINUTES LATER, THE *PRESS* EAGERLY ARRIVES UPON THE SCENE--

YOU AND THE TORCH WOULD MAKE A GREAT TEAM, SPIDER-MAN!

FORGET IT, GENTS! THE *LAST* THING I NEED RIGHT NOW IS A *PARTNER!*

HAVE YOU EVER *CONSIDERED*--?

WELL THEN, WHAT *DO* YOU NEED?

STAGE 7

PLANE FARE-- BACK TO *NEW YORK!* --BUT I CAN'T ADMIT THAT TO *THEM!*

HEY, SPIDEY-- *WAIT!!* I WANNA GIVE YOU YOUR SHARE OF THE *REWARD* FOR OUR NABBING THOSE TWO CLOWNS!

HUH? DID YOU SAY-- *REWARD?*

SURE! DIDN'T YOU *KNOW?* THEY'RE WANTED IN HALF THE STATES IN THE *COUNTRY!*

Y'KNOW SOMETHIN; HOT-HEAD? I THINK YOU'RE BEGINNING TO *GROW* ON ME!

THUS, AN HOUR LATER, A SOMEWHAT WEARY WEB-HEAD DOZES CONTENTEDLY, HIGH ABOVE THE CLOUDS...

HE MUST HAVE HAD TOO MUCH *SIGHT-SEEING* IN HOLLYWOOD!

I GUESS HE'S THE TYPE THAT *TIRES* EASILY!

WE DON'T KNOW ABOUT *PETE*-- BUT AFTER *WRITING 41 PAGES*-- WE'RE KINDA BUSHED OURSELVES! SO...'NUFF SAID!

THE END!

FOR THE MAN WHO HAS EVERYTHING, HIS OWN PERSONAL WEB-SHOOTER MAKES A UNIQUE AND WELCOME GIFT! CARTRIDGES ARE EXTRA, AND CAN BE OBTAINED PRACTICALLY NOWHERE AT ALL!

TO PREVENT ACCIDENTAL FIRING WHEN MAKING A FIST, IT IS NECESSARY TO TOUCH THE RELEASE BUTTON *TWICE*, IN A PRE-PROGRAMMED, PRE-SET PATTERN! IF YOU'VE SHORT, STUBBY FINGERS, FORGET IT!

THE AMAZING WEB FLUID CAN GUSH OUT IN MANY DIFFERENT FORMS, DEPENDING UPON *HOW LONG* SPIDEY'S FINGER REMAINS UPON THE SENSITIVE CONTROL BUTTON...

A *SHORT* TAP RELEASES A THIN, CABLE-LIKE *STRAND*, RECOMMENDED FOR SWINGING... OR STRINGING GUITARS!

A *LONGER* PERIOD OF PRESSURE RELEASES MORE FLUID, FORMING AN ICKY, ECHHY, BLOCHHY, STICKY *BLOB*... USEFUL IN PASTING A FOE AGAINST A WALL... LIKE!

A SERIES OF BRISK, *STACCATO* TAPS RELEASES MULTIPLE CABLE SHAPES WHICH CAN BE FORMED INTO A DECORATIVE *NETTING* PATTERN!

SPIDEY'S GREATEST TALENT

THE ABILITY TO CLIMB WALLS AND STICK TO ANY SURFACE.

I'M PROBABLY A FULL-TIME *IDIOT* FOR TAKING A *CHANCE* LIKE THIS, BUT--

UH OH!! *FOOTSTEPS!!* SOMEONE'S *COMING!*

WHEW! ANOTHER SECOND WOULD HAVE BEEN *TOO LATE!*

IT'S PROFESSOR *WARREN!*

PARKER! IS THAT *YOU?*

I *THOUGHT* I HEARD SOMEONE IN THE *GYM!*

I WAS-- JUST TAKING A LITTLE *WORKOUT*, SIR--!

I NEVER *REALIZED* YOU WERE SO *AGILE*, SON!

BETTER TUCK IN YOUR *UNDER-SHIRT*, THOUGH!

HUH? OH! YES SIR --I--I *WILL!*

WOW!-- LUCKY HE'S SO *NEAR-SIGHTED*-- HE DIDN'T SEE THE *WEB PATTERN!*

BUT DON'T *PANIC*, MY BOY!

NO ONE'S BEEN EXPELLED *YET* FOR A PRO-TRUDING UNDERSHIRT!

BY THE WAY, PARKER--I HAVE TWO EXTRA *TICKETS* TO TONIGHT'S *SCIENCE EXPOSITION!*

SO, IF YOU--AND A FRIEND-- WOULD LIKE TO BE MY *GUEST?*

THAT'S *GREAT*, PROFESSOR! I'VE BEEN *WANTING* TO GO!

GOOD! I'LL GIVE YOU A *LIFT*-- AFTER CLASS!

WHAT A *RELIEF!* HE DOESN'T SUSPECT A *THING!*

SAY! AREN'T *YOU* THE ONE WHO PICKED A PECK OF PICKLED PEPPERS?

GWEN!! JUST THE ONE I'M *LOOKING* FOR!

ARE YOU DOING ANY-THING *SPECIAL* TONIGHT, PRETTY GIRL?

EVERYTHING I DO IS SPECIAL, MR. PARKER!

WHAT I *MEANT* WAS-- OH, THERE'S *HARRY!*

HI, ROOMMATE! HOW'S IT GOIN'?

HELLO, PETE! FLASH SAID HE'LL LOOK FOR YOU AFTER CLASS, GWEN.

WHAT'S WITH *HIM?* WHY THE BIG *FREEZE?*

YOUR UNEXPLAINED *COMINGS AND GOINGS* SEEM TO BE SHAKING HIM UP, LADDIE!

BUT GREEDY *GWENDOLYNE* IS MORE INTERESTED IN WHAT YOU HAD IN MIND FOR *TONIGHT!*

IT'S THE *SCIENCE EXPO!* MAYBE IT'S NOT YOUR *CUP OF TEA,* BUT--

SILLY BOY! I THOUGHT YOU'D *NEVER* ASK!

IN CASE YOU'VE FORGOTTON, YOUR LITTLE BLONDE BUDDY IS A SCI MAJOR, *TOO!*

SOME TIME LATER, AFTER CLASS--

YOU'RE BRINGING *MISS STACY?*

I CERTAINLY ADMIRE YOUR *CHOICE,* PARKER!

NO TIME FOR YOU TO *CHANGE!* I'LL GET THE CAR--MEET YOU OUT FRONT!

HI, GORGEOUS! I KNEW YOU WOULDN'T KEEP OL' *FLASHEROO* WAITING!

HOW ABOUT A *RAIN CHECK,* GENERAL? I'VE A DATE WITH *PETE* TONIGHT!

'SPECIALLY WHEN WE'RE GONNA KNOCK 'EM DEAD AT THE *DISKO!*

GREAT LITTLE *KIDDER,* THAT CHICK!

SHE'S NOT *KIDDING!*

LISTEN, *CIVILIAN*--ARE YOU TRYIN' TO BEAT MY TIME WITH *GWEN?*

YOU NEVER *HAD* ANY TIME TO *BEAT!*

AND WHAT'S WITH THE *CIVILIAN* BIT? WHAT WERE *YOU* BEFORE THE *DRAFT?!!*

AT EASE, MEN! LET'S ALL MEET LATER AT THE *COFFEE BEAN,* AND PUFF A PURPLE *PEACE PIPE!*

OKAY--BUT ONE OF THESE DAYS THAT LOUDMOUTH'LL PICK ON THE *WRONG GUY*--!

YEAH--AND THAT'S WHEN I'LL *FLATTEN* YOU, PARKER --'CAUSE YOU WERE *BORN* THE WRONG GUY!

SPIDEY'S BIGGEST FAN! OH, BRO-THER!

LET'S *GO,* GWEN! THE PROF IS WAITING!

I NEVER COULD UNDERSTAND WHY HE *BUGGED* YOU, FLASH--BUT NOW--!

I CAN'T *EXPLAIN* IT, BUT HE ACTS LIKE HE'S IN HIS OWN PRIVATE *WORLD*--AND EVERY-ONE ELSE BETTER KEEP *OUT!*

AW, HE'S OKAY, HARRY!

WHAT?!!

SURE! NOTHING WRONG WITH HIM THAT A GOOD *LEFT* TO THE *LABONZA* COULDN'T CURE!

MINUTES LATER, IN PROFESSOR WARREN'S CAR--

I WONDER WHAT THEY'RE *FEATURING* AT THE SCIENCE EXHIBIT TODAY?

ACCORDING TO THE *PAPER*, IT'S A NEW TYPE OF MISSILE *DEFENSE*-- CALLED A *NULLIFIER!*

EXACTLY! AND, DO YOU KNOW HOW IT *WORKS?*

I IMAGINE IT NULLIFIES THE *HOMING DEVICES* OF ENEMY MISSILES!

YOU IMAGINE *RIGHT*, YOUNG LADY!

TODAY, THERE'LL BE A DEMONSTRATION OF THE NULLIFIER'S *STABILIZER CONTROL!*

SOMEHOW, IT ALL SEEMS LIKE THE START OF A *JAMES BOND* MOVIE--!

FOR MAXIMUM *SECURITY*, THE TWO *PARTS* OF THE STABILIZER WILL BE DELIVERED *SEPARATELY!*

IT *SURE DOES!*

BUT, THE *MOST* EXCITING PART IS JUST BEING WITH *GWEN!*

HOW CAN ANY-ONE SO *BEAUTIFUL* ALSO BE SO--*UH OH!!*

SOMETHING'S *WRONG!* MY *SPIDER SENSE* IS STARTING TO *TINGLE!*

PETE! YOU LOOK SO *STRANGE!* DO YOU--*FEEL* ALL RIGHT? PETE--?

WE'D BETTER SEE ABOUT FINDING OUR *SEATS!*

IT LOOKS AS THOUGH THE *DEMONSTRATION* IS ABOUT TO *BEGIN!*

I'M SURE YOU'LL SEE A *PRACTICAL* APPLICATION OF THE MANY SEEMINGLY UNRELATED *THEORIES* WE'VE BEEN DISCUSSING IN CLASS!

IT'S TINGLING MORE THAN *EVER* NOW!

BUT *HOW? WHY?* I DON'T SEE ANY-THING *HAPPENING!*--AND THERE ARE GUARDS ALL OVER THE PLACE!

HUM? OH--SURE--I FEEL *FINE!* I JUST THOUGHT-- I *RECOGNIZED* SOMEONE, GWEN!

FROM THE *LOOK* ON YOUR FACE--HE MUST HAVE BEEN A *GHOST!*

LET'S BE SEATED--!

THERE *MUST* BE SOME DANGER TO THE *NULLIFIER!* BUT-- I JUST *CAN'T* SLIP AWAY AND BECOME *SPIDER-MAN!*

NOT WITHOUT AROUS-ING TOO MANY *SUSPICIONS!!*

LADIES AND GENTLE-MEN--WITH *BOTH* PARTS OF THE STABILIZER SAFELY ON THIS PLATFORM, I SHALL *JOIN* THEM TOGETHER SO THAT OUR *DEMON-STRATION* CAN BEGIN!

OBVIOUSLY, WE HAVE TAKEN EVERY PRECAUTION FOR *MAXIMUM SECURITY* WITH THIS VITAL DEVICE!

GWEN! YOU AND PETER FOLLOW ME! WE'VE GOT TO GET OUT!

PETER? I-I THOUGHT HE WAS WITH YOU!

I'VE GOT TO SLIP AWAY--AND CHANGE TO SPIDER-MAN!

RUN, YOU HELPLESS WEAKLINGS --RUN!!

I CAN ALWAYS SAY WE JUST GOT SEPARATED IN THE CONFUSION!

RUN! THEY'RE USING TEAR GAS!

HE'S GOT THE NULLIFIER!! THIS'LL STOP 'IM!

-UNHH!- LOOK OUT FOR THOSE METAL ARMS OF HIS!

YOU THINK SOME MERE BURSTS OF TEAR GAS CAN STOP THE MOST DANGEROUS MAN ALIVE?

DON'T LET 'IM BLUFF YOU, BOYS!!

HE'S NOT WEARIN' A GAS MASK! AS LONG AS HE BREATHES--WE'VE GOT 'IM!

DR. OCTOPUS NEEDS NO GAS MASK!

MY ALL-PURPOSE ARMS CAN DO ANY-THING--!!

JUST WATCH!

LOOK OUT! HE'S WHIRLIN' THOSE TENTACLES AROUND FASTER 'N FASTER!

MEANWHILE, AMONG THE MANY SPELLBOUND SPECTATORS ON THE GROUND, WE FIND--

THERE'S NO SIGN OF PETER ANY-WHERE!!

WHAT COULD HAVE HAPPENED TO HIM?

I DON'T UNDER-STAND IT!

I CAN'T HELP FEELING THAT HE'S IN SOME SORT OF DANGER!

TALK ABOUT FEMALE INTUITION! GORGEOUS GWEN JUST COULDN'T BE RIGHTER!

HEADS UP, DOC!

YOU FIGURED YOU'D HAVE THE ADVANTAGE HERE ON THE ROOF-- 'CAUSE YOU COULD STAND ON YOUR FEET, AND USE ALL FOUR ARMS FOR FIGHTING EH?

WELL, YOU CAN'T HIT WHAT YOU CAN'T SEE--

--AND YOU WON'T SEE ME WHILE YOUR GOGGLES ARE COVERED WITH WEB FLUID!

YOU'RE TRULY CLEVER, SPIDER-MAN!!

BUT NOT CLEVER ENOUGH!

EVEN WITH MY VISION OBSCURED, MY ARMS WILL BRING ME VICTORY!

THE NULLIFIER!! YOU'RE DANGLING IT OVER THE STREET BELOW!

IF I DROP IT--DOZENS WILL BE CRUSHED!

SO YOU CAN'T EVEN FOLLOW UP YOUR SMALL VICTORY!

NOT WHILE INNOCENT PEOPLE NEED YOUR PROTECTION!

HE'S RIGHT! I CAN'T LET THAT FALL!

NOR CAN I RUN OFF-- WITHOUT PLANTING MY SPIDEY TRACER!

KLIK!

HE MEAN IT! THA' MADMA' LET IT GO!

--AND THE STREET IS PACKED WITH ONLOOKERS DIRECTLY BELOW US!

NO CHANCE TO *REACH* IT--BUT--

IF I CAN *SNARE* IT WITH MY *WEBBING* IN TIME--!!

GOT IT!

WHILE, ON THE ROOFTOP ABOVE--

IT'S *NO USE!* CAN'T GET THE FLUID *OFF!*

IT'S STUCK TOO *TIGHT!*

BUT, I CAN'T *REMAIN* HERE LIKE THIS-- I'M TOO *VULNERABLE* WITH MY *VISION* CLOUDED!

IF I USE MY TENTACLES AS *FEELERS*--

--I CAN *STILL* MAKE MY WAY TO SAFETY--

--SO LONG AS I KEEP MY SENSE OF *DIRECTION!*

AND, AS THE MULTI-ARMED MENACE FEELS HIS WAY INTO THE ALL-CONCEALING SHADOWS OF NIGHT--

HEADS UP, GANG! SEE IF YOU CAN *HANG ONTO* THIS *GIZMO* FROM NOW ON!

YOU DON'T FIND VALUABLE *NULLIFIERS* ON EVERY *STREET CORNER!*

WELL, THAT'S *THAT!* NOW, IF DOC-- *HEY!*

HE'S *GONE!* HE MANAGED TO CUT OUT-- EVEN WITH HIS EYES COVERED WITH *WEB FLUID!*

BUT I CAN ALWAYS TRACK HIM DOWN--SO LONG AS MY LITTLE *SPIDEY TRACER* HANGS IN THERE!

RIGHT *NOW,* I'D BETTER *CHANGE* AGAIN AND CUT BACK TO GWEN AND THE PROF!

I'M GONNA HAVE ME SOME TALL *EXPLAINING* TO DO--AS USUAL!

SHE'S THE ONLY GIRL--WHO'S NEVER ASKED ME--FOR ANY EXPLANATIONS!

IT'S A SHAME YOU MISSED SPIDER-MAN, PETE! HE WAS SIMPLY WONDERFUL!

IF ONLY HIS IDENTITY COULD BE EXPOSED! WHAT A SUBJECT HE'D BE--FOR A PSYCHOLOGICAL STUDY!

IMAGINE LEARNING WHAT MOTIVATES SUCH A MAN! IS IT ALTRUISM--OR DEEP-ROOTED SCHIZOPHRENIA?

I'LL BET HE'S EVEN AN ENIGMA TO HIMSELF!

MINUTES LATER--

CARE TO JOIN US FOR SOME COFFEE, SIR?

THANKS, BUT I'D BETTER BE GETTING BACK!

WE'LL TRY TO KEEP THE FAITH WITHOUT YOU, DR. WARREN!

THE ENTIRE SCIENTIFIC COMMUNITY MAY TOPPLE IF I DON'T GRADE SOME TERM PAPERS TONIGHT!

THE Coffee Bean

abandon hope all ye who enter here.

HE'S ABOUT THE GREATEST PROF THAT EVER --OH, LOOK!

THE PARKER FAN CLUB IS NOW IN SESSION!

LIKE HI, LITTLE ONES! THERE'S JUST ROOM FOR TWO MORE SOUL-MATES!

SAY, GORGEOUS! YOU STILL WITH PUNY PARKER?

HOW ABOUT LEVELLIN' DIDJA LOSE A BET OR SOMETHING?

FACE IT, FRIENDS! YOU'VE GOT YOUR GURU-- I'VE GOT MINE!

WHAT'S HARRY STONY-FACED ABOUT?

I ONLY LOANED HIM TO YOU, LADY!

IS HE JEALOU --OF GWE AND ME

PETER DEAR! I THOUGHT I SAW YOU WALK IN HERE!

AUNT MAY! AND MRS. WATSON!

THEY'RE ALL SMILES! SOMETHING MUST BE UP!

MAY COULDN'T WAIT TO TELL YOU THE NEWS--!

WE JUST PLACED AN AD IN TODAY'S NEWSPAPER!

AN AD?!

WE THOUGHT OF THE MOST DELIGHTFUL WAY TO MAKE SOME EXTRA PIN MONEY!

SINCE ANNA HAS AN EXTRA ROOM IN HER HOUSE--WE'RE GOING TO TAKE IN A BOARDER!

Room for rent. Comfortably furnished. Light and pleasant. Suitable for retired gentleman or lady. Call after 5 P.M. weekdays.

Beautiful room for young lady. A

IT'S A GREAT IDEA, AUNT MAY--

BUT BE CAREFUL WHOM YOU ACCEPT, HEAR?

YOU KNOW HOW CAUTIO WE ARE, PET

WE'LL INSIST ON THE VERY FINES REFERENCES!

I WOND IF CONR HILTO STARTI THIS W

FROM WHERE I SIT, IT SOUNDS REAL GROOVY!

THIS IS MY CHANCE TO *CUT OUT* NOW, AND GET BACK TO THE TRAIL OF *DOC OCK!*

SEE YOU *LATER*, GROUP! I'LL MAKE SURE NO ONE *FLIRTS* WITH THESE TWO PUSSYWILLOWS ON THEIR WAY HOME!

NO SKIN OFF *MY* NOSE! NOW WE DON'T HAVE ONE FELLA TOO *MANY!*

AW, *ONE* TIGER'S AS GOOD AS *ANOTHER*, SO LONG AS HE'S A REAL LIVE *MALE!*

EVEN WHEN NO ONE'S *AROUND*, HE'S ONE FELLA TOO MANY!

METHINKS THE LADY DOTH *PROTEST* TOO MUCH!

BUT, BEFORE OUR LITTLE SAGA TURNS INTO A SWINGIN' *SOAP OPERA*, LET'S SEE WHAT'S SHAKIN' IN THE DIABOLICAL DIGS OF DASTARDLY *DOC OCK*--

FORTUNATELY, I WAS ONE OF THE WORLD'S MOST COMPETENT *ATOMIC SCIENTISTS* BEFORE I TURNED MY TITANIC TALENTS TO THE CAUSE OF TOTAL *VILLAINY!*

THUS IT IS MERE *CHILD'S PLAY* FOR ME TO FIND A WAY TO EMPLOY SPIDER-MAN'S ELECTRONIC TRACER *AGAINST* HIM!

ALL I NEED DO IS CONSTRUCT A MAKESHIFT *REPLICA* OF MYSELF--SETTING IT IN FRONT OF A DUMMY *CONTROL PANEL*--!

THE SHEER *SIMPLICITY* OF THIS TRAP WILL MAKE IT VIRTUALLY *ESCAPE-PROOF!!*

THERE! EVERYTHING IS READY--AND WAITING--FOR THE ARRIVAL OF MY *DOOMED* ARCH-FOE!

THERE CAN BE NO DOUBT THAT HE *WILL* ARRIVE!!

SINCE I HAVE TAKEN THE PRECAUTION OF PLACING HIS OWN *SPIDER TRACER* EXACTLY WHERE I *WANT* IT!

AND, BEFORE THE NIGHT GETS VERY MUCH OLDER--

AUNT MAY AND MRS. WATSON ARE SAFELY BACK AT HOME--AND THEY GAVE ME THE PERFECT *EXCUSE* TO DUCK OUT OF THE *COFFEE BEAN*--

SO NOW I'M FREE AS A *BIRD* TO TAKE OFF AFTER THAT MULTI-ARMED *MISFIT!!*

I'VE JUST GOTTA PICK UP MY *TRACER SIGNAL*, AND THEN-- *ZOWEEE!*

SPECIAL NOTE FOR DO-IT-YOURSELF BUFFS: WE'VE GENEROUSLY LEFT ENOUGH SPACE FOR YOU TO ADD YOUR OWN IMPASSIONED *SOUND EFFECT!* A RESOUNDING *PTWEEOW* OR A ROLLICKING *BTOOOMM* MIGHT WELL FILL THE BILL! --STEREOPHONIC STAN.

MEANWHILE, WITHIN THE SAFETY OF HIS *REAL* HIDEOUT, DOC OCK FIENDISHLY GLOATS--ALBEIT *PREMATURELY*--!

I'VE DONE IT AT *LAST!*

I'VE DESTROYED *SPIDER-MAN* --FINALLY-- BEYOND ANY *DOUBT!*

BUT NOW, I'VE GOT TO FIND A *SAFER* HIDING PLACE!

AFTER MY ABORTIVE ATTEMP[T] TO STEAL THE *NULLIFIER,* EVERY FEDERAL AGENT IN TH[E] *COUNTRY* WILL BE SEARCHING FOR ME!

THUS, I MUST FIND A PLACE OF *SANCTUARY* --SO INNOCENT- APPEARING--SO MUCH *ABOVE SUSPICION*-- THAT NO ONE WOULD EVER *THINK* THAT *DOCTOR OCTOPUS* MIGHT BE HIDDEN THERE!

HAVING FINALLY *DESTROYED* MY GREATEST ENEMY, I CAN *AFFORD* TO LIE LOW--AND BIDE MY TIME!

BUT *WE* KNOW DIFFERENTLY, DON'T WE, WEB-SPINNERS?

IF NOT FOR [MY] *SPIDER SENS[E]* I'D BE *KAPU[T]* BY NOW!

JUST LI[KE] THAT SPOOKY S[PIDER] ARMED KILLER W[ILL] BE--ONC[E I] CATCH [UP] WITH HI[M!]

WHERE- EVER HE IS--

SOONER OR LATER-- I'LL *FIND* HIM!

AND, FIND HIM SPIDEY *WILL*-- BUT NOT THE WAY HE *EXPECTS*--!!

ROOM FOR RENT

CLASSIFIED

NEXT ISSUE!

OH! I JUST REMEMBERED!

DIDN'T I *HEAR* SOMETHING... ABOUT YOU BEING *WANTED*... BY THE *POLICE*?

OH, HEAVENS *NO*, MADAM!

THAT WAS JUST A *MISTAKE*!

THE *NEWSPAPERS* GOT THE STORY ALL *MIXED UP*, AS THEY SO OFTEN *DO*!

AS A DEDICATED *SCIENTIST*, I WAS MERELY SEEKING TO *PREVENT* A ROBBERY!

SPIDER-MAN WAS THE CULPRIT... I WAS TRYING TO *STOP* HIM FROM STEALING THE *NULLIFIER*!

OF COURSE! HOW PERFECTLY SILLY OF ME! I SHOULD HAVE KNOWN!

TO THINK YOU'D RISK YOUR OWN LIFE TRYING TO SAVE US ALL FROM THAT DREADFUL *SPIDER-MAN*!

HONESTLY! IT'S SO GOOD TO LEARN THAT *GALLANTRY* STILL EXISTS IN THIS *CALLOUS* WORLD!

DO COME IN, DEAR *DR. OCTOPUS!* THE ROOM IS *YOURS* IF YOU WANT IT!

MRS. WATSON, WITH WHOM I LIVE, IS AWAY ON A TRIP...

I'M DEEPLY *TOUCHED* BY YOUR KINDNESS, DEAR LADY!

THIS IS *PERFECT!* THEY'LL *NEVER* FIND ME, HERE!

BUT I JUST *KNOW* SHE'LL WELCOME YOU AS MUCH AS *I* DO!

MEANWHILE, EVEN AS ONE OF THE WORLD'S MOST DEADLY *ARCH-VILLAINS* FINDS SANCTUARY UNDER THE ROOF OF SPIDEY'S UNWITTING *AUNT*...

I'VE COVERED THE WHOLE *CITY*...

CAN'T FIND A *TRACE* OF HIM!

STILL, HE *MUST* BE HERE *SOMEWHERE* --BUT *WHERE*?

MY *SPIDEY SENSE* HASN'T EVEN *TINGLED* YET!

WHEREVER HE *IS*... I GUESS HE'S *SAFE* FOR NOW!

SO I MIGHT AS WELL HEAD *HOME* AND GRAB SOME *SHUT-EYE!*

I'M GETTING TO BE A MIGHTY *WEARY* LITTLE WEB-SWINGER!

THEN, AFTER A SPEEDY *COSTUME CHANGE...*

OCK IS *BOUND* TO SHOW HIMSELF SOONER OR LATER!

HMMM... HARRY MUST BE OUT ON A *DATE!*

GUESS I'LL PHONE *AUNT MAY* AND SEE HOW SHE'S FEELING!

AND SO, SECONDS LATER...

OH.. THE *PHONE!* IT MUST BE MY *NEPHEW!*

I'LL GIVE YOU YOUR FIRST MONTH'S RENT IN *ADVANCE,* DEAR LADY!

THAT SHOULD KEEP HER OUT OF MY HAIR UNTIL MY *PLANS* ARE COMPLETE!

YOU JUST MAKE YOURSELF *COMFORTABLE,* DOCTOR...

AND IF THERE'S ANYTHING YOU *WANT,* JUST *CALL!*

THANK YOU, MRS. PARKER! I'M SURE EVERYTHING WILL WORK OUT *FINE!*

PETER, DEAR! HOW NICE TO *HEAR* FROM YOU!

IT'S A GOOD THING SHE'S SO *UNSUSPECTING!*

BECAUSE, IF SHE EVER GUESSED WHAT'S IN *STORE...!!*

BUT THEN, IN THE PRIVACY OF HIS ROOM, DOCK OCK'S SPIRITS BEGIN TO RISE...

NOW THAT SPIDER-MAN IS DEAD... AND I'VE FOUND A FAR BETTER HIDE-OUT THAN I EXPECTED...

I CAN AGAIN MAKE PLANS TO STEAL THE PRICELESS NULLIFIER!

AND THIS TIME I WILL NOT FAIL!

...ESPECIALLY SINCE MY MENTAL CONTROL OVER MY POWERFUL ARTIFICIAL ARMS IS EVEN GREATER THAN EVER!

I AM STILL ONE OF THE MOST BRILLIANT SCIENTIFIC BRAINS OF THE CENTURY...

AND, AIDED BY MY TENTACLES, I CAN ACCOMPLISH ANYTHING!

NOW I'LL UNPACK THE COMMUNICATING EQUIPMENT I BROUGHT, AND CONTACT ONE OF MY WAITING AIDES..!

LUCKILY, ALL OF MY MEN WERE NOT CAPTURED WHEN MY CAREER AS THE MASTER PLANNER WAS CUT SHORT BY THE ACCURSED SPIDER-MAN! *

* IT STARTED IN SPIDEY #31... AND FINALLY PETERED OUT IN #33! OR MAYBE IT WAS THE OTHER WAY AROUND! --- SHEEPISH STAN.

BEFORE LONG, I'LL BE IN FULL COMMAND ONCE MORE!

AND SO...

DR. OCTOPUS!! I'VE BEEN WAITING TO HEAR FROM YOU!

YOUR WAIT IS OVER! SOON WE SHALL STRIKE AGAIN!

AND SO I BEGIN THE GREATEST SERIES OF *CRIMES* THE WORLD HAS EVER KNOWN!

NOW LISTEN CLOSELY... AS I GIVE YOU A LIST OF THE *MATERIAL* I WILL NEED..!

WHILE, ON THE FLOOR BELOW...

HOW *ODD!* I'VE NEVER HAD TROUBLE WITH THE TV BEFORE!

IT'S LIKE SOME SORT OF SILLY *ELECTRICAL* INTERFERENCE!

I WONDER IF *DR. OCTOPUS* COULD FIX IT FOR ME?

HE SEEMS SO VERY *CAPABLE.*

BUT, SINCE THE NAME OF THIS PUBLICATION IS NOT "*THE AMAZING AUNT-WOMAN*," LET'S TURN OUR ATTENTION ONCE AGAIN TO THE EVER-POPULAR PAD OF *PETER PARKER*... THE FOLLOWING MORNING...

PETE'S *DOOR* IS OPEN! HE MUST HAVE BEEN UP *EARLY!*

SOME ROOM-MATE! I'VE HARDLY *SPOKEN* TO HIM IN DAYS!

HEY, *PETE!* ARE YOU *THERE?* WANT SOME BREAK-FAST?

IT'S *HARRY!* I DIDN'T REALIZE IT WAS SO *LATE!*

CAN'T LET HIM FIND ME MIXING MY *SPIDEY FLUID!*

AND--IF HE EVER SAW MY *COSTUME*.. HANGING ON THE *DOOR*..!

I WAS A *FOOL* TO BE SO CARELESS!

I'VE GOTTA LOAD MY *WEB FLUID* IN MY BELT *NOW*...

MAY NOT GET A *CHANCE* LATER!

JUST A SECOND, HARRY! BE RIGHT *WITH* YOU!

THIK

THERE! THAT *DOES* IT!

BOY! TALK ABOUT *CLOSE CALLS*..!!

ZAK

NOW THEN, HARRY...DID I HEAR SOMEONE SAY *BREAKFAST?*

FORGET IT! I CAN'T WAIT FOR YOU TO LOCK EVERYTHING UP TIGHT AS A *DRUM* BEFORE YOU'LL *TALK* TO ME!

IF YOU'RE AFRAID I'LL *STEAL* SOMETHING.. JUST *MOVE OUT!*

C'MON, HARRY! YOU KNOW BETTER THAN *THAT!*

YEAH! BUT I'M NOT SURE *YOU* DO!

SEE YOU LATER! I'VE GOT TO VISIT MY *DAD* NOW!

BOTH THOSE LIVING DOLLS ACT LIKE PARKER'S THE ONLY ONE OF HIS KIND!

WHAT'S HE GOT, ANYWAY?

NOT A *THING*, JOE! TAKE AWAY HIS *LOOKS*... AND HIS *BRAINS*.. AND HE'S *NOWHERE*!

CARE TO HAVE A *TALK-IN* WITH A COUPLE OF WIDE-EYED WENCHES, MR. P. ?

BREAK IT TO HER *GENTLY*, PETEY-O!

THE POOR *CHILD* NEVER *HEARD* THAT THREE'S A CROWD!

DON'T BE *SILLY*, MISS WATSON!

WE DON'T WANT YOU TO LEAVE ON *OUR* ACCOUNT!

LOOK, KIDDIES..THIS IS ALL VERY *FLATTERING*, BUT I JUST REMEMBERED MY AUNT MAY HAS A NEW *BOARDER*, AND I'D BETTER SEE IF EVERY-THING'S OKAY!

AUNT MAY? WHO CAN BUCK COMPETITION LIKE *THAT?!*

I'D HAVE *LIKED* TO STAY WITH GWEN AND MJ, BUT MRS. WATSON IS OUT OF TOWN, AND... *HEY!!*

MY *SPIDEY SENSE!!* TINGLING LIKE *MAD!* SOMETHING'S *WRONG* INSIDE...!

I'VE GOT TO GET *IN* THERE.. *FAST!*

IT CAN'T BE...!!

BUT, NO SOONER DOES PETE ENTER THE HOUSE, WHEN..

IT'S... *DR. OCTOPUS!*

PETER *DEAR!* HOW *NICE* OF YOU TO DROP IN!

OH, THAT'S *RIGHT!* YOU'VE *MET* MY NEW BOARDER *BEFORE!* I HAD ALMOST *FORGOTTEN!*

COME *IN*, YOUNG MAN.. COME IN!

YOUR AUNT WAS JUST *TELLING* ME WHAT A BRILLIANT *SCIENCE STUDENT* YOU ARE!

YOUR NEW BOARDER??!

DON'T *STARE* SO, DEAR! IT'S *IMPOLITE!*

I DABBLE A BIT IN SCIENCE MYSELF!

AUNT MAY... DON'T YOU KNOW WHO HE *IS*... *WHAT* HE IS ??

HE'S A CRIMINAL!! A DEADLY MENACE!

YOU MUSTN'T SAY SUCH THINGS, DEAR! AFTER ALL, HE *IS* OUR GUEST!

FORGIVE MY NEPHEW, DOCTOR! HE'S SO HIGH-STRUNG!

OF *COURSE*, DEAR LADY! I *UNDERSTAND!*

HE'S JUST *OVER-EMOTIONAL*.. LIKE SO MANY OF TODAY'S TEENAGERS!

AUNT MAY... LISTEN TO ME..!

NOT ANOTHER *WORD*, PETER! YOU MUSTN'T *EXCITE* YOURSELF THIS WAY! YOU *KNOW* HOW FRAGILE YOU ARE!

DR. OCTOPUS EXPLAINED THE WHOLE *THING* TO ME! HE'S ENTIRELY *INNOCENT!*

HE WAS JUST TRYING TO STOP THAT HORRIBLE SPIDER-MAN!

HOW CAN I *TELL* HER?? HOW CAN I *EXPLAIN*... WITHOUT ONE OF THEM SUS-PECTING THAT *I'M* SPIDER-MAN!

PERHAPS IF YOU LET ME SPEAK TO HIM *ALONE*, MRS. PARKER...

I'LL TRY TO SHOW HIM HOW *WRONG* HE IS...MAN-TO-MAN!

THAT'S VERY KIND OF YOU, DOCTOR!

NOW *LISTEN*, YOU PUNK KID... AND LISTEN *GOOD!*

ONE MORE *PEEP* OUT OF YOU... TO YOUR *AUNT*... THE *PAPERS*... OR THE *COPS*.. AND IT'LL BE CURTAINS FOR *BOTH* OF YOU!

I'D *TACKLE* HIM *NOW*... BUT, I *CAN'T!* I DON'T *DARE* DO IT...!

THE *SHOCK* WOULD BE TOO MUCH FOR AUNT MAY'S WEAK *HEART!*

BUT, HOW CAN I *LEAVE* HER HERE... WITH THE MOST *DANGEROUS*, MOST *MANIACAL* ARCH-FIEND OF ALL ?!!

REMEMBER... HER LIFE'S IN YOUR HANDS!

I THINK YOUR NEPHEW UNDER-STANDS NOW, MRS. PARKER!

HOW *NICE!* I DO HOPE YOU'LL BECOME GOOD *FRIENDS!*

DR. OCTOPUS MIGHT EVEN BE ABLE TO HELP YOU WITH YOUR *SCIENCE,* PETER!

BUT...

WHAT'S THAT, KID?

N-NOTHING! FORGET IT!

I'LL..BE RUNNING ALONG NOW..AUNT MAY! I'VE SOME *STUDYING* -- TO DO!

REMEMBER, MY BOY..IF I CAN BE OF ANY *HELP* TO YOU WITH YOUR SCHOOL WORK--!

HOW *GENEROUS* OF YOU, DOCTOR!

IT'S LIKE A *DREAM* ... A CRAZY *NIGHT-MARE!*

THERE'S NOTHING I CAN *DO* IN THERE --

AND YET... I DON'T DARE *LEAVE*..!

I'LL WAIT TILL *DARK*--AND THEN CHANGE TO *SPIDER-MAN!*

MAYBE *THEN*.. I'LL THINK OF *SOMETHING!*

THUS, HOURS LATER...

I'VE NEVER FELT SO *HELPLESS!*

I DON'T DARE *ATTACK*--- BECAUSE OF *AUNT MAY!*

BUT HOW CAN I *LEAVE* HIM THERE ??!

SOMEONE MAKING A *DELIVERY!*

IT'S FOR *OCK!*

MUST BE EQUIPMEN FOR SOME NEW *CRIME*

NOW I *HAVE* TO ACT!!

HOW *EASY* IT WAS! THE OLD WOMAN IS *GULLIBLE* ENOUGH TO BELIEVE *ANYTHING!*

AND HER WHIMPERING, NO-ACCOUNT *NEPHEW* IS TOO *SCARED* TO CAUSE ME ANY FURTHER TROUBLE!

BUT, FASTER THAN YOU CAN WIGGLE A WEB...

NO! *NO!!* IT ISN'T *POSSIBLE!*

I *KILLED* HIM!! HE'S *DEAD!!*

THEN, BEFORE DOC OCK CAN REACH THE WINDOW... BY SCOOTING AROUND TO THE *SIDE* OF THE HOUSE, I'LL MAKE *HIM* COME TO *ME!*

I *CAN'T* FIGHT HIM INSIDE--WITH *AUNT MAY* THERE!

BUT, THE DIABOLICAL DO-BADDER HAS *OTHER* IDEAS...

IF HE *IS* ALIVE... HE'LL BE *EXPECTING* ME TO PURSUE HIM!

BUT, *SUCCESS* IS ONLY FOR THOSE WHO DO THE *UNEXPECTED!*

I'VE NO TIME TO WONDER HOW HE *FOUND* ME...INSTEAD, I'LL MAKE SURE HE DOESN'T ESCAPE *ALIVE!*

AND I KNOW JUST HOW TO *DO* IT!

I MUST SUMMON THOSE OF MY MEN WHO ARE STILL AT LARGE!

THOUGH *SPIDER-MAN* DEFEATED ME WHEN I ASSUMED THE IDENTITY OF THE *MASTER PLANNER,* ENOUGH OF MY MOST LOYAL AIDES *ESCAPED* TO FORM THE NUCLEUS OF A *NEW* ARMY OF CRIME!

AN ARMY WHICH I'LL SEND INTO BATTLE RIGHT *NOW*--AGAINST THE MOST *DANGEROUS* FOE OF ALL--

THIS TIME THERE'LL BE NO QUARTER GIVEN! *THIS* TIME SPIDER-MAN MUST BE *CRUSHED!*

WE'VE GOT 'IM NOW! THE GAS MADE HIM HELPLESS!

FINISH HIM OFF FAST! A CROWD'S BEGINNING TO GATHER! THIS PLACE'LL SOON BE CRAWLIN' WITH COPS!

WATCH IT, YOU FOOL! WE'RE BEGINNIN' TO TRIP OVER EACH OTHER!

LET ME HANDLE 'IM!

THAT'S ALL THE TIME I NEEDED! MY HEAD'S CLEAR AGAIN.... BUT THEY DON'T KNOW IT!

...EY! LOOK OUT! ...'S STARTIN' TO....!

UMMFFF!

HOLD 'IM! DON'T LET HIM...

:YUHHH:

BTOK!

...AY, FELLAS-- ...ERE DID WE ...VE OFF--?

WHY DOESN'T SOMEBODY STOP THEM?

GOOD IDEA! YOU WANNA TRY?

THE POLICE SHOULD BE HERE ANY MINUTE!

HEAR THAT, BOYS? SOMEONE CALLED THE LAW! THAT MEANS YOU WON'T HAVE TO WORRY ABOUT LODGINGS FOR TONIGHT!

THEY CAN'T ARREST US! WE HAVEN'T DONE ANYTHING YET!

AND FROM HIS VANTAGE POINT AT THE WINDOW, *DOC OCK* COMES TO THE SAME CONCLUSION ---

ALL OF THEM *TOGETHER* --- AGAINST *SPIDER-MAN* ...AND THEY'RE ACCOMPLISHING *NOTHING!*

AM *I* THE *ONLY* ONE *CLEVER* ENOUGH... *STRONG* ENOUGH.. TO *DEFEAT* HIM??

BUT SPIDEY HAS NO TIME TO PONDER SUCH INTERESTING PHILO-SOPHICAL QUESTIONS, AS HE CONTINUES DOING WHAT COMES NATURALLY...

PLEASANT DREAMS, PLAYMATES

ZOT!

YOU GENTS SHOULD BE GLAD I'M IN A *HURRY*...

OTHERWISE, I'D *NEVER* LET YOU OFF SO *EASY!*

WHO *ARE* THEY? WHAT DID THEY *DO*? WHAT'S IT ALL *ABOUT*?

ANYONE WHO CAN FIGHT LIKE *SPIDER-MAN* SHOULD BE *LOCKED UP!* HE'S A *MENACE!*

SECONDS LATER, THE "MENACE" COMPLETES HIS LITTLE TASK..

MAYBE THE POLICE *CAN'T* HOLD YOU FOR LONG ON ANY SPECIFIC CHARGE ...

BUT THINK OF THE *FUN* THEY'LL HAVE *TRYING!*

AUNT MAY!!

SHE MUST HAVE SLIPPED OUT TO SEE WHAT ALL THE *EXCITEMENT* WAS ABOUT!

THAT MEAN ..*OCK* WILL BE HOME *ALONE.*

THIS IS WHAT I'VE BEEN *WAITING* FOR!

ZOK!

BUT JUST THEN...

WHAT'S ALL THAT *NOISE* UPSTAIRS??

EEEEEEK!

IT'S *SPIDER-MAN!* HE BROKE IN HERE!

BUT DON'T WORRY... I'LL SAVE YOU FROM HIM!

OHHH...!

THE *SHOCK*... IT'S TOO MUCH FOR HER!

LET'S FINISH OUR BATTLE *ELSEWHERE*.. SAFE FROM INTERFERENCE BY THE *POLICE!*

CRASH!

SO! YOU CHOOSE TO REMAIN *BEHIND!*

BUT *THAT* WON'T SAVE YOU! I'LL FIND YOU *AGAIN*... AND *NEXT* TIME WILL BE THE *LAST* TIME!

BUT, THE ARCH-VILLAIN'S WORDS FALL UPON *DEAF EARS* AS THE HEARTSICK YOUTH CRIES OUT...

IT WAS *SPIDER-MAN* WHO SCARED HER... I'M THE ONE SHE FEARS!

I TRIED TO *SPARE* HER THIS... BUT *NOW*.. BECAUSE OF ME... SHE'S--SHE'S...!

IT'S *ALL RIGHT,* AUNT MAY! YOU'RE *SAFE!* YOU'VE NOTHING TO FEAR FROM *SPIDER-MAN!*

LOOK-- I'LL *PROVE* IT! JUST OPE YOUR EYES.. JUST WA UP!

IT'S *NO USE!* I CAN'T *REVIVE* HER!

I'VE GOT TO CALL THE *DOCTOR!*

I JUST *PRAY*... THERE'S *STILL TIME!!*

IT'S MY AUNT, DR. BROMWELL! SHE'S *COLLAPSED!*

CAN YOU LEAVE AT *ONCE ??* GOOD!

YES, OF *COURSE* I'LL STAY HERE WITH HER!

MY *COSTUME!* I ALMOST *FORGOT!*

I'LL CHANGE MY *CLOTHES* WHILE I'M WAITING FOR HIM!

THEN, AS THE LONG, TORTUROUS MINUTES TICK BY...

IF--IF SHE DOESN'T *RECOVER*..IT'LL BE MY *FAULT*...

BUT, SHE *MUST* PULL THROUGH... SHE *MUST!*

AFTE THE W ..SHE DEVOTE HER LI TO ME.. JUST CA END..LI THIS

the AMAZING
SPIDER-MAN

MARVEL
COMICS
GROUP
12¢ 55
IND. DEC
MCG

"DOC OCK WINS!"

HIDDEN?? DO YOU THINK I'M TRYING TO HIDE FROM YOU??

YOU ARROGANT FOOL! YOU'RE NOT IMPORTANT ENOUGH TO CONCERN ME RIGHT NOW!

NOT WHEN I'M ABOUT TO EXECUTE THE CRIME OF THE CENTURY!

HE MEANS IT! HE'S PLANNING SOMETHING BIG! THAT'S WHY HE'S GLOATING!

YOU'RE MERELY A PAWN... AN INCIDENTAL DETAIL THAT I CAN ATTEND TO ANY TIME I WISH ---

BUT NOW, I'LL SIGN OFF... LEAVING YOU ALONE WITH YOUR RAGE... AND YOUR FRUSTRATION!

THERE'S NOTHING I CAN DO... AND HE KNOWS IT!

SECONDS LATER, IN A SUDDEN PAROXYSM OF UNCONTROLLABLE FURY, THE SUPER-POWERED YOUTH GIVES VENT TO HIS EMOTIONS BY SHATTERING EVERYTHING IN SIGHT --!

HE'S THE ONLY ONE I'VE NEVER DECISIVELY BEATEN!!

BUT I'LL GET HIM YET! I WILL.. I MUST!!

THAT'S THE GUY WE TRIED TO FIGHT?!!

I WOULDN'T WANNA BE OCK.. IF HE EVER FINDS 'IM!

THEN, MINUTES LATER...

THE POLICE WILL TAKE CARE OF THOSE PENNY-ANTE HOODS!

BUT I'M TOO KEYED-UP TO GO HOME YET!!

I'VE GOTTA KEEP SEARCHING --- TILL I FIND HIM!

MAYBE HE RETURNED TO THE UNDERWATER HIDEOUT HE USED WHEN HE CALLED HIMSELF THE MASTER PLANNER!*

I CAN'T LET ANY CHANCES PASS BY!

*AS SEEN IN SPIDEY #31...OR #32! ..WOULDJA BELIEVE #33? --SLEEPY STAN.

NOT A SIGN OF LIFE!

SO I STRUCK OUT AGAIN!

DON'T KNOW WHERE ELSE TO LOOK!!

THERE'S NO POINT IN *AIMLESSLY* SWINGING AROUND TOWN!

I MIGHT AS WELL CALL IT A DAY AND GET SOME *REST!*

I'LL *NEED* ALL MY ENERGY FOR THE NEXT TIME I *FIND* HIM!

BUT, BEFORE I GO *HOME*, I'D BETTER CHECK ON HOW *AUNT MAY* IS FEELING!

HOWEVER, AS SPIDEY SWINGS PAST A DOWNTOWN BUILDING, LITTLE DOES HE *DREAM*... BEHIND ITS GRIM, GREY WALLS... A CERTAIN *MEETING* IS IN SESSION...

COLONEL JAMESON, SINCE YOU ARE IN CHARGE OF *SECURITY* FOR AMERICA'S *NULLIFIER WEAPON*, WOULD YOU PLEASE STATE YOUR PLANS..?

YES, SIR.. INASMUCH AS WE ALL POSSESS *TOP SECURITY* CLEARANCE!

SINCE *DR. OCTOPUS* IS AT LARGE... AND MAY STILL BE IN THIS AREA...

WE'VE DECIDED TO *MOVE* THE NULLIFIER... TO THE FACTORY OF *ANTHONY STARK*... WHERE IT CAN RECEIVE *TOP PROTECTION* WHILE FINAL MODIFICATIONS ARE MADE!

ARE ALL *PRECAUTIONS* BEING TAKEN TO PROTECT OUR WEAPON FROM *SPIDER-MAN*, AS WELL AS *DR. OCTOPUS?*

YES, SIR.. THEY *ARE!*

BUT I'D LIKE TO SAY *ONE* THING...

I'VE HAD A FEW *RUN-INS* WITH SPIDER-MAN IN THE PAST...

AND, DESPITE THE OPINIONS EXPRESSED IN MY FATHER'S *NEWS-PAPER*, I PERSONALLY FEEL THAT HE IS *NOT* AND NEVER *HAS* BEEN... IN LEAGUE WITH *DR. OCTOPUS.*

WELL, THAT'S NOT FOR *US* TO DECIDE, COLONEL!

SUPPOSE WE GET *ON* WITH THE MATTER AT HAND!

VERY WELL, SIR! I'LL CON-*TINUE* THE BRIEFING...!

AND THEN...

THIS IS IT!

LET'S START ROLLING!

PARKING $2.00

SO FAR, SO GOOD! NO SIGN OF TROUBLE!

ESTIMATED TIME OF ARRIVAL STILL UNCHANGED!

OVER AND OUT!

THERE'S SOMETHING UP AHEAD, COLONEL!

LOOKS LIKE AN ORDINARY PUBLIC UTILITY MAINTENANCE TRUCK!

BUT WE'LL TAKE NO CHANCES!

CUT YOUR SPEED! APPROACH WITH CAUTION!

EVERYTHING LOOKS NORMAL ENOUGH SO FAR ---!

BAR

WHY'D THEY SLOW UP?

WHAT'S THE DELAY?

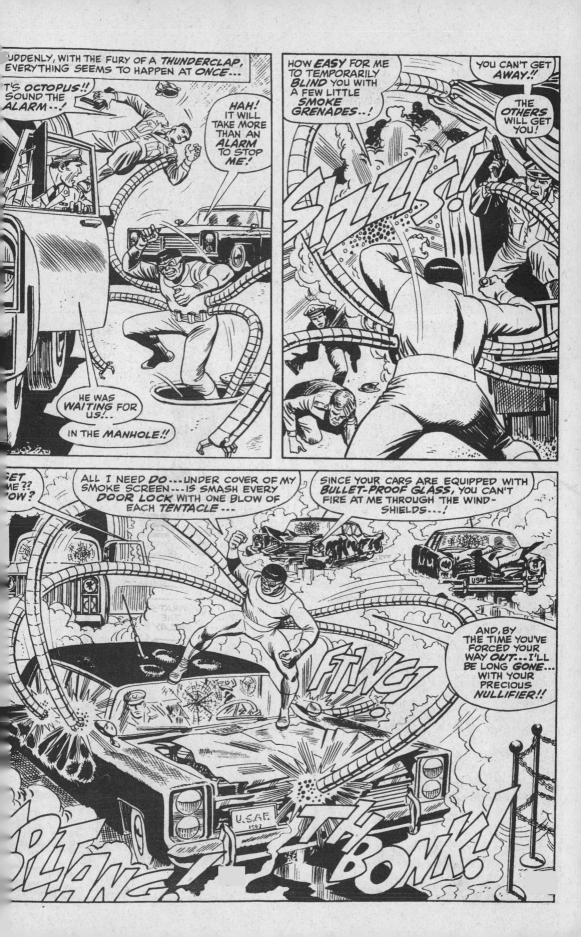

AND, WITHIN THE LEAD CAR...

THE *DOOR'S* JAMMED... CAN'T GET *OUT!*

AND CAN'T *SHOOT* OUT... THROUGH BULLETPROOF GLASS!

GET ME *SECTOR A* HEAD-QUARTERS!! *TOP PRIORITY!*

WE'VE GOT TO *SEAL OFF* THE AREA!

BUT BEFORE COLONEL JAMESON'S DESPERATE ORDERS CAN BE EXECUTED---

NOT EVEN AN *ARMY* COULD HAVE ACCOMPLISHED WHAT *I'VE* JUST DONE!

AND, BEFORE THEY CAN TAKE ANY *COUNTER-MEASURES,* I'LL HAVE SAFELY REACHED MY *NEXT* OBJECTIVE!

KEEP THAT *MOTOR* RUNNING!

EVERYTHING DEPENDS ON SPLIT-SECOND *TIMING!*

NOW *MOVE--* BEFORE ANY *HELP* CAN REACH THEM!

NO MATTER *HOW* FAST THEY ARE--- IT'LL TAKE A FEW MINUTES TO THROW A *CORDON* AROUND THIS SECTION--!

AND THOSE FEW MINUTES ARE ALL I *NEED!!*

WHEN THEY FIND ME *GONE,* THEY'LL LAUNCH THE *BIGGEST MANHUNT* IN HISTORY!!

BUT I'LL BE AT THE *ONE* PLACE THEY'D NEVER *DREAM* OF SEARCHING---!

INSTEAD OF TRYING TO LEAVE THE COUNTRY... WE'RE GOING TO STAY AND *TEST* OUR PRIZE!

AND WHAT *BETTER* PLACE FOR IT THAN THE NEARBY *MUNITIONS FACTORY* OF... *TONY STARK?!!*

IT'S WHAT'S LEFT OF A MILITARY *CONVOY...*

--LED BY COLONEL *JAMESON!*

IT CAN ONLY ADD UP TO *ONE* THING... OCK GOT THE *NULLI-FIER!*

WOW! THEY'VE GOT THE ARMY...THE *POLICE...* THE *F.B.I....* AND PROBABLY EVEN *SHIELD* IN ON THE CASE!!

BUT THEY HAVE NO *LEADS...* AND TIME IS WORKING *AGAINST* THEM!

NOBODY KNOWS OCK AS WELL AS *I* DO!!

HE ALWAYS DOES THE LAST THING YOU'D *EXPECT!*

INSTEAD OF *HIDING,* HE'LL WANT TO *FLAUNT* HIS POWER!!

AND WHAT BETTER..MORE *UNEXPECTED* PLACE TO DO IT...

...THAN THE MOST *IMPORTANT* FACTORY IN THE EAST?!!

AND, EVEN AS SPIDEY HURTLES TOWARDS LONG ISLAND, A FORBIDDING *TRUCK* RUMBLES INTO THE WORLD-FAMOUS FACTORY SITE OF *STARK INDUSTRIES...*

BUT WHAT IF *IRON MAN* IS ON DUTY NOW ??

YOU *FOOL!!* WITH THIS *NULLIFIER* IN MY POSSESSION, NO POWER ON *EARTH* CAN THWART MY PLANS!

AND THAT IS JUST WHAT I INTEND TO *PROVE* BY THIS UNEXPECTED LITTLE *VISIT!*

THE PHONE'S GONE **DEAD**!!

DON'T TAKE ANY **CHANCES**, PAL!! **FIRE**!!

THAT'S **DOC OCK** UP THERE!

I **CAN'T**!! MY GUN'S **JAMMED** OR SOMETHIN'!

SAY! FIRST THE **PHONE**... NOW MY **PISTOL**... MAYBE THAT NUTTY **RAY** OF HIS HAS SOMETHIN' TO **DO** WITH IT?!!

HAH! IT'S WORKING **PERFECTLY**!!

NOW, BY EFFORTLESSLY **INCREASING** THE POWER, I CAN MAKE THE BEAM COVER A **WIDER** RANGE!

WITHIN **MINUTES**, I'LL IMMOBILIZE EVERY MACHINE WITHIN THE ENTIRE **FACTORY**!! I'LL BRING EVERYTHING TO A COMPLETE **STANDSTILL**!

KEEP DRIVING! NO ONE CAN STOP US!

I'M **SUPREME**! **SUPREME**!!

MY **TENTACLES** GIVE ME THE STRENGTH TO DEFEAT ANY **LIVING** BEING...

WHILE MY CAPTIVE **NULLIFIER** MAKES ME SAFE FROM ANY **WEAPON** ON EARTH!

NOW AT **LAST**...BEYOND ANY SHADOW OF **DOUBT**...

THE WORLD IS **MINE**!!

LONG HOURS LATER, AFTER WORKING HALF-WAY THROUGH THE NIGHT, THE DEMONIACAL EX-ATOM SCIENTIST FINALLY EXCLAIMS...

OF COURSE! NOW I KNOW WHAT'S WRONG!

THERE'S ONE PART THAT'S STILL MISSING!

AS A SAFETY FACTOR, THEY DIDN'T ASSEMBLE THE ENTIRE THING!

I SHOULD HAVE GUESSED IT SOONER!

ALL I NEED IS A SMALL QUANTITY OF ISOTOPE 16... WHICH IS STORED AT FT. TYSON, A SCANT FEW MILES FROM HERE!

BUT IT'S AN ARMY POST! HOW CAN YOU HOPE TO GET IN THERE?

I?! I DON'T HOPE TO!

YOU'RE GOING TO DO IT FOR ME!

AND YOU'LL DO IT NOW!

WHY DO I FEEL THIS STRANGE SENSATION... THIS SUDDEN TINGLING... ALL THROUGH MY BODY!

IT'S LIKE A BUILT-IN WARNING OF SOME SORT...

...BUT, A WARNING OF... WHAT??

DON'T JUST STAND THERE WHEN I GIVE YOU AN ORDER!

AND ANOTHER THING... BEFORE YOU GO, TAKE THAT MORONIC MASK OFF!

I WANT TO SEE WHO YOU ARE!

YOU MEAN... YOU DON'T KNOW?!!

I WAS A FOOL! THAT WAS MY FIRST MISTAKE! NOW I'VE AROUSED HIS SUSPICIONS!

I'D LIKE TO KNOW WHO I REALLY AM, TOO!

BUT... IF YOU DON'T KNOW MY IDENTITY.. HOW CAN WE BE PARTNERS??

I *STILL* DON'T FEEL RIGHT ABOUT INVADING A MILITARY POST..!

BUT, UNTIL I GET MY *MEMORY* BACK... I'VE GOT TO SEE THIS THROUGH!

I DON'T EVEN DARE *THINK* OF WHAT WOULD HAPPEN...

...IF MY MEMORY SOMEHOW *NEVER* RETURNS!

THE ONLY THING I CAN'T *UNDERSTAND* IS...

IF I REALLY *AM* A CRIMINAL... WHY IS THIS SO *DISTASTEFUL* TO ME??

AND, IF I'M *NOT* A CRIMINAL... WHY DO I WEAR THIS *MASK*..?

AND WHAT'S MY CONNECTION WITH A FULL-TIME CREEP LIKE *DOC OCK*.!?

BUT I'D BETTER *FORGET* ABOUT THAT NOW!

AT LEAST-- UNTIL THE *JOB* IS DONE!

THAT *VENT* BELOW IS JUST WHAT I NEED!

WOW! I'M *LIFTING* IT LIKE IT'S *NOTHING!*

SURE WISH I COULD REMEM HOW I GO MY POWE

WELL, HERE GOES *NOTHING!*

I'LL JUST CRAWL THROUGH THE WHOLE *SYSTEM,* UNTIL...

THIS COULD BE WHAT I'M *AFTER!*

ANYTHING WITH SO MANY IRON *BARS...*

MUST BE GUARDING *SOMETHING* MIGHTY IMPORTANT!

THERE IT *IS...* INSIDE THAT *CELL!*

I COULDN'T *MISS* THAT PLATINUM *CANNISTER!*

HERE'S THAT SAME NUTTY *TINGLING* AGAIN!

IF ONLY I *KNEW* WHAT IT *MEANT!!*

POOR SPIDEY! IF NOT FOR HIS AMNESIA, HE'D KNOW IT MEANS *TROUBLE!!* ...LIKE SO...

IT'S *SPIDER-MAN!*

HE'S *BROKEN* INTO THE *ISOTOPE CHAMBER!!*

HE'LL *NEVER* GET *AWAY* WITH IT!

HOLD IT, MISTER!! DON'T MAKE A *MOVE...* OR WE *FIRE!*

GUARDS!! THEY'VE *FOUND* ME!!

HE MUST BE *NUTS...* TRYING A STUNT LIKE THAT!!

CAN'T LET THEM GET ME--NO MATTER *WHAT!*

I'VE GOTTA MOVE *FAST*... DO THE *UNEXPECTED!*

HE'S NOT *STOPPING!*

HE'S MAKING A *BREAK!*

NAIL 'IM!

BUT, BEFORE THE STARTLED GUARDS CAN GET THE FAST-MOVING FUGITIVE IN THEIR SIGHTS, OUR HERO... MOVING BY SHEER *REFLEX ACTION*... DISARMS THEM IN A LIGHTNING-LIKE MANEUVER..!

SORRY, GENTS!

SINCE I'M NOT *BULLETPROOF*, TARGET PRACTICE MAKES ME *NERVOUS.*

...SPECIALLY WHEN *I'M* THE TARGET!

HELP!

GET US *OUT* OF HERE!!

THEY MUST HAVE CORNERED *SPIDER-MAN!!*

SOUNDS MORE LIKE *HE* CORNERED *THEM!*

LISTEN!! HELP'S COMING!!

WHERE'S..?

=WHUPPP!=

LOOK OUT!

THUD!

NO TIME TO GO BACK THROUGH THE *VENT*..!

I'M HEADING FOR THE *OPEN*... BUT *FAST!!*

=UH OH!= I DROPPED THE MAP OCK GAVE ME!

BUT I'M NOT GOING BACK FOR IT NOW!

SECONDS LATER, SPIDEY SWINGS INTO THE ALL-CONCEALING SHADOWS OF NIGHT..!

IT'S STRANGE...I COULD HAVE WHISKED UP THE MAP WITH MY WEBBING!

--BUT I DIDN'T!

ALMOST AS IF I SUBCONSCIOUSLY WANT IT TO BE FOUND!

BUT...WHY WOULD I WANT THEM...TO BE ABLE TO TRACE ME??

PERHAPS THE PSYCHOLOGY MAJORS AMONGST YOU CAN ANSWER OUR WEB-SLINGER'S QUERY...

WE CAN ONLY SHOW WHAT HAPPENS NEXT...

IT'S HARD TO BELIEVE ONE MAN GOT AWAY WITH IT!

IS IT TRUE..??

NOT WHEN HIS NAME'S SPIDER-MAN!

DID HE GET THE ISOTOPE?

'FRAID SO, COLONEL!

BUT LOOK WHAT HE DROPPED!

IT'S A MAP...SHOWING THE ROUTE HERE...FROM THE HEIGHTS SECTION AT THE CITY'S OUTSKIRTS!

SPIDER-MAN'S CLEVER! IT COULD BE A RUSE...TO STALL US WITH A WILD-GOOSE CHASE!

STILL, IT'S OUR ONLY LEAD! LET ME SEE IT..!

HERE YOU ARE, SIR!

THIS IS GENUINE...IT PIN-POINTS THE AREA HE STARTED FROM...AND TO WHERE HE MAY BE RETURNING!

SERGEANT! I WANT A CHOPPER HERE WITHIN FIVE MINUTES...

...AND A SQUAD OF YOUR BEST MEN...ARMED TO THE TEETH!

WE'RE GONNA MOVE!!

THEN, AS THE NEWLY-ARRIVED WHIRLEYBIRD PREPARES FOR LIFT-OFF...!

REMEMBER...I WANT AN IRON CORDON THROWN AROUND THE ENTIRE AREA!!

IF A GRASSHOPPER SLIPS THROUGH, EVERY MAN RESPONSIBLE WILL ANSWER TO ME!

WE'LL MAINTAIN 24-HOUR RADIO-CONTACT!

GOOD HUNTING, SIR!

MEANWHILE, AT THE EXECUTIVE OFFICES OF THAT WORLD-FAMOUS CITADEL OF CULTURE, THE *DAILY BUGLE*...

MY OWN *SON*...IN CHARGE OF *OPERATION NULLIFIER*...AND NOT A PEEP *OUT* OF HIM!!

BE *REASONABLE*, CHIEF! YOU *KNOW* THE COLONEL CAN'T GIVE YOU ANY *CLASSIFIED* INFO!

REASONABLE?? I'M *ALWAYS* REASONABLE!

...BUT I *WANT* THAT BLANKETTY-BLANK *STORY* AND I WANT IT *NOW!!*

WHERE'S *PARKER??* MAYBE *HE* KNOWS WHERE *SPIDER-MAN* IS!

NOBODY'S *SEEN* PETER FOR *DAYS*, MR. JAMESON!

WHY IS THAT FROSTY-FACED *FINK* NEVER HERE WHEN I *NEED* HIM??

AFTER ALL, SIR...HE'S ONLY A *PART-TIME* PHOTO-GRAPHER!

IT'S NOT AS IF YOU PAY HIM A *SALARY!*

SHE'S *RIGHT*, JJ!

SURE!! SURE!!

SHE'S *RIGHT!!* HE'S *RIGHT!!* THEY'RE *RIGHT...* EVERYBODY'S *RIGHT...* EXCEPT J. JONAH JAMESON!!

AT LAST THE WORLD CAN SEE THAT *SPIDER-MAN* REALLY *IS* A *CROOK*...

AND I HAVEN'T *ONE* SINGLE PICTURE TO *GLOAT* OVER!

IT'S A COMMUNIST *PLOT...*

--TO DRIVE ME *BATTY!*

BUT, IF JOLLY *JONAH* THINKS THAT *HE* HAS TROUBLES, LET'S GET BACK TO *SPIDEY* ONCE MORE...

I *MADE* IT!

BUT WHY DO I FEEL SO *UNHAPPY*...SO *ASHAMED* OF MYSELF!!

HERE HE IS!

I *KNEW* THE FOOL WOULD *DO* IT!

ONCE I HAVE THAT CANNISTER OF *ISOTOPE 16*, THE NULLIFIER WILL BE *PERFECT*...AND THE WORLD WILL BE *MINE!*

WHAT KIND OF CROOK *AM* I, ANYWAY?

BE *CAREFUL*, BOSS!

I *STILL* DON'T TRU-- THAT WEB SLINGIN' WEASE--

IT'S AN *ARMY* 'COPTER! THE *MAP* HE DROPPED... MUST HAVE *LED* THEM HERE!

QUICK...GET THE *OTHERS*...HEAD THEM *OFF*!

IT'S *SPIDER-MAN'S* FAULT!

AND, IN THE HOVERING SHIP...

WE'VE *FOUND* THEM!

TAKE 'ER *DOWN*!

THEN, BEFORE THE MULTI-ARMED MENACE'S FEW REMAINING MEN CAN HEAD FOR SAFETY...

TAKE ANOTHER STEP AND WE *FIRE*!

DON'T SHOOT! *DON'T SHOOT*!

WE'RE NOT TAKIN' LEAD FOR *DOC OCK*!

HE'S THE ONE YOU WANT!

KEEP 'EM UNDER *WRAPS*, CORPORAL!

THE *REST* OF YOU...SURROUND THE *HOUSE*! ...MOVE!

MY *OWN* MEN... THEY LET ME *DOWN*!

BUT I DON'T *NEED* THEM! --DON'T NEED *ANYONE*!

...NOT AS LONG AS I HAVE... THE *NULLIFIER*!

BUT, EVEN AS THE GRASPING *TENTACLES* REACH ○ FOR THE STOLEN WEAPON...

SMOKE GRENADES!

COVERING THE WHO○ ROOM! I...I CAN'T *SEE*...!

THE *NULLIFIER*! IT WAS RIGHT *AHEAD* OF ME...I'VE GOT TO *REACH* IT!

HURRY...IT'S THE ONLY WAY TO *SAVE* YOURSELF! YOU'RE A *CRIMINAL*...LIKE ME! THEY'LL *FIGHT* YOU... *IMPRISON* YOU! YOU'VE GOT TO *DESTROY* THEM!

OUR *PETTY* QUARREL DOESN'T MATTER!

YOUR OWN *LIFE* IS AT STAKE! YOU CAN'T LET THEM *KILL* YOU!

NOBODY IS GONNA KILL ME! I'M *THROUGH* BEING PUSHED AROUND! HEAR *THAT?* YOU BETTER *RUN*... ALL OF YOU! CLEAR OUT WHILE YOU *CAN!*

YOU'RE NO MATCH FOR *SPIDER-MAN!*

AND YOU *KNOW* IT!

HE'S MY *PARTNER!* HE DOES WHATEVER I *SAY!*

HE CAN *BEAT* YOU WITHOUT HALF TRYING! SO *DOC OCK* WINS AGAIN!

THAT'S *IT! THAT'S IT!* GRAB THE *NULLIFIER!* THEY CAN'T STOP YOU!

DON'T *TRY* IT, MISTER! YOU CAN'T FIGHT THE *U.S. ARMY!*

IT'S *NOT* THE WHOLE *ARMY!* ...JUST A HANDFUL OF *FOOLS!*

ATTACK THEM...*SMASH* THEM! WHAT ARE YOU *WAITING* FOR?!!

LOOK, COLONEL...!

IT'S UP TO *YOU*, SPIDER-MAN! MAKE YOUR *MOVE*..!

I DON'T KNOW WHAT *HAPPENED* HOW I GOT *MIXED-UP* IN ALL THIS...

BUT, ONE THING I *DO* KNOW

I'M...*NO PARTNER*.. OF HIS...!

THEN...I W *RIGHT* AB YOU!

THE *NULLIFIER* IS *SAFE* ONCE MORE!

LOVELY PARTY, ISN'T IT? THERE'S NOTHING LIKE HAVING YOUR *DINNER* OUT-OF-DOORS!

THAT *SANDWICH*... FLOATING IN THE *AIR*!

I BEG YOUR PARDON??

ONE OF THE SANDWICHES IS...IS... *FLYING AWAY!*

LESTER, ARE YOU *SURE* YOU HAVEN'T BEEN DRINKING TOO MUCH *PUNCH*??

RIGHT *NOW* I..I'M NOT SURE OF *ANYTHING!*

MY COMPLIMEN TO THE *CHEF*

I'D LIKE TO GO BACK FOR *SECONDS*...

BUT NO SENSE PUSHING MY *LUCK* TOO FAR!

OKAY...SO I WON'T *STARVE* FOR A WHILE!

BUT WHAT DO I DO *NEXT?*

I DON'T EVEN KNOW WHERE I *LIVE!*

I'VE GOT TO FIND *SOME* PLACE TO SLEEP!

MY BEST BET IS TO SEEK THE *HEIGHTS*...

WHERE THE *POLICE* WON'T FIND ME!

I'M SURE TO FIND *SOME* LONELY LEDG WHERE I CAN GRAB A LITTLE SHUT-EYE!

IF ONLY MY *MEMORY* WOULD RETURN!

IF ONLY I KNEW WHO I *AM*... WHERE I'M *FROM!*

I NEVER REALIZED HOW *EMPTY* YOU CAN FEEL...

NOT EVEN KNOWING YOUR OWN *NAME!*

OH *NO!* NOW IT'S STARTING TO *RAIN!*

I CAN'T STAY *HERE!* I'VE GOT TO FIND A *DRY* SPOT SOMEWHERE!

BOY, I MAY NOT KNOW MY *NAME*, BUT I'M SURE OF *ONE* THING...

I'M PROBABLY THE *ORIGINAL* HARD-LUCK CHARLIE!

IT'S PROBABLY SMARTER FOR ME TO KEEP MY *MASK* ON!

THERE MUST BE *SOME* REASON WHY IT'S PART OF MY COSTUME!

THER THA LOO LIKE GOO SPO

WELL, IT'S NOT EXACTLY THE *WALDORF*...

BUT AT LEAST IT'S *DRY!*

AND SO, WEARY AND WAN...UNAWARE OF HIS PAST...UNSURE OF THE PRESENT...AND UNSUSPECTING THE MENACE OF THE FUTURE -- THE AMNESIA-STRICKEN YOUTH FINALLY DROPS OFF INTO A FITFUL, TROUBLED SLUMBER ATOP THE CAVERNOUS RAILROAD TERMINAL ---

MEANWHILE, INSIDE THE MODEST HOME WHICH HIS *AUNT MAY* SHARES WITH HER CLOSEST FRIEND, WE FIND MRS. PARKER FAR TOO *WORRIED* ABOUT HER NEPHEW'S *DISAPPEARANCE* TO BE ABLE TO FALL ASLEEP...

HE'S *NEVER* BEEN AWAY THIS LONG --- WITHOUT *CALLING ME*...WITHOUT *SOME EXPLANATION!*

SOMETHING *TERRIBLE* MUST HAVE HAPPENED!

I...I JUST *KNOW* IT!

WHAT IF HE'S *HURT*... IN *TROUBLE* SOMEWHERE..?

WHAT IF HE *NEEDS ME..?*

HOW CAN I LIE IN *BED* THIS WAY-- WITHOUT *KNOWING*...WITH-OUT ANY *WORD* FROM HIM?

I'VE GOT TO CALL HIS *ROOMMATE* AGAIN!

PERHAPS YOUNG *OSBORN* HAS HEARD SOMETHING BY NOW!

OR...ARE THEY *KEEPING* ANYTHING FROM ME?

WHAT IF... THEY'RE *AFRAID..* TO *TELL* ME..?

EXACTLY FIFTEEN SECONDS LATER...

MAY!

IT'S WHAT I'VE BEEN *DREADING..!*

WORRYING ABOUT *PETER* HAS BEEN TOO *MUCH* FOR HER!

SHE'S *COLLAPSED!*

3.

DR. BROMWELL... YOU'VE GOT TO COME AT ONCE!

OR... PERHAPS IT WOULD BE BETTER... TO SEND AN AMBULANCE!

AND, AS THINGS SEEM TO GET FROM BAD TO WORSE...

IF I HAD MY WAY, YOU'D BE BUSTED TO PRIVATE, COLONEL JAMESON!

HE HAD NO RIGHT TO LET SPIDER-MAN ESCAPE!

LET'S NOT FLY OFF THE HANDLE UNTIL WE'VE HEARD FROM THE COLONEL GENTLEMEN

THANK YOU CAPTAIN STACY

COLONEL JAMESON IS UNDER MY COMMAND!

HIS ORDERS WERE TO RETRIEVE THE STOLEN NULLIFIER...

--NOT TO APPREHEND COSTUMED CRIMINALS!

HOWEVER, THE CITY COUNCIL DOES DESERVE AN EXPLANATION, COLONEL!

WHY DID YOU MAKE NO ATTEMPT TO CAPTURE THE SO-CALLED SPIDER-MAN?

BECAUSE HE HAD SAVED MY LIFE THREE TIMES IN THE PAST, SIR!

I--COULDN'T OVERLOOK THAT FACT!

SAVED YOUR LIFE?

WHEN? HOW?

I'VE MADE A STUDY OF SPIDER-MAN'S RECORD, GENERAL!

ONE OF HIS EARLIEST EXPLOITS WAS SAVING A SPACE-CRAFT WHICH THE COLONEL WAS PILOTING ---

WHILE HE LATER RESCUED HIM FROM THE RHINO... AND FINALLY FROM DR. OCTOPUS HIMSELF! *

IN FACT, HIS RECORD MAKES IT DIFFICULT TO BELIEVE SPIDER-MAN COULD REALLY HAVE TURNED BAD!

*SPI. # 1, 41 AND 56. -- SUCCINCT STAN.

I CAN SEE YO POIN CAPTA STACE

FINALLY, AT THE CONCLUSION OF THE STORMY MEETING ...

I NEVER KNEW YOU WERE SO FAMILIAR WITH SPIDER-MAN'S BACKGROUND, CAPTAIN!

AS AN EX-POLICE OFFICER, I FIND HIS HISTORY FASCINATING!

THE MORE I LEARN... THE MORE HE MYSTIFIES ME!

JOHN! I THOUGHT YOU'D NEVER COME OUT, BLAST IT!

IS IT TRUE? DID YOU LET THAT WEBBED WEASEL ESCAPE??

I DID WHAT I THOUGHT WAS RIGHT, DAD!

BY THE WAY, DO YOU KNOW CAPTAIN STACY? HE ACTS AS A SPECIAL CONSULTANT TO THE CITY COUNCIL ON POLICE MATTERS...!

NEVER MIND THAT! ALL I CARE ABOUT IS MY OWN SON LETTING THAT MASKED MURDERER GO SCOT FREE!

THERE'S NO PROOF THAT HE'S EVER MURDERED ANYONE, JAMESON!

WHO NEEDS PROOF??

EVERYONE KNOWS HE'S A ROTTEN, LOW-DOWN, NO-GOOD KILLER!

BUT *THIS* TIME I *KNOW* HOW TO FINISH HIM OFF!

THERE'S SOMEONE *ARRIVING* IN THE CITY... SOMEONE WHO'LL BE ABLE TO MAKE *MINCEMEAT* OF THAT COSTUMED CREEP!

YOUR FATHER IS A VERY *DETERMINED* MAN, MY BOY!

THAT'S PUTTING IT *MILDLY*, CAPTAIN!

I'LL FIND A WAY TO DO WHAT MY OWN *SON* WOULDN'T *DO!*

AND, AT THAT VERY MOMENT... AT *JFK* AIRPORT...

LORD PLUNDER... IS IT TRUE THAT YOU PREFER BEING CALLED *KA-ZAR*, LORD OF THE JUNGLE??

AND, WOULD YOU TELL US *WHY* YOU'VE COME TO THE *UNITED STATES?*

WHAT ABOUT THE FACT THAT IT TOOK AN *ACT OF CONGRESS* TO ALLOW YOU TO BRING THAT *BEAST* WITH YOU?

I TRAVEL *NOWHERE* WITHOUT *ZABU!*

THE WHOLE *NATION* IS WONDERING WHY YOU'VE COME HERE...!

IT IS PURELY *PERSONAL!*

I MUST DISCUSS *LEGAL MATTERS* ABOUT MY ESTATE... WITH MY *LAWYER!*

HOW ABOUT A STORY FOR OUR *FEMALE* READERS, KA-ZAR?

WHAT DOES IT *FEEL* LIKE TO BECOME A BLUE-BLOODED *NOBLE-MAN* AFTER HAVING LIVED AS A *SAVAGE* ALL YOUR LIFE?

YOU'D BETTER KEEP ...A TIGHT REIN ON THAT *SABER TOOTH!*

IF HE EVER... BREAKS *LOOSE...!!*

HOW DO YOU PLAN TO *USE* YOUR NEWLY-INHERITED *FORTUNE??*

I HAVE NOTHING MORE TO *SAY!*

5.

THEN, SECONDS LATER...

L-LORD PLUNDER...ARE YOU S-SURE YOUR P-PET IS...HARMLESS??

HE WILL NOT ATTACK...WITHOUT MY COMMAND!...DRIVE ON!

THERE ARE MANY PEOPLE WHO WANT TO SEE YOU, M'LORD!

I WISH TO SEE NO ONE!

MINUTES LATER...

BUT...WHAT ABOUT THE PRESS? ---THE TV..??

THEY ARE NO CONCERN OF MINE!

NOW GO! KA-ZAR WISHES TO SPEAK NO MORE!

AT LAST!!

I CAN FREE MYSELF OF THE UNBEARABLE TRAPPINGS OF CIVILIZATION!

AT LAST I CAN MOVE... I CAN BREATHE...

...I CAN BE... KA-ZAR!

WHILE, OUTSIDE THE JUNGLE LORD'S DOOR...

IMAGINE THEM TELLING ME THAT THE WILD MAN DOESN'T WANT TO BE DISTURBED!

AS IF J. JONAH JAMESON WILL EVER TAKE NO FOR AN ANSWER!

C'MON!! OPEN UP IN THERE

YEOWR!

DOWN, ZABU!!

KA-ZAR GAVE NO COMMAND!

WERE YOU NOT TOLD I WILL SEE NO ONE?

YES! BUT...WHAT I HAVE TO SAY TO YOU...IS VITALLY IMPORTANT.

THEN SPEAK!

BUT, YOU *MUST* KNOW! HE WAS TRYING TO GET SOME *NEWS PHOTOS* OF YOU!

EASY, GWEN! TRY NOT TO *ANTAGONIZE* HIM!

IF HE REALLY *HAS* AMNESIA---IF HE CAN'T REMEMBER THE *PAST*...

THEN, HE MIGHT DO *ANYTHING!*

WE'RE *NOT GETTING* ANYWHERE!

WAIT! DON'T *GO*--! THERE *MUST* BE A WAY...!

IT'S *NO USE*, COLONEL! THERE'S NO STOPPING HIM *NOW!*

I THOUGHT YOU'D BE ABLE TO *HELP*...

BUT I'M MORE *CONFUSED* THAN EVER!

IF HE'D ONLY GIVEN US MORE *TIME!*

DAD...DO YOU THINK... HE'S *HURT* PETER PARKER?

IN HIS CONDITION... *ANYTHING* IS POSSIBLE!

AND THE SAME GOES FOR *KA-ZAR*, AS WELL---!

I HAVE HEARD *ENOUGH!*

I WILL *FIND* YOUR SPIDER-MAN!

GOOD! GOOD!

HE'LL MAKE *MINCEMEAT* OUT OF THAT WEB-HEAD!

THE MAN *JAMESON* REMINDS ME OF A HUMAN *JACKAL*...

BUT IT IS NOT FOR *KA-ZAR* TO JUDGE!

HEAD DUE *SOUTH*...TOWARDS *GRAND CENTRAL STATION!*

THAT'S WHERE HE WAS LAST *SIGHTED!*

AND, WHEN YOU *FIND* HIM---

GIVE 'IM ONE FOR *ME!*

THOUGH THE *JUNGLE* IS MORE TO MY *LIKING*... THIS *CITY* MAY PROVE MORE *INTERESTING* THAN I HAD HOPED!

BUT NOW... I NEED A *WEAPON!*

HEY! COME *BACK* HERE!

YOU CAN'T TAKE THAT *ROPE*... AND *GRAPPLING HOOK!!*

ON THE *CONTRARY*... I JUST *DID!*

I SHALL *RETURN* THEM WHEN I AM DONE!

THIS IS *GRAND CENTRAL* TERMINAL!

AND THE SCENT OF A *MAN* STILL LINGERS FROM THE *RAFTERS!*

THE *SPOOR* TELLS ME HE *LEFT*... SCANT MINUTES AGO!

I MUST *FOLLOW* THE SCENT... FOR AS LONG AS I *CAN!*

AH! THIS TELLS ME I AM ON THE RIGHT *TRACK!*

A PIECE OF *FIBRE*... FROM SOME SORT OF *COSTUME!*

I'M *GAINING* ON HIM--!

THE SCENT IS GROWING *STRONGER* EVERY SECOND!

IT LEADS INTO THAT *WINDOW* YONDER...!

HOW CAN WE PROVE SPIDER-MAN *INNOCENT*... WHEN EVEN *HE* CAN'T HELP US NOW?

I'M *HOPING* THAT HE *RETURNS!*

HAH! THE TRAIL GROWS EVER *WARMER!*

11.

THESE THINGS IN MY *BELT* COULD BE THE FLUID *CARTRIDGES!* BUT I DON'T REMEMBER HOW TO *USE* THEM!

AND THEY FEEL *EMPTY,* ANYWAY!

BUT NOW *KA-ZAR'S* HEADING BACK FOR ME--!

THIS TIME I GIVE YOU *NO SECOND CHANCE!*

COME *BACK!* NO ONE CAN ESCAPE FROM KA-ZAR!

WELL, HERE'S *ONE* WALL-CRAWLER WHO'S GONNA *TRY!*

I'M NOT *NUTTY* ENOUGH TO FIGHT SOME-ONE WHEN I DON'T KNOW *WHY!*

SO LONG, MUSCLE-BOUND!

I'LL SEND YOU A *POST CARD* SOME TIME!

≡ UH OH! ≡ WHAT'S HE DOING ON THAT *TV AERIAL?*

THIS FLEXIBLE STEEL DEVICE IS LIKE A JUNGLE *SAPLING!*

ALL I NEED DO IS BEND IT *BACK*... AND *THEN...!*

17.

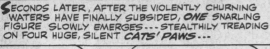

SECONDS LATER, AFTER THE VIOLENTLY CHURNING WATERS HAVE FINALLY SUBSIDED, *ONE* SNARLING FIGURE SLOWLY EMERGES --- STEALTHILY TREADING ON FOUR HUGE, SILENT *CATS' PAWS*...

ZABU! YOU SOUGHT TO PROTECT YOUR *MASTER!*

BUT, WHAT OF THE ONE CALLED *SPIDER-MAN?*

NEVER HAVE I FACED SO *POWERFUL*...SO *AGILE* A FOE!

ALTHOUGH YOU COULD NOT HAVE *KNOWN,* I DID NOT *DESIRE* YOUR AID!

THE *VICTORY* SHOULD HAVE BEEN WON BY *KA-ZAR*...ALONE!

BUT, WHAT OF THE *MASKED ONE?* HE DOES NOT *APPEAR!*

CAN IT BE A *TRAP*...OR..

I MUST PLUNGE BELOW AND *SEE!*

SWIFTLY, WITH POWERFUL, SEEMINGLY-TIRELESS STROKES, THE JUNGLE LORD PROBES THE MURKY WATERS OF THE LONELY LAKE...AS HIS MIGHTY LUNGS FILL NEARLY TO THE BREAKING POINT...

UNTIL, AT LAST... THE BATTLE HAS *ENDED*...

FOREVER!

YOU MUST *BE* HERE NEXT ISSUE

YET, DESPITE HIS UNBELIEVABLE STRENGTH...

IF NOT FOR KA-ZAR'S JUNGLE KNOWLEDGE OF SURVIVAL AID...

AHH! HE BEGINS TO STIR... AT LAST!

UNHHH...

NEVER HAS KA-ZAR FOUGHT MORE VALIANT A FOE!

I COULD NOT BRING MYSELF TO ALLOW YOU TO PERISH!

EVEN THOUGH THE MAN NAMED JAMESON EXPLAINED WHAT A MENACE YOU ARE...

KA-ZAR MUST LEARN THE TRUTH FROM YOUR LIPS ALONE!

JAMESON!! SO HE PUT YOU UP TO ATTACKING ME!

YOUR VOICE! IT HAS A DIFFERENT QUALITY!

IT IS NO LONGER HESITANT... NO LONGER UNSURE!

SOMEHOW... YOU ARE... CHANGED!

CHANGED??! OF COURSE! THAT'S IT!

I CAN REMEMBER NOW! MY AMNESIA IS GONE!

THE SHOCK.. OF HITTING THE WATER.. MUST HAVE CURED IT!

AND SO, AS A GREAT WAVE OF RELIEF ENGULFS MARVELDOM ASSEMBLED, WE RETURN ONCE MORE TO THAT PEERLESS PARAGON OF PUBLISHING POMPOSITY— JOLLY JONAH JAMESON HIMSELF...

SPEAK UP, MISS BRANT! DON'T MUMBLE!

WHAT IS IT NOW??

PROFESSOR SMYTHE IS ON THE PHONE!

HE'S THAT NITWIT WHO BUILT A ROBOT TO DEFEAT SPIDER-MAN!

BUT HE FAILED, LIKE EVERYONE ELSE!

SMYTHE? OH YEAH--NOW I REMEMBER!

* WE THINK IT WAS ISH #25! ---SMILEY.

SMYTHE? THIS IS JAMESON!

DIDN'T THINK YOU'D HAVE THE *NERVE* TO CALL ME --- AFTER YOUR LAST *FIASCO!*

WHAT'S THAT? YOU'VE GOT A *NEW* HARE-BRAINED SCHEME FOR POLISHING OFF *SPIDER-MAN?!!*

GO TELL IT TO *CITY HALL,* YA BUM!

NOW *CALM DOWN,* JJ!

I'M JUST AS DISAPPOINTED AS *YOU* ARE ABOUT OUR PREVIOUS FAILURE! BUT...

WE *NOW* HAVE A CHANCE TO COMPLETELY *CRUSH* THE WEB-SPINNER!

AND *THIS* TIME... *IT CAN'T FAIL!*

BUT, IF SPIDEY HAS UNRELENTING *ENEMIES...* HE ALSO HAS DEDICATED *SUPPORTERS...* SUCH AS ---

I JUST CAME TO SAY *GOODBYE,* MR. STACY!

MY NEW *ORDERS* FINALLY ARRIVED... AND I'M HEADED *OVERSEAS!*

I'M SORRY I CAN'T *STAY* TO HELP CLEAR *SPIDER-MAN!*

SO AM *I,* COLONEL!

EVEN THOUGH YOU'VE *RETIRED* FROM THE POLICE, DO YOU THINK THERE'S A *CHANCE..?*

DON'T WORRY, MY BOY!

I FIND THIS *SPIDER-MAN* MATTER COMPLETELY *FASCINATING!*

I WON'T *REST* TILL I GET TO THE *BOTTOM* OF IT!

BUT, WHAT ABOUT YOUR *FATHER?* DOES HE STILL *HATE* SPIDER-MAN WITH THE SAME *FANATICISM* AS EVER?

I'M AFRAID SO, CAPTAIN! IT'S BECOME QUITE A *SORE POINT* BETWEEN US!

I'VE KNOWN MEN LIKE *JONAH JAMESON* BEFORE! IRON-WILLED, VAIN, AND UNWILLING OR UNABLE TO EVER CHANGE THEIR MINDS!

I'D BETTER TELL HIM *GOODBYE* BEFORE I GO!

AND WOULD YOU GIVE MY REGARDS TO YOUR DAUGHTER, GWEN, AS WELL?

CERTAINLY, COLONEL! I THINK SHE'S AT THE *HOSPITAL* NOW, VISITING *MRS. PARKER!*

AND IF YOU THINK IT WAS *EASY* TO SQUEEZE ALL OF *THAT* INTO ONE PANEL, FORGET IT! ANYWAY, SPEAKING OF GORGEOUS *GWENDOLYN...*

I'M AFRAID SHE CAN'T SEE *ANYONE* RIGHT NOW!

THE ONLY ONE SHE KEEPS *CALL-*ING FOR IS HER *NEPHEW...* PETER!

IF ONLY WE KNEW WHERE TO *FIND* HIM!

DON'T WORRY GWEN! HE'S *BOUND* TO SHOW UP!

4.

I KNOW HE'S TAKEN OFF ON THOSE MYSTERIOUS *PHOTO ASSIGNMENTS* BEFORE---

IF HE WAS *HURT*... OR *WORSE*... SOMEONE WOULD HAVE *FOUND* HIM BY NOW!

BUT NEVER THIS *LONG*...NEVER WHILE HIS *AUNT* WAS SO *ILL!*

NO! DON'T EVEN *SAY* IT!

BUT, FOR ONCE, OUR YOUTHFUL ADVENTURER *ISN'T* HURT--OR *WORSE!* ALTHOUGH, WE MUST ADMIT, HE'S NOT EXACTLY A CARE-FREE CAVORTER...

...AND THAT'S THE *STORY,* WILD MAN!

I MUST HAVE BEEN *INJURED* WHILE FIGHTING *DOC OCK,* AND... WITH MY MEMORY *GONE*---HE TRIED TO CONVINCE ME WE WERE *PARTNERS!*

IN THE *JUNGLE,* WE LEARN TO SENSE *TRUTH* FROM *FALSEHOOD!*

KA-ZAR *KNOWS* YOU SPEAK THE *TRUTH!*

BUT NOW THERE IS MUCH TO *DO!*

KA-ZAR WILL AID YOU TO CLEAR YOUR--- *WAIT!*

THAT GUTTERAL *SOUND*... IN THE *STREET* FAR BELOW!!

THE WARNING ROAR OF *ZABU!!*

HEY!! WATCH IT, MAN!

IF YOU MISS THAT *LEDGE*...!

KA-ZAR DOES NOT *MISS!*

AND, IN THE STREET BELOW...

...A GRIMLY GROWLING *SABER TOOTH* PROWLS THE PAVEMENT, SEARCHING FOR HIS *MASTER*...!

GRRRRRR RRRRR

GUNS AGAINST ZABU?? *NEVER!*

LOOK OUT! IT'S KA-ZAR! HE'S TRYING TO SAVE THE *TIGER!*

FROM *WHAT?* ALL WE WANNA DO IS GET 'IM OFF THE *STREETS!*

HOLD YOUR FIRE, MEN! DON'T *SHOOT!*

SPINN!

HOLD IT, FELLA! THERE'S NO *NEED* FOR THAT!

GUNS! KA-ZAR *HATES* GUNS!!

KA-RUNCH

NO MORE WILL ZABU BE PURSUED BY CARS! NOT WHILE KA-ZAR LIVES!

CIVILIZED MEN--BAH! ALWAYS FIGHTING --CHASING--- TRYING TO HARM OTHERS!

LOOK HOW HE'S BENDIN' THAT *LAMP POST* OVER THE CAR!!

DON'T TRY TO *STOP* HIM! HE DOESN'T MEAN ANY *HARM!*

BESIDES, HIS ESTATE IN *ENGLAND* HAS ENOUGH DOUGH TO SETTLE UP FOR ALL THE *DAMAGES!*

6.

ALL STAND BACK! WHOEVER HARMS ZABU MUST ANSWER TO KA-ZAR, THE JUNGLE LORD!

NOW CLEAR THE WAY! WE WOULD BE GONE!

IT'LL BE A PLEASURE TO SAY GOODBYE!

WE WERE ONLY TRYING TO PROTECT THE PEOPLE, MISTER!

KA-ZAR SPEAKS NO MORE!

MAN! WHAT A CORKER!

I'D RATHER FACE THAT KING-SIZE KITTY THAN TACKLE HIM WHEN HE'S ANGRY!

BUT, EVEN AS THE FAR-OUT PAIR WALKS OFF OUR SCENE CHANGES ONCE MORE...

I JUST REMEMBERED... AUNT MAY!!

SHE MUST BE WORRIED SICK ABOUT ME!

I'VE GOT TO GET TO HER, FAST!

BUT... I'M ALL OUT OF WEB FLUID!

CAN'T SWING ACROSS TOWN WITHOUT IT!

I'LL HAVE TO TRAVEL BY WALL-CRAWLING!

FIRST, BACK TO THE APARTMENT... FOR MY CLOTHES!

EASY, SPIDEY! YOU'RE STILL KIND'A WOOZY!!

Y'KNOW SOMETHING? IT'S HARD TO KICK THIS SCENE CHANGING HABIT! LIKE F'RINSTANCE...

AHH, MR. JAMESON! I THOUGHT YOUR CURIOSITY WOULD NOT LET YOU STAY AWAY!

SKIP THE SPEECHES, SMYTHE!

I KNOW THIS A BLINKIN' WASTE OF TIME... SO LET'S GET IT OVER WITH!

JUST TROT OUT WHAT YOU WANT TO SHOW ME!

STEP IN, MY FRIEND! AND PREPARE FOR A STARTLING SURPRISE!

SEE HOW MUCH MORE *SOPHISTICATED* THESE CONTROLS ARE?

HE'S TWICE AS *SENSITIVE* AS MY FIRST PROTOTYPE WAS!

SURE! SURE! BUT WHAT CAN HE *DO*?

I WAS *HOPING* YOU'D ASK!

HE'S BUILT TO *TRACK DOWN* ANYTHING THAT HAS A SPIDER SCENT!

HE COULD LOCATE ONE LONE SPIDER IN THE MIDDLE OF A *JUNGLE*!

YOUR *OTHER* ROBOT DID THE SAME THING...!

BUT THE WEB-SLINGER *STILL* DEMOLISHED HIM!

BUT THE *FIRST* ONE DIDN'T HAVE MY SPIDER-SLAYER'S INVINCIBLE *STRENGTH*!

SEE HOW EASILY HE SHATTERED THAT *FOOT-THICK* WALL TO REACH A TINY SPIDER!

NOW THINK WHAT HE'LL DO TO... *SPIDER-MAN*!

I'M SOLD! I'M SOLD! HURRY--LETS GET HIM *STARTED*!

BUT, LUCKILY, *ALL* JAMESONS ARE NOT OF JONAH'S ILK!

DON'T *WORK* TOO HARD, HONEY!

CAN'T HAVE YOU YAWNING AT OUR *WEDDING*!

I'LL TRY TO STAY *AWAKE* DURING THE CEREMONY, DARLING!

HATE TO INTER-*RUPT* YOU LOVEBIRDS...

BUT I'D LIKE TO SEE MY *FATHER*, MISS BRANT!

COLONEL JAMESON! SORRY, THE CHIEF ISN'T *IN* RIGHT NOW!

ANYTHING *I* CAN DO TO HELP?

'FRAID NOT, NED! I JUST WANTED TO SAY *GOOD-BYE*!

I HAVE MY ORDERS TO *SHIP OUT* WITHIN THE HOUR!

OH! IF ONL I KNEW WHER MR. JAMESO IS...!!

COULDN'T
HELP OVER-
HEARING,
COLONEL!

THANKS, MR. ROBERTSON! TELL ME
...DO *YOU* EVER FEEL LIKE
GETTING BACK IN UNIFORM?

AT *MY AGE?* BEING *CITY
EDITOR* IS EXCITEMENT
ENOUGH!

ALL THE *BEST*
ON YOUR NEW
ASSIGNMENT,
MY BOY!

ANY-
WAY, TELL
DAD I
DROPPED
BY!

SURE
WILL, SON!

AND *NOW,* GANG... YOUR PATIENCE IS ABOUT TO
BE REWARDED! 'CAUSE HERE WE *GO*...

I'M *STILL* FEELING
TOO WOOZY TO
CRAWL MY WAY
ACROSS TOWN!

I'VE
GOTTA
GET
MYSELF
A *RIDE*...!

AND THIS IS *ONE*
WAY TO DO IT!

Q41 UPTOWN

GHREN BUS INC.

KEEP
YOUR CITY
CLEAN

IT'S KINDA
SLOW...
BUT AT LEAST
I'M GOING IN
THE RIGHT
DIRECTION!

THIS *REST*
IS WHAT I
NEEDED!

I'M FEELING
BETTER
ALREADY!

BUT, THERE ALWAYS SEEMS TO BE ONE
PARTY-POOPER ON THE SCENE...

HELP!
POLICE!
I *SEE*
HIM!

IT'S
*SPIDER-
MAN!*

ON TOP
OF THAT
BUS!

I'VE
FOUND
*SPIDER-
MAN!!*

OH,
NO..!

WELL, IT'S
BACK TO THE
ROOFTOPS
FOR ME!

I CAN'T
LET THEM
CATCH
ME...

TILL I FIND A
WAY TO *CLEAR*
MYSELF!

10

BUT, IF SPIDEY THINKS HE'LL HAVE TIME FOR MAKING LEISURELY *PLANS*... FORGET IT!!

HOP IN, JAMESON! WE'LL FOLLOW THE *SPIDER SLAYER* HERE IN MY *CAR!*

GOOD! I DON'T WANT TO BE TOO FAR *AWAY* WHEN HE CATCHES UP WITH THAT MASKED *MISFIT!*

HE WALKS LIKE HE KNOWS WHERE HE'S *GOING!*

MAYBE HE'S PICKED UP THE TRAIL *ALREADY!*

OF COURSE! IF SPIDER-MAN IS ANYWHERE IN THE *CITY*, HE'S AS GOOD AS *TRAPPED!*

WHAT A *FUN* WAY TO PASS THE TIME!

AND SO THE DEADLY MECHANICAL CREATION PLODS ON... STOPPING FOR NOTHING... AND WE MEAN *NOTHING*...!

I'M IN *LUCK!* THE APARTMENT'S *EMPTY!*

HARRY MUST BE *OUT* SOMEWHERE

WHILE A WEARY *SPIDEY* FINALLY REACHES HIS GOAL...

FIRST THING TO DO IS GET OUT OF THESE DUDS AND CHECK WITH *AUNT MAY!*

≡WHEW!≡ I'VE NEVER FELT SO *TIRED* BEFORE!

NO ANSWER!

MAYBE IT'S JUST AS *WELL!* I'M NOT SURE WHAT I'D *TELL* HER, ANYWAY!

AFTER I GET SOME *SHUT-EYE*, I'LL... *SAY!* WHY'S MY SPIDE SENSE *TINGLING* LIKE THIS?!!

SOMETHING'S WRONG!

14

JUST MY *LUCK!* I DON'T KNOW HIS *FIRST* NAME!

AND THERE ARE A COUPLE *DOZEN* SMYTHES LISTED!!

HOW AM I GONNA TELL WHICH ONE IS *WHICH...??*

I *KNEW* IT! I *KNEW* YOU'D CRACK UP UNDER THE *STRAIN!*

ONLY A *FOOL* WOULD WASTE TIME WITH A *PHONE BOOK* WHEN HIS MINUTES ARE *NUMBERED!*

WRONG, SMYTHE! I *FOUND* WHAT I NEED!

LUCKILY, YOU'VE GOT THE WORD *SCIENTIST* AFTER YOUR *NAME!*

OKAY, MASKED MAN! SEE HOW MUCH *GOOD* IT DOES YOU!

JUST KEEP *WATCHING*, BIG MOUTH!

YOU'LL SEE A LOT MORE THAN *THAT!*

KRAKK!

SMYTHE! IF HE HADN'T LEAPED *OUT* IN TIME...

I TOLD YOU TO *BUTT OUT* JAMESON. I'LL *HANDLE* THIS!

IN A WAY, IT'S EVEN *BETTER* THAN I *HOPED!*

THE MORE HE FRANTICALLY TRIES TO *FLEE...* THE MORE *SATISFACTION* I'LL GET WHEN HE'S FINALLY *BEATEN!*

YOU DON'T *CARE* ABOUT HIM BEING A MENACE TO MANKIND!

YOU JUST WANT TO *KILL* HIM --- FOR PERSONAL *REVENGE!*

DON'T TALK TO *ME* ABOUT MOTIVES, YOU PIOUS *HYPO-CRITE!*

YOU'VE *LIED* ABOUT HIM IN YOUR PAPER FOR *YEARS!*

NOW STAY *BACK* WHILE I *CONCENTRATE!*

HE MUST BE OUT OF HIS *MIND!* HE'S HEADING FOR MY LAB... IN SHEER, STARK PANIC!

THE *FOOL!* HE DOESN'T SUSPECT WE'RE *HERE,* IN YOUR OFFICE AT THE *BUGLE!*

ONCE HE REACHES THE LAB, HE'LL BE TRAPPED! MY ROBOT WILL *NEVER* LET HIM ESCAPE FROM THERE!

A SHORT TIME LATER, OUR YOUTHFUL ADVENTURER *ENTERS* THE FATEFUL CHAMBER--

EVERYTHING DEPENDS ON THE NEXT FEW MINUTES!

IF I GUESSED *WRONG,* I'M *FINISHED!*

NO! IT'S *OKAY!* FOUND WHAT I WANT!

AND JUST IN *TIME!* I HEAR HIM COMING *NOW!*

THIS IS *IT,* SPIDER-MAN! YOU'VE NO PLACE LEFT TO *RUN!*

SPKANNCH!

I'VE GOT *NEWS* FOR YOU, SMYTHE...

I'M *THROUGH* RUNNING!

I'LL SAY YOU'RE *THROUGH* RUNNING!

YOU'RE *THROUGH EVERYTHING!*

YOU'RE.. *WAIT!* WHAT'S *THIS...?!!*

SO COME AND *GET* ME, SWEETIE!

THE *CONTROLS* ARE MALFUNCTIONING!

SOMETHING'S *WRONG!* HE--HE'S NOT *RESPONDING!*

BUT *WHY??* WHAT *HAPPENED??*

CLICK!

18

I CAN'T FAIL *NOW*...NOT WHEN I ALMOST *HAVE* HIM!

I'LL *INCREASE* THE POWER...GIVE IT *ABSOLUTE MAXIMUM*..!

CLICK

THIS WILL DO IT! IT *HAS* TO..!

AND *DO IT,* IT DOES -- THOUGH NOT QUITE THE WAY PRO- FESSOR SMYTHE *EXPECTS*...

RRROONWWW

TOO BAD YOU CAN'T STILL *HEAR* ME, SMYTHE!

I'D BE *GLAD* TO EXPLAIN WHAT HAPPENED!

I *KNEW* YOUR MAN-SHAPED RATTLETRAP WAS ACTIVATED BY *SPIDER* IMPULSES--

THAT'S WHY HE WAS ABLE TO TRACK *ME* DOWN SO EASILY!

SO, IT WASN'T HARD TO FIGURE OUT THAT *TOO MANY* SPIDER IMPULSES MIGHT JUST *SHORT CIRCUIT* HIM!

...LIKE A *FUSE BOX* THAT CAN'T TAKE AN ELECTRIC *OVERLOAD*!

ALL I NEEDED WAS A PLACE WHERE THERE'D BE *ENOUGH* SPIDERS TO DO THE TRICK...

AND *THAT'S* WHY I CAME TO YOUR LAB, SMART GUY... NOT FOR *YOU*...FOR YOUR *SPIDERS*!

I JUST HEAPED THEM ALL *TOGETHER,* FOR MAXIMUM IMPACT...THEN-- *BLOOIE!*

AND JUST BETWEEN *US,* SMYTHEY..I'M *BUSHED!*

WHILE, AT THE OFFICE OF *JONAH JAMESON,* MOOD IS SOMEWHAT *LESS* THAN TRIUMPHANTU HILARIOUS...

IF YOU'D HAVE BEEN SATISFIED TO JUST *CAPTURE* HIM...LIKE I *WANTE* YOU TO... WE'D HAVE *WON!*

GET *OUT,* YOU BUM !! I'VE GOT A GOOD MIND TO TURN YOU OVER TO THE *POLICE!*

YOU NEUROTIC *NUT!* YOU DON'T EVEN *HAVE* A MIND!

OUT! OUT! OUUUUT!

THE AMAZING SPIDER-MAN! ™
THE BRAND OF THE BRAINWASHER!"

AHH--*THERE'S* WHAT I NEED!

THE DIRECTORY OF *PATIENTS!*

JUST MY LUCK--

AUNT MAY'S ON THE *TOP* FLOOR!

WELL, WE ING'S OR RE--

I'D BETTER NOT TAKE THE PASSENGER ELEVATOR!

AND EVEN THE *STAIRS* WOULD BE TOO RISKY!

WHAT WOULD I EVER *DO* WITHOUT AIR SHAFTS?

THIS IS THE FLOOR!

I'LL CHANGE MY CLOTHES AND-- ≡UH OH!≡

SOMEONE'S *COMING!*

THE NITOR-- TTING MOP!

AT A FE! MOP THE FLOOR, DRY THE FLOOR! MOP THE FLOOR, DRY THE FLOOR!

IF HE THINKS *THAT'S* BAD--HE SHOULD TRY BEING *SPIDER-MAN* FOR A WHILE!

HERE'S THE ROOM NOW!

I HOPE-- SHE'S ALL RIGHT!

AUNT MAY!

WHO--? I THOUGHT I HEARD--

PETER! IS IT *YOU?* --IS IT-- *REALLY YOU??*

I WAS-- BEGINNING TO FEAR-- I'D NEVER *SEE* YOU AGAIN--!

DON'T EVER *SAY* THAT, AUNT MAY!

PETER--PETER! I'M FEELING BETTER *ALREADY*--JUST *SEEING* YOU--JUST KNOWING YOU'RE *SAFE*!

I'D HAVE RETURNED *SOONER* --IF I *COULD*!

BUT, WHERE *WERE* YOU? WHAT *HAPPENED*?

WHY DIDN'T YOU *CALL*?

NOW WHAT DO I SAY? I WAS SO ANXIOUS TO *SEE* AUNT MAY--I FORGOT TO MAKE UP A *STORY*!

I DARE NOT SAY ANYTHING THAT'LL LET HER SUSPECT I'M *SPIDER-MAN*!

WHO ARE *YOU*? WHAT ARE YOU *DOING* HERE?

HE'S MY DEA... *NEPHEW*-- PETER! HE'S BACK AT LAS...

-WHEW!- SAVED BY THE BELL!

THE ONE WHO WAS *MISSING*?

GLAD YOU'RE *BACK*, SON! YOUR AUNT WAS MIGHTY *WORRIED* ABOUT YOU!

BUT SHE MUSTN'T HAVE ANY *EXCITEMENT*!

YOU'D BETTER *LEAVE*--AND LET HER REST!

I'LL BE *BACK*, AUNT MAY-- SOON AS I *CAN*!

I JUST *KNOW*--I'LL SLEEP LIKE A BABY-- *NOW*!

THE *SIGHT* OF YOU WAS BETTER FOR HER THAN A *TONIC*, PARKER!

SHE TOOK IT PRETTY *HARD* WHEN YOU WERE LISTED AS A *MISSING PERSON*.

MISSING PERSON? HOOO BOY!

I ALMOST *FORGOT*! I HAVE TO REPORT TO THE *POLICE*!

AND I'D BETTER HAVE A GOOD *STORY* FOR THEM!

THEN, A SHORT TIME LATER--

HI! I'M PETER PARKER!

PARKER?!! WE'VE GOT HALF THE *FORCE* OUT LOOKING FOR YOU!

YOU *HAVE*? WHY?

'CORDING TO THE *DAILY BUGLE*, YOU WERE *CAPTURED* BY *SPIDER-MAN*!

GREAT! THAT'S MY *STORY*!

WITHIN MINUTES, OUR HERO FINDS HIMSELF THE CENTER OF ATTRACTION

WHY DID SPIDER-MAN DO IT?

COULD YOU LEAD US TO HIS *HIDE-OUT*?

EH--*NO*! I WAS *BLIND-FOLDED* ALL THE TIME!

SPIDER-MAN *CAN'T* BE ALL *BAD*--

--OR HE WOULDN'T HAVE SE... THE BO... FREE...

DON'T JUST *SIT* THERE, YOUNG MAN! TELL US EVERYTHING YOU *LEARNED* ABOUT THAT MASKED *MENACE*!

BRO-TH... WHAT I... I SA... NOW...

I'M *GEORGE STACY*, YOUNG MAN-- CAPTAIN OF POLICE, RETIRED!

GWEN'S DAD! I'VE *HEARD* HER *MENTION* HIM!

WHEN LAST SEEN, SPIDER-MAN CLAIMED TO HAVE LOST HIS *MEMORY!*

DO *YOU* KNOW ANYTHING ABOUT THAT?

YES, SIR! HE *DID* HAVE AMNESIA!

THAT'S HOW *DOC OCK* CONVINCED HIM THEY WERE *PARTNERS!*

WHEN HIS MEMORY *RETURNED* TO HIM, HE SET ME *FREE* AGAIN!

WELL, THAT'S MY STORY-- AND I'M *STUCK* WITH IT!

BUT WHY DID HE *CAPTURE* YOU IN THE *FIRST* PLACE?

THINK FAST, MR. PARKER!

I WAS ON A *PICTURE-TAKING* ASSIGNMENT-- FOR THE DAILY BUGLE!

HE SAW ME *FOLLOWING* HIM--AND THOUGHT I WAS AN *ENEMY!*

BUT, WHEN HIS *MEMORY* RETURNED, HE REALIZED I WAS HARMLESS--AND *RELEASED* ME!

ARE YOU SAYING HE'S *NOT* AS DANGEROUS AS WE THOUGHT?

IF YOU ASK *ME,* HE'S SORT OF *LOVABLE!*

THIS IS NO LAUGHING MATTER, PARKER!

COMMISSIONER-- THIS IS THE REPORT YOU'VE BEEN *WAIT-ING* FOR!

LOOKS LIKE YOUR QUESTION-ING IS *OVER,* SON!

REPORT--??

WE'VE A MORE *URGENT* MATTER TO ATTEND TO NOW, PARKER!

IF YOU THINK OF ANYTHING YOU MAY HAVE *FORGOTTEN* TO TELL US ABOUT SPIDER-MAN, CONTACT ME AT ONCE!

YOU MAY *GO* NOW!

THANK YOU, SIR!

SO FAR, SO GOOD!

THEY *STILL* DON'T SUSPECT MY *REAL* CONNECTION WITH SPIDEY!

I'LL SEE YOU TO THE DOOR!

THE REPORT IS JUST WHAT WE *FEARED!*

ANOTHER BATCH OF THE MOST *DANGEROUS* MOBSTERS IN TOWN HAVE BEEN RELEASED ON BAIL!

BUT WHO'S *BEHIND* IT? WHAT'S THE *EXPLANATION?*

SOUNDS LIKE SOME-THING *BIG* IN THE WIND! WISH I COULD *STAY!*

CAN YOU SPARE A FEW MINUTES, PETER?

I-- GUESS SO!

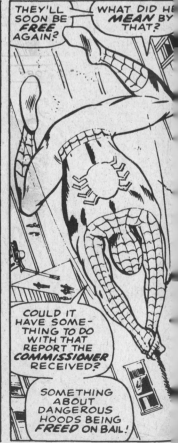

WELL, NOTHING MORE I CAN DO *NOW!*

BETTER GET *HOME* AND GRAB SOME *SHUT-EYE!*

I WANNA BE ALL *RESTED UP* FOR MJ'S GRAND *OPENING* TOMORROW NIGHT!

I BET SHE'LL BE A *WOW!*

AND SPIDEY ISN'T THE *ONLY* ONE WHO THINKS SO--

FACE IT, FEMALE-- YOU'LL KNOCK 'EM *DEAD* TOMORROW!

AWRIGHT, KID! THAT'S ENOUGH FOR *NOW!*

SAVE IT FOR THE *LIVE ONES* AT SHOW TIME!

OW DID I *DO,* MR. SLADE?

FINE, FINE! BUT WHAT ABOUT THE *CAMERA?*

SURE YOU CAN *HANDLE* IT, OKAY?

NO SWEAT, BOSS MAN!

REPEAT YOUR INSTRUC- TIONS --JUST TO MAKE *SURE!*

BETWEEN NUMBERS, I WALTZ AROUND THE PLACE SNAPPING *FREE* PICS OF THE PILGRIMS! HOW'SZAT?

YOU FORGOT *ONE* THING--!

YOU *ONLY* TAKE PICTURES OF THOSE SITTING AT TABLES WITH A *STAR* ON THEM!

I *READ* YOU, MAN!

BE SURE THERE ARE NO *SLIP- UPS!*

WITH MJ AT THE HELM? BITE YOUR TONGUE!

...UT FINALLY, JUST BEFORE TOTAL *SHELLSHOCK* ...ETS IN--

...OLD IT, MJ! ...REN'T YOU ...ONNA TAKE ...OUR PIC?

SORRY, SWEETIES! I'M ONLY SUPPOSED TO SNAP THE *CELEBRITIES* TON'IGHT!

THAT'S *STRANGE!* I WONDER *WHY?*

I *MUST* HAVE BEEN GROOVY IF *YOU* ADMIT IT, BLUE EYES!

WELL, KEEP IT COOL, CHILDREN!

YOUR FOOTWORK WAS FROM *FABSVILLE,* TWINKLE-TOES!

...NAP YOUR MAP, GENTS? ...COMPLIMENTS OF THE HOUSE!

FREE ...HOTO-...RAPH?

HOW NICE!

I'LL HAVE IT *READY* FOR YOU IN A HALF-HOUR--

IF *HOLLYWOOD* DOESN'T GET YOU *FIRST!*

WHAT'S *WRONG,* COUNCIL-MAN?

I--DON'T KNOW--!

ALL OF A SUDDEN-- I FEEL *DIZZY!*

PERHAPS-- I NEED-- SOME *AIR--!*

...AY I TAKE YOUR ...PICTURE, SIR?

THERE'S *NO CHARGE* FOR THE SNAPSHOTS!

CERTAINLY, YOUNG LADY!

I ENJOYED YOUR *DANCING* VERY MUCH!

BY THE WAY, I BELIEVE YOU KNOW MY DAUGHT-- --*OHH!--*

IS SOMETHING *WRONG,* SIR?

EH, *NO--* I DON'T *THINK* SO!

IT'S PROBABLY THE SUDDEN FLASH OF THE *BULB--* IT *STARTLED* ME!

UH OH! MY *SPIDEY SENSE* IS AT IT AGAIN!

SOMEONE'S ATTACKING FROM *BEHIND!*

THIS'LL PUT YOU OUTTA THE WAY UNTIL WE CAN--*HEY!!*

HOW'D YOU *DODGE* THAT??

WITH *EASE,* SONNY BOY!

I DON'T KNOW WHAT'S GOING *ON* IN THERE--

BUT IF IT NEEDS A COUPLE OF ARMED *HOODS* TO GUARD THE SECRET--

YOU CAN BET YOUR BOTTLE-TOPS I'M GONNA *FIND OUT!*

WHAP

AND, WHEN IT COMES TO A LITTLE WAY-OUT *WALL-CRAWLING--*

THERE'S NO TIME LIKE THE *PRESENT!*

THE *ALARM!* --I'VE GOTTA-- SOUND-- THE *ALARM--!*

THE *SIGNAL!!* SOMEONE'S BROKEN *IN!*

WELL, WE'VE GOT ENOUGH *MUSCLE* TO MAKE SURE HE NEVER GETS *OUT* AGAIN--

--UNLESS IT'S *FEET FIRST!*

--AND 'FAR BE IT FROM *ME* TO STOP YOU FROM *GETTING IT!*

ZONK!

OKAY-- FUNTIME'S *OVER!*

NOW I WANNA KNOW WHAT'S *UP?!!*

D-DON'T *HIT* ME! DON'T *HIT* ME!

I'LL TALK, I'LL TALK

BUT, AT THAT CRUCIAL INSTANT--*FATE* INTERVENES--IN THE PULCHRITUDINOUS PERSON OF A MYSTIFIED *M. J. WATSON*--

MARY JANE!!

WH-WHAT'S *WRONG??*

ALL THAT *NOISE!!* --WHAT'S *HAPPEN-ING?*

NOW'S MY *CHANCE*--

IF I CAN GRAB THE *GUN*--!

OKAY, WALL-CRAWLER--!

HE'S *USING* HER --AS A *SHIELD!!*

NOW IT'S *OUR* TURN!

SPIDER-MAN!

LET 'IM HAV IT, LOUI

THAT'S *IT!* IT'S WORKING *PERFECTLY!*

IN A MATTER OF *SECONDS* HE'LL BE OUR UNWITTING, TOTALLY-OBEDIENT TOOL!

NOW... REPEAT AFTER ME, STACY...

THE *KINGPIN* IS MY *MASTER!* I WILL OBEY... HIS *ORDERS!*

THE KINGPIN... MY MASTER! ---I WILL OBEY... HIS ORDERS

AND, AS THE MASTER EVIL-DOER CONTINUES HIS SINISTER BRIEFING---

I CAN'T SHAKE THE FEELING THAT THERE'S SOMETHING *WRONG* HERE!

LIKE *WHAT,* GWEN?

I DON'T *UNDERSTAND* IT! FIRST *DAD*...AND NOW *PETER* HASN'T RETURNED, EITHER!

GWEN! WHERE'S YOUR *FATHER?*

I'VE GOT TO *SEE* HIM!

THERE'S SOMETHING *HAPPENING* OUTSIDE... SOMETHING HE SHOULD *KNOW!*

MJ! YOU LOOK A THOUGH YOU'V SEEN GHOS

WHAT *IS* IT, GIRL? SPEAK UP!

I WAS BACKSTAGE...AND I SAW A *FIGHT*...THEN ONE OF THE MEN *GRABBED* ME... USING ME AS A *SHIELD*...

A *SHIELD!* AGAINST *WHAT??*

AGAINST *SPIDER-MAN!* LIKE..IT WAS *HIM* THEY WERE FIGHT-ING!

I'M SURE THAT... THERE'S NOTHING... TO WORRY ABOUT... YOUNG LADY!

OH! CAPTAIN *STACY!* I..I DIDN'T KNOW YOU WERE *THERE!*

DAD! YOU' *BACK!* YOU'R AL *RIGHT!*

I WAS GETTIN SO *WORRIEE*

WORRIED? ...ABOUT *WHAT..?*

MIGHT AS WELL *FACE* IT---

I'M NO GOOD TO *ANYONE* LIKE THIS!

BETTER GET BACK *HOME*... FAST!

EVEN CRAWLING DOWN THE *WALL* WASN'T EASY!

IF THIS DOUBLE VISION DOESN'T *LEAVE* ME SOON..

THEN SPIDER-MAN'S *HAD* IT!

CAN'T EVEN *TRUST* MYSELF TO CROSS ANY *STREETS!*

I'D BETTER TAKE A *BUS* HOME!

...IF I CAN CLIMB ABOARD THRU THE RIGHT *DOOR!*

ECONDS LATER, AS PETER PARKER FALTERINGLY ALKS IN THE OPPOSITE DIRECTION---

STILL THINK WE HOULD HAVE WAITED OR *PETER* TO RETURN!

AW, YOU *KNOW* THAT ROVIN' ROOMIE OF MINE, GWEN!

HE COULD BE GONE FOR *DAYS!*

WHEN THAT SHUTTERBUG IS AFTER SOME *NEWS PIX*...FORGET IT!

DAD, DO *YOU* THINK THAT---*DAD?*

IS - IS ANYTHING *WRONG?*

NO!...I'M JUST... TIRED!

UT, THERE ARE SOME THINGS EVEN ORSE THAN FATIGUE...AS OUR ORELY-TROUBLED HERO CAN ESTIFY...

WEN'S DAD... ACING SOME NKNOWN ANGER... T THE HANDS F THE KING- PIN...

AND NOTHING I CAN *DO* ABOUT IT!

FOR A WHILE, EVERYTHING SEEMED TO BE GOING *MY* WAY!

AUNT MAY WAS RECOVERING... *HARRY* WAS FRIENDLY AGAIN... AND *GWEN...*

MOST OF ALL... *GWEN!*

I WAS BEGINNING TO REALIZE... HOW MUCH SHE *MEANT* TO ME!

WITH SPIDER-MAN *HELPLESS* ...IF ANYTHING SHOULD HAPPEN ...TO *GWEN...!!*

BUT SUDDENLY, EVERYTHING'S *CHANGED!*

WHAT IF CAPTAIN STACY IS *MORE* THAN THE KINGPIN'S *PRISONER?*

WHAT IF THAT MACHINE HAS SOMEHOW TURNED HIM INTO A FELLOW *CRIMINAL?*

SOONER OR LATER... *SPIDER-MAN* WILL HAVE TO *FACE* THEM... TO FORCE A *SHOWDOWN!*

BUT *HOW?* HOW DO I TREAT *GWEN'S* DAD... AS AN *ENEMY?*

HOW CAN I BATTLE THE FATHER OF... THE GIRL I..I.. *LOVE?*

THE GIRL I LOVE!

IT'S...THE *FIRST TIME*... I EVER *ADMITTED* IT... TO MYSELF!

CAN'T SLEEP! NO SENSE EVEN *TRYING!*

I'VE GOT TO SEE *GWEN*... LEARN MORE ABOUT HER *DAD*... SOMEHOW!

I'M ALMOST *AFRAID*... TO LOOK AT ANYTHING!

WHAT'LL I *DO*...IF I STILL HAVE... THAT *DOUBLE VISION?*

BUT, I'VE GOT TO DO IT... I *MUST* LOOK....

EVERYTHING IS STILL *BLURRED*...BUT IT'S *BETTER* THAN IT WAS!

THAT MEANS...IT'S SLOWLY *IMPROVING!* I'LL FIND *SOME* WAY TO MANAGE!

NO SENSE DISTURBING HARRY! I'LL JUST LET HIM SLEEP!

THE LESS EXPLAINING I HAVE TO DO, THE BETTER!

SLOWLY, PETE... SLOWLY!

TAKE IT EASY, FELLA...TILL YOUR VISION'S OKAY AGAIN!

EVEN THOUGH EVERYTHING'S BLURRED...

AT LEAST I DON'T SEE TWO IMAGES ANY MORE!

I COULDN'T WAIT ANY LONGER!

I'VE GOT TO KNOW ...HAS GWEN'S DAD RETURNED YET?

AND, IS HE OKAY?

PETER! I...NEVER EXPECTED..!

WHERE'VE YOU BEEN? WHAT HAPPENED TO YOU?

IT'S A LONG STORY..!

IS YOUR DAD HOME?

MAY I COME IN FOR A MINUTE?

IT'S NOT VERY FLATTERING TO ME...IF YOU ONLY WANT TO STAY A MINUTE!

WOULDJA BELIEVE... FOREVER?

TRY ME, MR. PARKER!

GOOD EVENING, YOUNG MAN!

I THOUGHT I HEARD SOMEONE!

ISN'T IT RATHER LATE TO COME CALLING, PARKER?

I'M SORRY, SIR!

BUT, I HAVE SOME... INFORMATION ...FOR YOU!

THAT'S MY CUE TO MAKE SOME COFFEE!

'TIS THE UNKINDEST CUT OF ALL!

TIME WAS WHEN THE GROOVY YOUNG GENTS CAME TO SEE GWENDOLYNE!

TO THINK THAT I'VE BECOME AN EIGHTEEN-YEAR-OLD HAS-BEEN --ALAS!

HE'S CHANGED! THE WARMTH... THE FRIENDLINESS.. ARE GONE!

BUT GWEN DOESN'T YET REALIZE...!

COME INTO THE STUDY, PARKER!

AND, NO SOONER DOES CAPTAIN STACY STRIKE THE FLOOR, THAN PETER PARKER'S MOST DESPERATE FEAR IS DRAMATICALLY *REALIZED*...

DAD! YOU'RE *HURT!* WHAT *HAPPENED??*

GWEN! WHATEVER HE *SAYS*... WHATEVER YOU *HEAR*...

IT *ISN'T*... WHAT IT *SEEMS!*

HE'S *MAD!* HE *ATTACKED* ME... FOR NO REASON AT *ALL!*

CALL THE *POLICE...* DO YOU *HEAR?* THE BOY IS *DANGEROUS!*

YOU... YOU TELL ME NOT TO *BELIEVE...* WHAT I SEE WITH MY OWN *EYES!*

YOU STRUCK MY OWN *FATHER*---AN OLD MAN---THE DEAREST... THE GENTLEST MAN WHO EVER *LIVED!*

NO, GWEN... *NO!*

THEN *DENY* IT! LET ME HEAR YOU *DENY* IT!

I...I *CAN'T!*

THERE'S NOTHING I CAN *TELL* HER...NO WAY TO *EXPLAIN!*

HOW? HOW COULD I EVER HAVE THOUGHT... THAT I *CARED* FOR YOU--??

I'VE NO *PROOF...* OF ANYTHING!

ALL I CAN DO... BY TELLING HER THE *TRUTH* ABOUT HER FATHER... IS TO MAKE HER *HATE* ME... EVEN *MORE!*

GET OUT, PETER---GET OUT! AND NEVER COME *BACK!*

I NEVER WANT TO *SEE* YOU AGAIN ---*EVER!*

I CAN'T *BLAME* HER! AND YET...

WHAT DO I DO *NOW??*

IT ALMOST BROKE MY HEART... TO SEE THE *TORMENT* IN HER EYES!

SHE COULDN'T HAVE BEEN SO *HURT*... UNLESS SHE FELT ABOUT ME... THE WAY I FEEL ABOUT *HER!*

BUT, WHAT *GOOD* DOES IT DO ME... TO KNOW THAT *NOW?* NOW... WHEN I'VE *LOST* HER... FOREVER!

IT ALL STARTED AT THE *CLUB*... WHERE I FOUND THE *KINGPIN!*

HE'S THE ANSWER TO THE ENTIRE RIDDLE!

BUT, I CAN'T GO AFTER HIM *YET!*

I'VE GOT TO WAIT A LITTLE *LONGER*...TILL MY VISION IS *PERFECT* AGAIN!

HE'S TOO *STRONG*..TOO *DANGEROUS* TO TACKLE WITH A *HANDICAP*.

AND, EVEN AS THE TORMENTED YOUTH RIDES INTO THE NIGHT...

WHAT MADE HIM *DO* IT, DAD? WHY DID HE *ATTACK* YOU?

I'M *TIRED*, NOW, GWEN! I WANT TO *SLEEP!* WE'LL DISCUSS IT IN THE MORNING!

I JUST *COULDN'T* BRING MYSELF TO CALL THE POLICE!

BUT, I'LL NEVER *FORGIVE* HIM! NEVER!

ARE YOU *SURE* I SHOULDN'T CALL THE *DOCTOR?*

POSITIVE! I JUST NEED SOME SLEEP!

BUT, NO SOONER HAS THE GORGEOUS, GRIEF-STRICKEN GIRL DEPARTED, WHEN...

AT *LAST*, SHE'S *GONE!*

THE *KINGPIN* MUST BE ALERTED ... AT ONCE

AHH, *STACY!* WHY BOTHER TO CALL?

YOUR ORDERS WERE TO *BE* HERE TONIGHT... REMEMBER?

WHAT? WHAT DID YOU *SAY?*

A *TEEN-AGER? SUSPICIOUS* OF US??

TELL ME HIS *NAME*... WHERE DOES HE *LIVE?*

HE MUST BE *SILENCED*... WITHOUT DELAY!

Panel 1:

EXACTLY TEN SECONDS LATER... (FOR THOSE OF YOU WHO WANT TO TEST YOUR STOP-WATCHES)...

HIS NAME IS *PETER PARKER*...AND I JUST GAVE YOU HIS ADDRESS!

SO WHAT ARE YOU *WAITING* FOR? *MOVE!*

CHOMP! CHOMP!

Panel 2:

BUT...YOU SAID HE WAS...JUST A *KID!*

HE'S JUST *SUSPICIOUS*...HE DON'T REALLY *KNOW* ANYTHING!

SUPPOSE WE JUST *LEAN* ON 'IM A LITTLE...AND SCARE 'IM OFF?

HOW *ABOUT* IT, BOSS?

BOSS?...WHY DON'T YOU...*ANSWER..??*

Panel 3:

...YOU INCONSEQUENTIAL, BRAINLESS *INCOMPETENTS!*

NOBODY GIVES THE *KINGPIN* ANY SUGGESTIONS!

NOW DO AS I *SAID*...OR IT'LL BE *YOUR* NECK...AS WELL AS *HIS!*

BLAM!

SURE, BOSS...*SURE!*

WE WERE ONLY *ASKIN'*, THAT'S ALL!

YOU CAN COUNT ON *US!*

Panel 4:

BUT, AS LUCK WOULD HAVE IT, *PETER PARKER* SPENDS THE REST OF THE NIGHT AIMLESSLY WALKING THE STREETS...LOST IN HIS OWN TORTURED THOUGHTS...UNTIL, AT DAYBREAK...

MRS. WATSON,...IS MY *AUNT MAY* HERE?

IS SHE...ALL RIGHT?

WHY, *YES*, PETER!

COME *IN*, SON! I WAS JUST ABOUT TO FIX HER BREAK-FAST!

YOU...LOOK *TIRED*, PETER!

I WAS *UP* KIND OF LATE...STUDYING!

Panel 5:

PETER, DEAR! WHAT A *WONDERFUL* SURPRISE!

I NEVER *EXPECTED* YOU SO EARLY!

I COULDN'T WAIT TO SEE HOW YOU *FELT*, AUNT MAY!

YOU SURE LOOK *SPRY!* STILL PLAYING FULL-BACK FOR THE *JETS?*

PETER, THESE *VISITS* FROM YOU ARE BETTER THAN A *TONIC* FOR YOUR AUNT!

ISN'T HE THE DEAREST *PUSSYWILLOW*, ANNA?

Panel 1: THEN, AS THE LONG, FATEFUL MINUTES TICK BY...

IS SOMETHING *WRONG*, DEAR? YOU DON'T SEEM *YOURSELF*, TODAY!

DON'T WORRY ABOUT *ME*, AUNT MAY!

I HOPE YOU'VE BEEN TAKING YOUR *VITAMIN* PILLS, PETER!

I'M ALWAYS A LITTLE KEYED-UP...JUST BEFORE EXAMS!

YOU KNOW HOW *EASILY* YOU TIRE!

Panel 2: MEANWHILE, AT PETE'S APARTMENT...

WHOM DID YOU SAY YOU WANT?

A PUNK NAMED *PARKER*... AND *YOU* DON'T FIT HIS DESCRIPTION!

WE GOT TIRED OF *WAITIN'* OUTSIDE... SO WE FIGURED WE'D COME AND *GET 'IM!*

HE'S NOT HERE!

AND, EVEN IF HE *WERE*...

Panel 3: SHUDDUP! IF WE WANTED *CONVERSATION*, WE'D LISTEN TO *SUSSKIND!*

STOP! YOU CAN'T... ⸓UNHH!⸓

DON'T *BET* ON IT!

LET'S GIVE THE JOINT THE ONCE-OVER!

Panel 4: *NUTS!* EVEN A *BEDBUG* COULDN'T HIDE IN *HERE!*

MAYBE SOMEONE TIPPED 'IM OFF AND HE FLEW THE COOP!

YEAH! A FAT LOTTA *GOOD* IT'LL DO HIM!

Panel 5: WE'LL BE *BACK*, JUNIOR!

AND IF WE FIND OUT THAT YA TIPPED PARKER OFF...WE'LL BE REAL *UNHAPPY!*

AND YOU WOULDN'T WANT US TO BE *UNHAPPY*, WOULDJA?

SO KEEP YER TRAP *SHUT*... OR WE'LL CLOSE IT FOR YA...FOR *GOOD!*

Panel 6: TALK ABOUT *TIMING!* GUESS WHO COMES IN, ABOUT FIVE MINUTES LATER...

HI, HARRY! I....HEY! WHAT *HAPPENED* HERE?

SUPPOSE *YOU* TELL ME, ROOM-MATE?

THEY WERE YO[U] PEN PALS NOT MIN[E]

THEY?? WHO'S *THEY?*

C'MON, HARRY! *SPILL IT!*

I DON'T KNOW WHAT KIND OF *TROUBLE* YOU'VE GOTTEN YOURSELF INTO, PETE...

BUT YOU'RE PLAYING IN A MIGHTY *DANGEROUS* LEAGUE!

THEY WERE TWO GUNMEN... WHO *WANTED* YOU... REAL *BAD!*

AND IT'S JUST DUMB LUCK THAT *YOU* WEREN'T HURT!

LOOK, HARR... I DON'T WANT *YOU* MIXED UP IN ANY OF THIS!

WHY DON'T YOU STAY WITH YOUR *DAD* FOR A WHILE... UNTIL I TAKE *CARE* OF IT!

NO DICE, PETE! I'M NOT CHICKENING OUT WHEN YOU MAY *NEED* ME!

BUT I WISH I KNEW WHAT WAS GOING *ON!*

SO DO *I,* PAL! SO DO *I!*

THAT *SINKS* IT! I CAN'T AFFORD TO LET ANOTHER *MINUTE* GO TO WASTE!

HARRY WILL BE GOING *OUT* SOON... AND WHEN HE *DOES...*

NO TELLING *WHO* MAY BE ENDANGERED NEXT!

SPIDEY'S GONNA STRIKE AGAIN!

THINGS ARE *STILL* A LITTLE BLURRED... BUT THE *HECK* WITH IT!

I'VE STILL GOT MY *SPIDER POWERS...* AND MY *SPIDER STRENGTH!*

TH ANG ANG

EVEN IF THINGS *DO* LOOK A LITTLE *HAZY* TO ME...

THAT'S NOT GONNA STOP ME FROM REACHING THE *KINGPIN!*

THERE'S TOO MUCH *RIDING* ON THIS FOR ME TO HOLD BACK *NOW!*

THE *POLICE* ARE STILL AFTER ME! I'M WASHED UP WITH *GWEN!*...EVEN *HARRY'S* BECOME INVOLVED!

SO WHAT HAVE I GOT TO *LOSE?!!*

THERE'S THE CLUB *NOW!* I'LL JUST SWING DOWN AND... *WAIT!*

THERE'S GWEN'S *DAD*... LEAVING WITH THOSE *HOODS!*

THIS MAY BE THE *BREAK* I'VE BEEN *WAITING* FOR!

I'VE GOT TO SEE WHERE THEY *GO...!*

I DON'T *GET* IT! HE'S LEADING THEM RIGHT INTO *POLICE HEADQUARTERS!*

GOOD EVENING, CAPTAIN!

BECAUSE OF HIS *POSITION,* NO ONE WOULD *QUESTION* HIM!

HE'S TAKEN THEM TO THE SOUND-PROOF, STEEL-WALLED *VAULT CHAMBER*...

WHERE THEIR *VITAL RECORDS* ARE STORED!

WELL, FOR *ONCE* I'M GONNA HAVE *PROOF POSITIVE!*

THERE! MY AUTO-MATIC *CAMERA'S* IN POSITION...

SO HERE GOES *NOTHING!*

'VE GOT TO 'ELIVER THE 'CTURES TO 'AMESON!

HE'LL PRINT THEM IN THE *BUGLE* FOR THE WORLD TO SEE!

IT'S THE ONLY WAY TO *HELP* GWEN'S DAD!

I *KNOW* HE'S NOT *HIMSELF!* I *KNOW* THE KINGPIN HAS FOUND A WAY TO *CONTROL* HIM!

BUT HE CAN'T BE *CURED* TILL THE KINGPIN'S *SMASHED!*

FORGIVE ME, GWEN... I'M DOING IT FOR HIS *OWN* GOOD... AND *OURS!*

MR. JAMESON... I *BROUGHT* SOME NEW *PICTURES* FOR YOU!

TOO BAD I LET THE *BRASS BAND* GO HOME!

WAS BEGINNING TO LOOK LIKE 'U FORGOT HOW TO TAKE ANY --- *HEY!!*

THESE ARE WHAT *THINK*... THEY'RE 'YNAMITE!!

THEY'RE WHAT YOU *THINK*, ALL RIGHT!

GEORGE STACY... STEALING POLICE RECORDS!!

ROBBIE, BABY... THIS IS JJ!

SCRATCH THE FRONT PAGE, SWEETIE! THE *SCOOP OF THE YEAR* JUST DROPPED IN OUR LAP!

YEAH --- *HOORAY!*

FINALLY, THE NEW EDITION IS DELIVERED THRUOUT THE CITY...

PERHAPS READING THE *PAPER* CAN HELP ME STOP THINKING OF *PETER*...

OH, IT'S A *SPECIAL* EDITION!

WHY, IT'S A PICTURE OF -- OF... OH, *NO!*

DAD -- COMMITTING A *CRIME!*

-- AND, TO MAKE IT *WORSE* --

DAILY BUGLE

EX-POLICE OFFICIAL ROBS P.D. FILES!

RETIRED CAPTAIN GEORGE STACY PHOTOGRAPHED IN ACT OF STEALING TOP SECRET DATA!

EXCLUSIVE PHOTO BY PETER PARKER

IT WAS *PETER* WHO TOOK THE PICTURE!

NEXT: THE **WEB** TIGHTENS!

I HAD TO GIVE THAT PHOTO TO THE *DAILY BUGLE*...

PROVING THAT *CAPT. STACY* TRIED TO STEAL THE POLICE DEPARTMENT *RECORDS!*

IT'S THE ONLY POSSIBLE WAY TO *SAVE* HIM!

GWEN'S DAD DIDN'T KNOW WHAT HE WAS DOING!

THE *KINGPIN* SOMEHOW MANAGED TO PUT HIM UNDER HIS *INFLUENCE!*

...AND THE ONLY WAY TO *SMASH* THE WHOLE SCHEME...

BUT NOW.. WHAT HAPPENS *NEXT?*

...IS TO *EXPOSE* IT... NO MATTER *WHAT!*

BUT I CAN'T TELL *GWEN* WHAT I KNOW...WITHOUT TELLING HER *HOW* I LEARNED IT!

...WITHOUT GIVING MYSELF AWAY... AS *SPIDER-MAN!*

WELL, SINCE PETE ASKED...LET'S *FIND OUT*...

UNAWARE THAT HER FATHER IS *STILL* AFFECTED BY THE *BRAINWASHING* HE SUFFERED UNDER THE *KINGPIN'S* STRANGE MACHINE...

GORGEOUS *GWEN STACY* TEARFULLY, UNCOMPREHENDINGLY STARES AT THE INCRIMINATING FRONT-PAGE NEWS PHOTO, UNTIL...

WHAT *IS* IT, GWEN? WHAT HAVE YOU *GOT* THERE?

LET ME *SEE* THAT...!

DAD! THIS *PICTURE*...OF *YOU*...BREAKING INTO THE *POLICE FILES* AT HEADQUARTERS..

HOW..? HOW CAN IT *BE??*

I *HAD* TO DO IT! IT *HAD* TO BE DONE!

THEN... IT'S *TRUE!*

I CAN'T EVEN HOPE ...CAN'T EVEN *PRAY*...THAT IT WAS A *MISTAKE!*

IF ONLY I COULD *REMEMBER*...WHY IT WAS...SO *IMPORTANT!*

THINGS IN MY BRAIN..THEY'RE ALL SO *BLURRED*...SO *HAZY!*

DAD! I SHOULD HAVE *GUESSED SOONER*..

YOU'RE *ILL!*

SOMETHING'S *HAPPENED* TO YOU! YOU DON'T KNOW WHAT YOU'RE *DOING!*

BUT... I MUST FOLLOW *ORDERS!* I CANNOT..DISOBEY!

ORDERS? *WHOSE* ORDERS? WHO'S *BEHIND* ALL THIS?

I DON'T KNOW... CAN'T *REMEMBER!* EVERYTHING IS... ONE BIG, CLOUDED *BLUR!*

WHO'S CHANGED YOU--- *DONE* THIS HORRIBLE THING TO YOU?

I MUST GO! I HAVE TO *HIDE..!*

NO! YOU *CAN'T!* YOU CAN'T BECOME... A *FUGITIVE!*

I *MUST!* BECAUSE HE WANTS IT THAT WAY!

PLEASE... DON'T TRY TO *STOP* ME!

I *DARE* NOT LEAVE HIM ALONE!...NOT *NOW!*

WHATEVER HAPPENS...I'LL BE *WITH* YOU, DAD!

I'LL LOOK AFTER YOU--UNTIL YOU CAN *REMEMBER!*

BUT, GWEN---I DON'T WANT *YOU* TO BECOME ...*INVOLVED!*

I'M YOUR *DAUGHTER!* IF THERE'S *DANGER* AHEAD..WE'LL FACE IT *TOGETHER!*

AND, AS THE DOOR SOFTLY CLOSES BEHIND THEM...

BRINNNNG BRINNNNG BRINNNG BRINNG

NO ANSWER! WHERE CAN THEY *BE?*

I WAS A *FOOL!* I NEVER SHOULD HAVE *LEFT* THEM.. NO MATTER *HOW* GWEN LOATHED ME!

WHAT IF THE *KINGPIN* TRIES TO *SILENCE* STACY...FOR *GOOD?*

I'VE GOT TO GET *BACK* TO THEM... WHILE THERE'S STILL *TIME!*

THAT IS... IF IT'S NOT ALREADY *TOO LATE!*

BUT I DON'T DARE *THINK* OF THAT!

ESPECIALLY WHEN I KNOW I *LEFT* HIM THERE ALONE...WITH *GWEN!*

I SHOULDN'T BE CUTTING CLASSES NOW...

BUT THAT'S THE *LEAST* OF IT AT A TIME LIKE *THIS!*

ALL I WANT.. IS TO FIND THEM BOTH *SAFE!*

BUT, SECONDS LATER, AS SPIDEY FINALLY REACHES HIS GOAL...

SOME OF THE *KINGPIN'S* MUSCLE MEN...

THEY JUST FORC[E] STACY'S *FRON*[T] DOOR OPEN[.]

I'M NOT A MINUTE TOO SOON!

HOLD IT, PUNKS!

THAT'S AS *FAR* AS YOU GO!

GRAB YOUR *HARDWARE!* IT'S *SPIDER-MAN!!*

OKAY, CHARLIE---WE'VE GOTTA STOP *SOME-TIME!*

SPINNG!

HTANNG

WE DON'T WANNA MAKE A *FEDERAL CASE* OUT OF THIS!

HEY, HOLD IT!

I DIDN'T MEAN YOU WERE OFF THE *HOOK* YET!

WANT SOME QUESTIONS ANSWERED... AND GUESS *WHO'S* GONNA ANSWER THEM FOR ME!

BUT, A FEW SECONDS LATER...

IT'S *NO USE!*

THE *KINGPIN* DIDN'T TAKE ANY *CHANCES!*

YOU'VE BEEN BRAINWASHED, TOO! YOU'RE *NO GOOD* TO ME!

BUT NOW LET'S TURN OUR ATTENTION TO SOMEONE WHOM *NOBODY* COULD EVER SAY THAT ABOUT...

HI, HARRY-O! WHAT'S GROOVIN', GOOD GUY?

MARY JANE! BUT, WHY SO *CHEERFUL?*

WHY *NOT*, DAD? THERE ARE MORE THAN *TWO BILLION* PEOPLE ALIVE TODAY!

...AND *HALF* OF THEM ARE... MMMMALES!

MY MEMORY OF THAT EVENT IS ALMOST A TOTAL *BLUR!*

I KNOW THERE WAS A *FIRE* WHICH STARTED DURING *SPIDER-MAN'S* BATTLE WITH THE GOBLIN!

...THE BATTLE IN WHICH THE *GREEN GOBLIN* LOST HIS LIFE!

WHEN I AWOKE IN THE *HOSPITAL* I WAS TOLD THAT THE MASKED WEBSLINGER CREDITED *ME* WITH HELPING HIM TO BEAT THE *GOBLIN*...

* DON'T TAKE *OUR* WORD FOR IT...CHECK IT OUT IN *SPIDEY #40!* ...SQUARE-DEAL STAN.

BUT, I CAN'T *REMEMBER!* I CAN'T REMEMBER *ANY* OF IT!

DON'T WORRY, DAD! IT'LL COME *BACK* TO YOU SOME DAY... I'M *SURE* IT WILL!*

MEANWHILE, BACK AT PETEY'S PAD...

THAT SHOULD DO IT!

IF HE TRIES TO STOP ME WITH *GAS* AGAIN...

---THE *KINGPIN* WILL BE IN FOR A LITTLE *SURPRISE!*

THIS IS ONE TIME OL' SPID ISN'T TAKIN ANY *CHANCE.*

* BUT, LET'S HOPE THE UNSUSPECTING HARRY IS *WRONG!* THINK HOW *COMPLI-CATED* THINGS WOULD BECOME IF NORMAN OSBORN EVER REMEMBERED THAT IT WAS *HE* HIMSELF WHO HAD BEEN--THE *GOBLIN!*   ...SCARE-MONGER STAN.

MY MAKESHIFT LITTLE *GAS MASK* SHOULD FILTER OUT JUST ENOUGH *FUMES* TO DO THE TRICK!

AND EVEN IF I *WON'T* NEED IT, IT'S LIGHT ENOUGH NOT TO *BOTHER* ME!

...IF I DON'T HAVE TO *WEAR* IT TOO LONG!

AND NOW, MY *FIRST* JOB IS TO FIND *GWEN* AND HER DAD!

...BEFORE THE *KINGPIN* DOES!

HEAVENLY Hair Spray

WILBERFORCE, LOOK! THERE IS OUR DREAM COME TRUE!

WH--WHAT IS IT, MR. BLISS?

THE WINDOW! LOOK OUT THE WINDOW! SHE'S MADE TO ORDER! SHE'S ABSOLUTELY PERFECT!

WE'VE BEEN SEARCHING FOR SOMEONE WHO COULD BE A TRADEMARK FOR OUR HEAVENLY HAIR SPRAY...

AND THERE SHE IS!

THINK OF THE ADVERTISING CAMPAIGN WE COULD BUILD AROUND HER..!

"THE LOVELY LADY WITH THE LIVING LOCKS USES HEAVENLY HAIR SPRAY!"

OH...I COULD CRY!

T, MR. ISS... AT IF E SAYS O?

NOBODY SAYS NO TO MONTGOMERY G. BLISS! NOW DON'T JUST STAND THERE, MAN...

SHE'S STARTING TO LAND...ON THE STREET BELOW US!

GO GET HER!

THIS IS A LIKELY SPOT!

THERE ARE ENOUGH AVERAGE PEOPLE IN THE STREET TO ENABLE ME TO LEARN WHAT I MUST KNOW!

I SHALL DESCEND AMONG THEM ...AND SEE HOW THEY RECEIVE ME!

4.

IT IS *INCREDIBLE!* THEY PANIC LIKE *CATTLE!*

WHY DO HUMANS ALWAYS *FEAR* THAT WHICH THEY DO NOT FULLY *UNDERSTAND?*

DIRECTLY *BEFORE* ME...A CHILD'S GOVERNESS HAS *FAINTED*...

...AND THE CONFUSED YOUNGSTER RUNS BLINDLY INTO THE *CROWD*...WHERE HE MAY BE *TRAMPLED!*

LOOK! THE LONG-HAIRED CREATURE *CAUGHT* THAT BOY...

BEFORE HE COULD BE *INJURED!*

THERE'S NO NEED TO *RUN!* SHE MEANS US NO *HARM!*

THEIR FLIGHT HAS *STOPPED!*

THEY SEEM TO GROW MORE *TRUSTFUL!*

I AM *MEDUSA!*

I HAVE COME TO YOUR LAND IN *PEACE!*

THE CHILD IS *SAFE* NOW!

I MERELY *DESIRE* TO WALK *AMONG* YOU...AS AN *EQUAL!*

THERE NO LA AGAIN THA LAD

RAS I ...N TELL, ...U HAVEN'T ...ROKEN A ...NGLE ...AW!

AND IF HAVING *LONG HAIR* WAS A CRIME... WE'D HAVE TO HAUL AWAY HALF THE *KIDS* IN TOWN!

PERHAPS I HAVE JUDGED MANKIND TOO *HASTILY!*

PERHAPS IT IS TIME FOR THE *INHUMANS* TO COME OUT OF HIDING!

BUT I MUST LEARN *MORE!* I MUST BE *SURE!*

SHE MAKES RAQUEL WELCH LOOK LIKE A *BOY!*

IF *SHE'S* NOT HUMAN, I'M *RESIGNING!*

FROM *WHAT?*

...THE *HUMAN RACE!*

...PARDON ME, MADAM--- ...WISH TO MAKE ...U AN *OFFER!*

AN *OFFER?!!!* THEN *SPEAK!*

MY *EMPLOYER* WOULD LIKE YOU TO BE THE *HEAVENLY HAIR SPRAY GIRL!* WE'RE PREPARED TO PAY YOU AS MUCH AS---

MONEY DOES NOT INTEREST *MEDUSA!*

BUT YOUR *OFFER* DOES!

WORKING FOR HUMANS WOULD GIVE ME A RARE OPPORTUNITY TO *STUDY* THEM!

...EANWHILE, A HEAVY-HEARTED YOUTH TRUDGES ...RVOUSLY TOWARDS A QUIET, WELL-KEPT GARDEN ...ARTMENT...

...EN GWEN SAW ...I HIT HER FATHER--- ...THEN, WHEN I ...LD THAT *PICTURE* ...HIM TO THE BUGLE...

...E COULDN'T ...W I WAS ...NG IT...FOR ...WN *GOOD!**

* BUT THOSE OF US WHO READ THE LAST ISH---*WE* KNOW, DON'T WE ? ...SMUG STAN.

PETER! I...*WOULDN'T* HAVE THOUGHT...YOU'D HAVE THE *NERVE---* TO COME HERE!

GWEN..YOU'VE GOT TO LET ME *EXPLAIN!*

I DON'T HAVE TO DO... *ANYTHING!*

6

WHEN DAD AND I...NEEDED A *FRIEND*...

WHEN NEITHER OF US KNEW WHERE TO *TURN*...

THAT WAS WHEN... *YOU* BETRAYED US!

BUT, IT *WASN'T* WHAT YOU THOUGHT! YOU'VE GOT TO *LISTEN* TO ME...!

OH, PETER... I *WANT* TO BELIEVE YOU!

I'LL LISTEN! BUT--LISTEN TO *WHAT?*

I... DON'T *KNOW!*

I DON'T KNOW... HOW... TO EX-*PLAIN!*

SHE *DID* WANT TO BELIEVE ME... I *KNOW* IT!

SHE'S *HEART-BROKEN* ABOUT WHAT HAPPENED... AS *I* AM!

BUT, THERE'S *NO WAY* TO EXPLAIN...WITHOUT REVEALING...THAT I'M REALLY *SPIDER-MAN!*

...AND *THAT*... I *DARE NOT* DO!

WHO WAS THAT, DEAR?

IT WAS *PETER PARKER*, DAD! I SENT HIM *AWAY!*

YOU *DID?* WHAT ON EARTH *FOR?*

I THOUGHT... YOU FELT HE WAS *THE BOY!*

I DID, DAD... I *DID!*

BUT, YOU DON'T *REMEMBER* WHAT HAPPENED... WHILE YOU WERE UNDER THE *BRAINWASHER'S* INFLUENCE!

AND I DON'T THINK...I CAN BEAR TO *TALK* ABOUT IT NOW!

IT'S ALL SO *DIM* AND *CLOUDED* TO ME...

...LIKE A SLOWLY FADING *NIGHTMAR*

BUT, FOR THOSE OF YOU WHO HATE TO SEE A LOVELY LADY *CRY*, WE'LL CHANGE OUR SCENE ONCE MOR AS WE ENTER THE PALATIAL OFFICE OF *MONTGOMERY G. BLISS*...

HERE SHE *IS*, M.B.! *MADAME MEDUSA!*

IS IT *YOU* WHO OFFER ME *EMPLOYMENT?*

COME IN, MY DEAR... COME *IN!*

YOU ARE JUST WHAT WE'VE BEEN *LOOKING* FOR!

YOU'LL HELP *DOUBLE* OU HAIR SPRA' SALES II NO TIME

EVERYTHING IS *SET!* I HAVE THE *CONTRACTS* ALL READY!

There is no NEED for contracts! MEDUSA'S WORD is her BOND!

CERTAINLY, MY DEAR... CERTAINLY! ANYTHING YOU SAY! I'LL CALL OUR ADVERTISING AGENCY IMMEDIATELY!

THEY'LL START DESIGNING THE ADS AT ONCE!

BEFORE LONG, I SHALL BE ABLE TO BRING A MOST COMPLETE REPORT BACK TO MY WAITING PEOPLE!

AND, SPEAKING OF PEOPLE, HERE'S ONE OF OUR FAVORITES...THE BLUSTERING, BOMBASTIC BUREAUCRATIC BOSS OF THE DAILY BUGLE...LOVABLE OLD J. JONAH JAMESON, SPENDING A RELAXING FEW MINUTES AT HIS CLUB...

WHAT?!! SOME FEMALE REFUGEE FROM A FREAK SHOW NAMED MUDUSA...WITH LIVING HAIR YET...IS IN TOWN?!!

...AND NOT ONE BUGLE PHOTOGRAPHER WAS ON HAND TO SNAP HER PICTURE?!!

HEADS WILL ROLL WHEN I GET BACK, BLAST IT!

IDIOTIC, INSECT-BRAINED INCOMPETENTS... ALL OF THEM!

I TELL YOU, OSBORN, THE WORKING MAN ISN'T WORTH A ROW OF BEANS TODAY!

NO MATTER HOW GOOD TO THEM YOU ARE.. IT DOESN'T PAY!

NOW TAKE THAT LAZY, GOOD-FOR-NOTHING PARKER, FOR EXAMPLE...!

OSBORN!! YOU'RE NOT LISTENING TO ME!

WHY DON'T YOU GIVE YOUR LARYNX A REST, JONAH?

I'VE GOT TROUBLES OF MY OWN, RIGHT NOW!

≡HRRUMMPH!≡ I WAS JUST MAKING CONVERSATION, OSBORN!

WELL, MAKE IT SOMEWHERE ELSE! YOU'RE GIVING ME A HEADACHE!

8

I'VE GOT TO GO HOME!

I CAN'T BEAR ANY MORE!

THE IMAGES KEEP GETTING STRANGER... MORE REALISTIC... MORE STRANGELY FRIGHTENING!

IT'S ALWAYS THE SAME... ALWAYS THE GREEN GOBLIN... AND A HELPLESS, UNMASKED SPIDER-MAN!

BUT I CAN NEVER REALLY SEE HIS FACE... ALTHOUGH IT SEEMS TO GET CLEARER EVERY TIME!

I MUST BE... GOING MAD!

BUT, IF I AM... WHAT ABOUT MY SON ...HARRY?

THERE'S NO ONE ELSE... TO LOOK AFTER HIM!

AND, IN CASE YOU'RE WORRIED ABOUT PETER'S ROOMMATE, TOO---LET'S LOOK IN ON HAPLESS HARRY OSBORN...

IT ISN'T FAIR! I STUDY AND STUDY---AND JUST GET BY!

WHILE EVERYTHING SEEMS TO COME SO EASY TO PETE!

HE WAS JUST BORN LUCKY!

HI, HARR--- I DIDN'T THINK YOU'D STILL BE UP!

HAVING TROUBLE WITH YOUR COURSES?

NO---I'M JUST TRYING TO LEARN TO LIVE WITHOUT SLEEP!

SORRY, PETE... DIDN'T MEAN TO SNAP AT YOU LIKE THAT!

HOW'S IT GOING? HAVE A GOOD TIME WITH GWEN TONIGHT?

GWEN? THAT LITTLE LADY CAN'T SEE ME FOR DUST!

ARE YOU KIDDING? SHE WAS BATTY ABOUT YOU! WHAT HAPPENED?

AW, IT'S A LONG STORY..!

NO SENSE BORING THE TWO OF US WITH MY HANG-UPS!

ANYWAY, THERE'S NOTHING ELSE LEFT TO HAPPEN!

BUT ALAS, PETEY DOESN'T SUSPECT HOW WOEFULLY WRONG HE IS! FOR, AT A MIDTOWN PHOTO STUDIO---

LOOK OUT! SHE'S A TIGRESS!

NO! SHE'S PERFECT!

THAT SAVAGE EXCITEMENT IS JUST WHAT WE WANT!

SHE'LL BE A SENSATION!

10

However, as the hours of *modeling* crawl by...

I grow *bored* at having my hair *arrange itself* in different styles for your amusement!

But, you *must* do it! We're not playing *games!* This is an *ad* campaign!

Heavenly hair spray will make you *famous!*

KR-K!

Fame? What does *Medusa* care for *fame? None may* tell a daughter of *Attilan* what she must d—

Wait! *Stop* ...that equip- ment cost *thousands.* ...*Don't.*

Mr. Bliss... what have we gotten our- selves *into?*

Shut up, Wilberforce!

You're just *overwrought,* my dear! Why not take the rest of the day *off?*

We'll tidy things up here while you're gone!

Medusa shall not return! There is *nothing more* for me to *learn,* here!

She's gone... at last! At least we took *some* pictures of her that we can use!

That's *not enough,* do you hear?

Montgomery G. Bliss will not be *frustrated* this way! I planned to get a *million dollars worth* of *publicity* out of that female... and we'll do it *yet!!*

Nobody walks out on a *Heavenly Hair Spray* campaign! I've got to think of some- thing *clever* ...something *big,* before she's gone *forever!*

...UT, MR. BLISS...WE CAN'T FORCE ANYBODY TO WORK FOR US! AND LEAST OF ALL... HER!

QUIET, YOU INCONSEQUENTIAL INCOMPETENT!

THERE'S THE ANSWER TO MY PRAYERS RIGHT NOW!

IF I CAN JUST ATTRACT HIS ATTENTION!

MIGHT AS WELL HEAD BACK TO THE APARTMENT NOW!

EVERY CRIMINAL IN TOWN MUST BE HOME WATCHING THE LATE SHOW!

QUICK! MESS UP THE STUDIO EVEN MORE...

WHILE I GET TO THE WINDOW AND SHOUT...!

Heavenly Hair Spray

HELP! HELP!

HELP US, SOME-BODY!

HURRY!!

HELP!

WHOOPS! HOLD IT, SPIDEY! YOU MAY HAVE HIT THE JACKPOT YET!

Heavenly Hair Spray

HEY! WHAT HAPPENED HERE?

LOOKS LIKE A CYCLONE JUST HIT THE PLACE!

IT WAS WORSE THAN THAT!! IT WAS MEDUSA!!

SHE MUST BE MAD! SHE SAID THIS IS JUST A SAMPLE... OF WHAT SHE'LL DO TO THE CITY!

SHE'S MUST BE CAUGHT... STOPPED!

YOU CAN DO IT, SPIDER-MAN!

12

BUT...I DON'T GET IT! DID SHE ROB YOU?

NO! ALL SHE WANTED TO DO WAS WRECK THE PLACE! DON'T WASTE TIME TALKING! NO TELLING WHO SHE'S ATTACKING NOW!

BUT WHY DID SHE DO IT? WHAT'S SHE AFTER?

WHY ASK ME?? I'M NOT HER HEAD-SHRINKER!

JUST GO GET HER!

IT STILL DOESN'T MAKE SENSE TO ME!

HURRY! SHE CAN'T HAVE GONE FAR!

HE'S RIGHT ABOUT ONE THING...

IF SHE IS DANGEROUS, I'VE GOT TO STOP HER FIRST...AND ASK QUESTIONS LATER!

IT WORKED! HE'S GOING AFTER HER!

I'M A GENIUS, WILBERFORCE!

NOW MOVE! CALL OUR ENTIRE PUBLICITY DEPARTMENT!

I WANT EVERY CAMERA-MAN WE CAN GET UP ON THE ROOFTOPS!

HISTORY WILL RECORD THIS AS HAIR SPRAY'S FINEST HOUR!

AND, EVEN AS MONTGOMERY G. BLISS CHORTLES IN TOP-LEVEL, MADISON-AVENUE-TYPE GLEE...

THOUGH THE HUMANS ARE NOT AS HOSTILE AS WE MAY HAVE FEARED...

THEIR INTELLIGENCE LEAVES MUCH TO BE DISIRED!

I'M IN LUCK! THERE SHE IS NOW!

SOMEHOW, YOU DON'T STRIKE ME AS A GAL WHO'D TOY WITH THE *TRUTH!*

BUT, IF *YOU'RE* ON THE LEVEL... THAT MAKES *BLISS* A LIAR!

WHAT HAS *HE* TO DO WITH THIS?

I HAVE NOT *SEEN* HIM SINCE I *REFUSED* TO ADVERTISE HIS HAIR SPRAY PRODUCT!

WAIT A MINUTE! NOW I *GET* IT!

HE WANTED YOU AS A LIVING *TESTIMONIAL* TO HIS HAIR GOO! BUT YOU *CUT OUT!*

THEN, HE TRIED TO TRICK US INTO *BATTLING*... HOPING HE COULD *CASH IN* ON THE *PUBLICITY!*

LADY, WE'VE *BOTH* BEEN HAD!

NOBODY MAY TAKE ADVANTAGE OF *MEDUSA!*

I SHALL *RETURN* TO HIM, AND...

WHOA, RUSTY. NOT SO FAST!

YOU'RE IN THE CLEAR NOW... WHY NOT *STAY* THAT WAY?

I'LL SEE THAT HE GETS WHAT'S *COMING* TO HIM!

I NO LONGER KNOW *WHOM* TO TRUST--- OR *WHAT* TO BELIEVE!

WITHOUT FURTHER ADO, LET ME *LEAVE* YOUR RACE OF *MADMEN*...!

BRO-*THER!* I'D HATE TO THINK WHAT WOULD HAVE *HAPPENED*...

...IF I HADN'T BEEN LUCKY ENOUGH TO *CALM* HER DOWN!

BUT, SPEAKING OF THINGS *HAPPENING*, LET'S VISIT *MONTGOMERY G. BLISS* ONCE MORE... JUST A SHORT TIME LATER...

THE PICTURES OF THEIR *BATTLE* MADE ALL THE FRONT PAGES...

AND THE *TV NEWS* PROGRAMS, EH?

GOOD! GOOD!

MR. BLISS! MR. BLISS!

DISASTE HAS STRUCK.

HOLD IT... MY IDIOT *ASSISTANT* JUST BARGED IN!

NO! YOUR EYES DO **NOT** DECEIVE YOU! THIS IS INDEED THE **ORIGINAL** VULTURE... THE MYSTERIOUS WINGED MENACE WHO **DIED** WHILE IN PRISON, IN ISSUE #48... OR, SO WE **THOUGHT..!**

I HAVE REMAINED IN HIDING **LONG** ENOUGH!

IT'S TIME ONCE MORE FOR THE **REAL** VULTURE TO **FLY** AGAIN!

NONE BUT **I** HAVE THE SKILL, AND THE CUNNING, AND THE **POWER** TO CARRY OUT MY CAREFULLY-LAID **PLAN..!**

NO ONE CAN SUCCESSFULLY DUPLICATE MY **FEATS.**

WHEN HE THOUGHT ME **DEAD,** MY EX-CELLMATE, **BLACKIE DRAGO,** TRIED TO TAKE MY PLACE!

BUT HE WAS EASILY **DEFEATED** BY THAT SNIVELLING, SO-CALLED SUPERHERO... **SPIDER-MAN!**

AND NOW, DRAGO IS IN **PRISON...** WHILE SPIDER-MAN HAS CROSSED THE **VULTURE** OFF HIS LIST!

...WHICH WILL PROVE TO BE... THE WEB-SLINGER'S **BIGGEST MISTAKE!**

AND, SPEAKING OF OUR FRIENDLY NEIGHBORHOOD **SPIDER-MAN...**

I DON'T MIND A LITTLE **RAIN...**

BUT IT'S STARTING TO COME DOWN IN **BUCKETS!**

AND THAT MEANS **BIG TROUBLE** FOR ME!

3

THEN, A FEW SOGGY, RAIN-DRENCHED MOMENTS LATER...

C'MON, SPIDEY... YOU CAN'T STAY HERE ALL *NIGHT!*

LET'S GET A *MOVE* ON, SON!

OH, *BROTHER!* MY SHOULDER FEELS LIKE IT WAS MASSAGED BY THE *HULK!*

THE *PAIN* MUST BE MAKING ME *DELIRIOUS!*

THOUGHT I SAW... THE *VULTURE...* FLYING BY!

HAVE TO IGNORE THE *ACHE...* ...AND GET ON MY *FEET!*

GOOD THING THAT *COP* DIDN'T SEE ME!

I WOULDN'T HAVE A *CHANCE* TO GET AWAY FROM HIM NOW!

WELERY

KEEP *WALKING,* MISTER... I CAN'T *STICK* HERE MUCH LONGER!

MADE IT! BUT, IF THAT *WAS* THE VULTURE I SAW--

NO! IT CAN'T BE! THE ORIGINAL VULTURE IS *DEAD!* AND HIS WOULD-BE *IMITATOR* SAFELY BEHIND BARS!

I SURE WOULDN'T WANNA TACKLE *EITHER* OF THEM---*NOW!*

ACCORDING TO THE OLD PROVERB, *IGNORANCE IS BLISS!* BUT, IN THIS PARTICULAR CASE, WHO KNOWS...?

AHH, *THERE'S* WHAT I'M LOOKING FOR---DOWN BELOW!

SEE THAT IT'S PAST CLOSING TIME!

BUT THAT WON'T AFFECT ME!

MUSEUM

HOURS 9:00 A.M. TO 5:00 P.M. WEEKDAYS

I'M REAL FLATTERED THAT THEY DEEMED MY WINGS, TAKEN FROM BLACKIE DRAGO, TO BE WORTHY OF DISPLAY IN A MUSEUM!

The WINGS of the NOTORIOUS VULTURE

BUT THEY FORGOT TO ASK FOR MY PERMISSION!

WHO'S THERE? YOU CAN'T... UNHH!!

THE VULTURE CAN DO ANYTHING!

AND NO ONE BUT ME HAS THE RIGHT TO THESE WINGS... SINCE I CREATED THEM!

SOON, THE NEWS WILL BE OUT---

THE VULTURE LIVES AGAIN!

BUT, BY THEN IT WILL BE... TOO LATE!

5

As a matter of fact, our high-flying VILLAIN would probably feel more CONFIDENT than ever if he could see his most dedicated ARCH-ENEMY at this particular moment--!

HOME... AT LAST! FOR A WHILE THERE... I WAS BEGINNING TO FEAR...I WOULDN'T MAKE IT!

LUCKY IT'S SO LATE... HARRY IS CERTAIN TO BE ASLEEP!

I FEEL TOO BEAT EVEN TO TAKE OFF MY COSTUME!

BUT, I LOCKED THE DOOR---!

SO I GUESS I' SAFE ENOUG TO HIT THE SACK IN MY SPIDEY DUDS!

IF ONLY M ARM WOUL STOP THROBBING

WOULDN'T YOU KNOW IT? TIRED AS I AM...I CAN'T FALL ASLEEP!

CAN'T STOP THINK-ING OF GWEN...OF THE MESS I MADE OF THINGS...BETWEEN THE TWO OF US!

PETER! HOW COULD YOU?!!

WHEN WE NEEDED YOU MOST...YOU TURNED AGAINST US!*

I'LL NEVER BE ABL TO EXPLAIN THIS TO GWEN...WITHOUT REVEALING MY SECRET IDENTITY!

AND THAT'S THE ONE THING ---I CAN'T EVER DO!

*IT ALL HAPPENED JUST A FEW ISSUES AGO, AS IF YOU DIDN'T KNOW! ---SICK-OF-SUMMARIZING STAN.

FINALLY, AFTER A FITFUL, PAIN-WRACKED EVENING, PETER PARKER REACHES THE CAMPUS OF E.S.U.!

A LOTTA GOOD MY SPIDEY STRENGTH IS DOING ME!

--THE PAIN IS AS BAD AS BEFORE!

SAY! THERE'S PETE!

PLEASE, HARRY...DON'T CALL TO HIM!

I'D PREFER NOT TO SEE HIM!

LOOK, GWEN...I DON'T GET IT! EVERYONE FIGURE YOU AND MY GLOOMY-ROOMIE WERE A REAL ITEM AND NOW...

LET'S JUST SAY THEY ALL FIGURED WRONG, SHALL WE?

IF ONLY HARRY WOULD LAY OFF!

HE'S NOT DOING ME ANY GOOD!

OKAY, GWEN-- HAVE IT YOUR WAY!

SEE YOU IN CLASS, PETE!

BECAUSE I AM THE *REAL* VULTURE... NOT A MERE, UNTALENTED *IMITATOR*!

HEY! HOW CAN YOU... GET UP SO *HIGH*... SO *FAST*?

FOLLOW ME AS BEST YOU *CAN*!

I'LL EXPLAIN MY *PURPOSE* ONCE WE'RE IN THE *CLEAR*!

...HILE, AT THAT VERY MOMENT...

...'S *NO USE*! MY *SHOULDER'S* ...ORTURING ME... AND I CAN'T ...T *GWEN* OUT OF MY MIND!

...ESS WHAT, ...R. PARKER..?

MIGHT AS WELL NOT EVEN *TRY* TO STUDY TONIGHT!

WE GOT A LETTER FROM *FLASH*!

READ IT TO ME, HARR!

HE DOESN'T SPELL IT OUT, BUT READING BETWEEN THE LINES, I'D SAY HE'S HEADING FOR *VIET NAM*!

THE ARMY'S *MATURED* HIM, PETE... HE DOESN'T SOUND LIKE THE SAME OLD *WISE-GUY*!

IT MUST BE A *FORGERY*!

HE EVEN SENDS *YOU* HIS BEST REGARDS!

YOU TWO'LL PROBABLY END UP *BEST FRIENDS* SOMEDAY!

YEAH... ESPECIALLY SINCE I'M OUT OF THE RUNNING WITH *GWEN*!

Y'KNOW, I'VE BEEN *THINKING*, HARRY.. I CAN'T KEEP SHARING THIS PAD WITH YOU... AND LETTING *YOU* FOOT ALL THE *RENT*!

HOW COME? I'M NOT COMPLAIN-ING!

IT JUST DOESN'T SEEM *RIGHT*!

9.

BUT IT'S NOT COSTING *ME* ANYTHING, EITHER! YOU KNOW MY *DAD* PAYS THE BILLS!

AND EVEN THOUGH YOU'RE ALWAYS IN A *JAM*, YOU'RE BETTER THAN *NO* COMPANY AT ALL! ANYWAY, I ALWAYS MANAGE TO BEAT YOU TO THE *SHOWER!* THAT'S WORTH *SOMETHING!*

BUT, I *STILL* THINK...

FORGET IT, SON... JUST REMEMBER ME IN YOUR *WILL!*

MY *WILL!* IF HE ONLY *KNEW* HOW CLOSE I'VE BEEN TO *DEATH* THESE PAST FEW YEARS!

IF ONLY THERE WERE *SOME-ONE* I COULD REALLY *CON-FIDE* IN --- SOMEONE TO *SHARE* MY SECRET!

HARRY'S TOO *YOUNG*...TOO *OUT-GOING!* HOW CAN I BURDEN *HIM* WITH SUCH A RESPONSI-BILITY?

NO! I DON'T DARE TELL *ANYONE!* IF IT EVER LEAKED OUT...IF AUNT *MAY* EVER SUSPECTED... THE SHOCK WOULD *KILL* HER!

I WONDER IF *GWEN* IS HOME YET? WHAT HARM CAN THERE *BE* IN ANOTHER *TRY?*

SORRY, PETER...SHE'S *OUT* TONIGHT...ON A *DATE*, I SUPPOSE! BUT I'M *GLAD* YOU CALLED, SON! I'VE BEEN *WANT-ING* TO SPEAK TO YOU!

I WONDER IF YOU'D HAVE *LUNCH* WITH ME TOMORROW?

YOU *WILL? GOOD!* SEE YOU THEN!

CAPTAIN STACY HAS MADE A *HOBBY* OF STUDYING *SPIDER-MAN!*

HAS HE FINALLY... *LEARNED* SOME-THING??

WHY WOULD HE ASK ME TO *LUNCH*, UNLESS...?

KNOCK! KNOCK!

UH OH! WHO CAN *THAT* BE AT THIS HOUR?

PARKER! LET ME *IN!* I WANT TO SEE *HARRY!*

MR. *OSBORN!* IS...ANYTHING *WRONG*, SIR?

OF *COURSE* NOT! CAN'T I VISIT MY OWN *SON*, IF I WANT TO?

WHY DOES MY MIND RETURN TO THE *GREEN GOBLIN* WHENEVER I SEE *PARKER?*

I'VE NEVER SEEN HIM SO *DISTRAUGHT!* HE HARDLY LOOKS LIKE THE *SAME* MAN!

LET ME *IN! I'M* NOT ACCUSTOMED TO *WAITING!*

YOU MUSTA *NEEDED* ME REAL BAD TO HELP ME BREAK *OUT* LIKE YA DID!

SO THAT MAKES *ME* TOP DOG AROUND HERE NOW!

NEEDED YOU? YOU BLOCKHEADED *FOOL,* YOU'VE GOT IT ALL *WRONG!*

AWRIGHT... NEVER MIND *THAT...*

I WANNA KNOW HOW COME YOU'RE STILL *ALIVE!*

THINK *BACK,* BLACKIE! BACK TO THAT DAY IN PRISON WHEN WE THOUGHT I WAS *DYING...* AND I TOLD YOU WHERE I HAD HIDDEN MY *WINGS...!*

I *TRUSTED* YOU... THOUGHT YOU WERE MY *FRIEND!*

"BUT THEN... ONCE YOU KNEW MY *SECRET*... I SAW YOU FOR WHAT YOU REALLY *WERE!* I REALIZED HOW YOU HAD *DUPED* ME!"

"IT WAS *THEN* THAT MY *WILL TO LIVE* GREW STRONGER THAN MY ILLNESS! I KNEW I *HAD* TO RECOVER... I *HAD* TO HAVE... MY *REVENGE!*"

"*YOU* WERE SO BUSY TRYING TO STEAL MY HIDDEN *WINGS* THAT YOU NEVER LEARNED WHAT HAPPENED *NEXT!* YOU NEVER KNEW THAT I MADE MY MOVE DURING THE *CONFUSION* CAUSED BY YOUR OWN *ESCAPE!*"

"IT WASN'T HARD TO START A *FIRE* IN THE HOSPI-SUPPLY ROOM, AND TO *SLIP OUT* IN THE UNIFO OF THE GUARD I HAD OVERPOWERED--!"

15

IT'S...THE *TWO VULTURES*!!

DRAGO MUST HAVE BROKEN OUT OF *JAIL*!

BUT...I THOUGHT... THE ORIGINAL VULTURE WAS... *DEAD*?!!

WELL, MAYBE IF I'M *LUCKY*, THEY'LL POLISH EACH OTHER *OFF*!

I WOULDN'T BE MUCH GOOD AGAINST *ANY-ONE* WITH THIS *SHOULDER* OF MINE!

I MIGHT AS WELL SEE IF *JAMESON* WANTS....UH OH! THERE HE *IS*!

PARKER! IT'S ABOUT *TIME* YOU SHOWED UP!

WE'VE GOT THE *PICTURE SCOOP* OF THE YEAR--- AND ALL MY PHOTOGS ARE *OUT* ON ASSIGNMENTS!

DON'T JUST *STAND* THERE, KID!

WE'VE GOT TO REACH THE *ROOF*---ON THE *DOUBLE*! THAT'S WHERE IT'S *HAPPENING*

I NEVER THOUGHT I'D BE SO *GLAD* TO SEE THAT INSIPID-LOOKING *FACE* OF YOURS!

THANKS A *LOT*!

SKIP THE *SARCASM!* KEEP *MOVING!*

THERE THEY *ARE*... THE TWO *VULTURES*... *FIGHTING* EACH OTHER!

IF YOU DIDN'T BRING YOUR *CAMERA*--- I'LL *ANNIHI-LATE* YOU!

YOU NEVER SHOULD'A COME *BACK*, GRAMPA!

I BROUGHT IT... I BROUGHT IT!

IT W... YOU BIGGE... MISTA...

19.

The Vulture's PREY!
NEXT

the AMAZING SPIDER-MAN

™

APPROVED BY THE COMICS CODE AUTHORITY

MARVEL COMICS GROUP

12¢ IND.

64 SEPT

THE VULTURE'S PREY!

HE *KNOWS* ABOUT MY *ARM!* THAT GIVES HIM THE *ADVANTAGE*-- BUT I MUSTN'T *PANIC!*

I'VE GOT *NEWS* FOR YOU, BALDY-- I COULD POLISH *YOU* OFF WITH MY HANDS TIED *BEHIND* ME!

--EVEN IF *NEITHER* OF US *BELIEVES* IT!

SPOK!

I APPLAUD YOUR *BRAVADO*, SPIDER-MAN! A *PITY* YOU CAN'T BACK IT UP WITH *POWER!*

I PUT *EVERYTHING* INTO THAT KICK-- BUT WHILE HE'S IN *FLIGHT*, HE USES THE *AIR* TO CUSHION THE IMPACT!

STAY WHERE YOU *ARE*, WALL-CRAWLER--

YOU WON'T BE *NEGLECTED* MUCH LONGER!

JUST MY *LUCK*--! HE'S EVEN *FASTER* THAN HE WAS BEFORE!

THEY WERE *LUCKY*-- I ONLY *GRAZED* THEM!

SPIDER-MAN-- *WATCH IT!* HE'S COMING AT YOU *AGAIN!*

WHAT ARE YOU *WARNING* HIM FOR? I'M *ROOTING* FOR THE *VULTURE!*

HAH! NOW THAT MY LEGS ARE *FREE* AGAIN, I'LL USE THEM TO-- --*UHH!*--

BLAST IT!! HOW DID YOU MOVE SO *FAST?*

IF HIS FEET HAD *CONNECTED,* GOING AT THAT SPEED, HE'D HAVE *STOMPED* ME TO-- --UH OH!--

BLAME IT ON *CLEAN LIVING,* FEATHER-BRAIN!

THE IMPACT *LOOSENED* SOM CHUNKS OF THE *BUGLE* SIGN!

THEY'RE *FALLING*-- TOWARDS JAMESON AND ROBBIE!

WE'LL BE *CRUSHED!*

THE VULTURE'S HOLDING BACK NOW--SEARCHING FOR A NEW METHOD OF ATTACK!

BUT JAMESON IS GETTING TO BE A PROBLEM!

YOU CAN'T ESCAPE HIM FOREVER! YOU'VE FINALLY MET SOMEONE WHO CAN ATTACK YOU--OVER AND OVER AGAIN!

YOU'RE FINISHED, SPIDER-MAN--AND YOU KNOW IT!

I WISH YOU WERE AN OFFICIAL, CARD-CARRYING SUPER-VILLAIN--

SO I'D REALLY HAVE AN EXCUSE TO LEAN ON YOU!

THWIP!

HEY! STOP--!

BUT, TILL THEN, THIS'LL HAVE TO DO!

GET ME OUT OF HERE! YOU CAN'T DO THIS TO ME, YOU BUM!

PIPE DOWN, SUGAR-LIPS! THE WEBBING'LL SOON WEAR OFF--I'M SORRY TO SAY!

ROBERTSON'S STARTING TO MOVE! DON'T SEEM TO BE ANY BONES BROKEN!

JJ--LOOK OUT--HAVE TO GET OFF--THE ROOF--!

EASY, FELLA! YOU'LL BE OKAY!

THAT'S MORE THAN I CAN SAY FOR YOU!

IT'S THE VULTURE! HE'S ATTACKING AGAIN!

MEANWHILE, A SWEET LITTLE OLD LADY OPENS THE DOOR OF HER SWEET LITTLE OLD HOUSE IN THE SUBURBS, TO FIND--

OH! IT'S MARY JANE!

IT'S MY GINCHY NEW HAIRDO, MRS. PARKER!

I DIDN'T RECOGNIZE YOU FOR A MOMENT, DEAR!

COME IN, DEAR--

12

I WAS WONDERING IF YOU'VE HEARD FROM PETEY?

NOT LATELY, DEAR! WE WERE JUST TALKING ABOUT HIM!

HE HASN'T CALLED ME FOR DAYS! IT ISN'T LIKE THE DEAR BOY!

I'LL CASE THE CATS AT THE COFFEE BEAN! MAYBE THEY'VE SEEN HIM!

IT'S MY CHANCE TO KNOCK 'EM DEAD WITH THE BRAND NEW ME!

DIG YOU LATER, PEOPLE!

MARY JANE HASN'T SEEN HIM, EITHER!

WHERE CAN PETER BE?

YOU KNOW YOUNG PEOPLE, MAY DEAR! THEY GET SO CARRIED AWAY BY THEIR OWN LITTLE PURSUITS, THAT THEY LOSE ALL TRACK OF TIME!

I'M SURE YOU'LL HEAR FROM HIM SOON!

TSK! HOW COULD THAT NIECE OF MINE HAVE CUT HER HAIR?

AND, WHILE WE'RE ON THE SUBJECT OF YOUNG PEOPLE--

DAD! WHAT A WONDERFUL SURPRISE!

THIS MEANS YOU'RE ALL WELL AGAIN!

NATURALL LOOK AT THE NURS I HAD!

I THOUGH I'D WALL YOU HOME DEAR

I'VE SOME THING TO TELL YOU--

WITH MY RECOVERY, MY MEMORY OF THE KINGPIN RETURNED!

I KNOW NOW THAT PETER DIDN'T REALLY ATTACK ME THAT DAY-- HE WAS TRYING TO HELP ME!*

OH, DAD! IS IT REALLY TRUE? CAN I BELIEVE IT?

DO YOU WANT TO BELIEVE IT, GWEN?

MORE THAN ANYTHING ELSE-- IN THE WORLD!

*AS SUPERBLY SHOWN IN SPIDER-MAN #60! --STURDY STAN.

IT'S TRUE DARLING.

THEN PETER DIDN'T BETRAY US!

HE DIDN'T!

CALLED THE AD--TO TELL HIM I UNDERSTAND--BUT HE WASN'T HOME! NOR WAS HIS ROOMMATE, HARRY!

THEY MIGHT *BOTH* BE WITH HARRY'S *FATHER!* MR. OSBORN HASN'T BEEN *WELL* LATELY!

BUT TELL ME MORE ABOUT *PETER!*

FIRST TELL ME WHAT'S WRONG WITH *NORMAN OSBORN,* DEAR!

I *WONDERED* WHY I HADN'T SEEN HIM AT THE *CLUB* LATELY! IT'S NOTHING *SERIOUS,* I HOPE!

I DON'T *KNOW,* DAD! HARRY THINKS IT MIGHT BE A *NERVOUS BREAKDOWN*--DUE TO OVERWORK! BUT, HE'S BEEN ACTING VERY--*OH! LOOK*--!

SOMETHING *HAPPENING*--ATOP THE *DAILY BUGLE* BUILDING!

LOOK AT THE *CROWD!* IT MUST BE *SERIOUS!*

THERE'S *BETTY BRANT*--AND HER FIANCE, *NED LEEDS!* THEY BOTH WORK FOR THE *BUGLE!*

PERHAPS *THEY'LL* KNOW WHAT'S WRONG!

LOOK! THE *VULTURE'S* DIVING TOWARDS *SPIDER-MAN* AGAIN!

BUT WHO *ELSE* IS UP THERE *WITH* THEM?

MISS BRANT, DO YOU--*OH!* NOW I SEE IT!

THAT'S THE *VULTURE*--SWOOPING TOWARDS THE *BUGLE* ROOF!

BUT *WHY?* WHAT IS HE *AFTER* UP THERE?

IT'S AWFUL! HE'S BEEN BATTLING *SPIDER-MAN!*

MR. JAMESON RAN UP THERE--WITH *JOE ROBERTSON,* AND *PARKER*--TO COVER THE STORY!

PETER? UP THERE *NOW?* OH--NO!

BUT, IF GORGEOUS GWENDOLYNE IS WORRIED ABOUT PETER *NOW*--IMAGINE IF SHE KNEW THE *REAL IDENTITY* OF--*SPIDER-MAN!*

THE VULTURE'S IN HIS *GLORY*--HAMMING IT UP FOR THE *CROWD* BELOW!

BUT THAT DOESN'T MAKE HIM ONE IOTA LESS *DANGEROUS!*

THIS TIME HE'S ZEROING IN --FOR THE *KILL!*

GET *OUT* OF HERE, MAN! RUN FOR *COVER,* BELOW!

NO! I'VE GOT TO SEE IT THRU--NO MATTER WHAT!

14

I'M ALMOST *HELPLESS* HERE--AND HE *KNOWS* IT!

BUT, NO MATTER *WHAT* HAPPENS-- I'M NOT *HANDING* HIM A VICTORY!

ARM OR *NO* ARM--I'VE STILL GOT MY *WITS*-- AND MY *STRENGTH!*

OKAY, *VULCH!* YOU *WANT* ME? COME AND *GET* ME!

THAT'S JUST WHAT I HAD IN *MIND!*

GOTTA *TIME* THIS--TO THE *SPLIT-SECOND*--

YOUR GRIP IS *WEAKER* THAN EVER! WE *BOTH* KNOW YOU HAVEN'T A *CHANCE!*

NOW!

BUT I'LL BE HAPPY TO *PROVE* IT--THE *HARD* WAY!

--UHHH--!

16

HA HA HA HA HA HA HA

I'VE DONE IT! I'VE DONE IT! I'VE BEATEN SPIDER-MAN!

BUT, EVEN AS THE VULTURE GLOATS--

TOO FAR FROM WALL TO GRAB IT--

BUT, IF I CAN FORM A WEB CUSHION IN TIME--

THWIPP!

IT WORKED!

--JUST ENOUGH TO BREAK MY FALL!

SSHOOOM!

WHAT HAPPENED DOWN THERE?

IT LOOKED AS THOUGH --HE LANDED ON SOMETHING!

I'D BETTER MAKE SURE HE'S FINISHED!

HAH! LOOK AT THEM RUN-- PANICKY AT THE MERE SIGHT OF THE DEADLY VULTURE!

NOW THAT I'VE DEFEATED SPIDER-MAN, THERE'S NO ONE WHO'LL DARE OPPOSE ME!

18

HE'S LYING *STILL*-- HASN'T MOVED A *MUSCLE!*

NOW THAT IT'S *OVER,* I CAN'T QUITE *BELIEVE* IT!

BUT, HE HAS A *WEB CUSHION* BENEATH HIM!

WHY DIDN'T IT BREAK HIS *FALL?*

I'VE *NEWS* FOR YOU, BALDY--

IT DID!

YOU'RE STILL *ALIVE!*

YOU WERE PLAYING *POSSUM!*

AND EVEN MORE THAN *THAT*--

I WAS RESTING MY *ARM*--GETTING MY *SECOND WIND*--

WAITING FOR A CHANCE TO GRAB YOUR *BUILT-IN POWER PACK*--

WHICH GIVES YOUR WINGS THE *STRENGTH* THEY NEED!

I *DID* IT! I FELT IT *SNAP* BENEATH MY FINGERS!

HAVE TO GET *AWAY*-- FAST-- WHILE I *CAN!*

HE MANAGED TO *SHORT-CIRCUIT* THE UNIT!

I'M *LOSING* PRECIOUS *ENERGY!*

19

NEXT: THE MAN BENEATH THE MASK!

20

the AMAZING

SPIDER-MAN ™

MARVEL ™ COMICS GROUP

12¢ IND. 65 OCT

ESCAPE IMPOSSIBLE!

Panel 1:

WHERE'S THAT BLASTED AMBULANCE?

WE'VE GOTTA GET HIM TO SAFETY BEFORE THE CROWD GETS HOLD OF HIM!

WADDAYA THINK, CAP'N STACY? MAYBE WE SHOULD TAKE HIS MASK OFF WHILE HE'S JUST LYIN' THERE?

I WOULDN'T DO IT, TOM!

--NOT WITHOUT EXPERT LEGAL ADVICE!

I'LL SEE YOU LATER, DAD--

I'VE GOT TO FIND OUT WHAT HAPPENED TO PETER!

Panel 2:

HE HAD BEEN ON THE ROOF WHEN THE BATTLE STARTED! BUT NO ONE'S SEEN HIM SINCE!

WHAT IF HE WAS INJURED--BY THE VULTURE--OR BY SPIDER-MAN?

HOLD IT! DON'T TAKE OFF THAT CREEP'S MASK WITHOUT ME!

RELAX, JAMESON! WE'RE NOT UNMASKING HIM!

I'VE WAITED TOO LONG FOR THIS GLORIOUS MOMENT!

YOU'RE NOT? WHAT ARE YOU, STACY-- SOME KINDA NUT?

Panel 3:

MY NEWSPAPER'S BEEN CRUSADING TO LEARN WHO THAT WALL-CRAWLING WEASEL IS FOR YEARS!

AND NOW--WE CAN FIND OUT! SO WHAT'S STOPPING US??

A LITTLE THING CALLED THE LAW, MY FRIEND!

WE'RE NOT POSITIVE WHAT THE SPECIFIC CHARGES AGAINST HIM ARE--

AND EVEN A HELPLESS MASKED MAN HAS HIS RIGHTS!

RIGHTS?!! AT A TIME LIKE THIS?!!

I KNEW IT! YOU'RE A RELIGIOUS FANATIC!!

Panel 4:

ALL THIS WRECKAGE ON THE ROOF.!!

ARE THERE--ANY BODIES--UNDERNEATH?

NOTHIN' BUT RUBBLE, LADY!

THE ONLY ONES THOSE TWO COSTUMED FREAKS HURT WHEN THEY WERE FIGHTING WAS THEM- SELVES!

THEN PETER IS SAFE!

BUT, WHERE IS HE? WHY DID HE VANISH?

2

DAD! THERE'S NO TRACE OF *PETER*-- ANYWHERE!

AND NOBODY KNOWS WHERE HE *WENT!*

C'MON, C'MON-- *MOVE ALONG!* THE PARTY'S *OVER!*

BUGL

DON'T WORRY, DEAR! YOUR MR. PARKER KNOWS HOW TO TAKE CARE OF HIMSELF!

HE'S PROBABLY AT SOME *LAB*, HAVING HIS NEWS PHOTOS *DEVELOPED* RIGHT NOW!

BUT WHY DIDN'T ANYONE *SEE* HIM?

OH, DAD--I *KNOW* I SHOULDN'T GET SO *EMOTIONAL*--

BUT I COULDN'T *BEAR* IT--IF *SOMETHING HAPPENED*-- BEFORE WE HAD A CHANCE TO *MAKE UP!*

NOTHING WILL HAPPEN, GWEN! IF YOU *HEAR* ANYTHING, I'LL BE AT THE *INFIRMARY* WITH SPIDER-MAN! CALL ME THERE!

ULANCE

BIG NEWS, ROBBIE! THE POLICE HAVE *SPIDER-MAN!*

C'MON! WE'VE GOT A *SPECIAL EDITION* TO GET OUT!

I'LL BE RIGHT *WITH* YOU, J.J.!

YOU'RE MIGHTY *LUCKY* YOUR INJURIES AREN'T *WORSE*, MISTER ROBERTSON!

LUCKY, MY *FOOT!*

OL' *JONAH JAMESON* WAS THERE-- LOOKING *AFTER* HIM!

WHAT ABOUT THE *VULTURE?*

DID *HE* GET AWAY?

YEAH! BUT WHO CARES ABOUT *HIM?*

THE *BIG* THING IS--SOMEONE FINALLY STOPPED *SPIDER-MAN!*

EVEN THOUGH THAT BLEEDING-HEART DO-GOODER, *STACY,* STOPPED EVERYONE FROM *UNMASKING* HIM--

IT'S ONLY A MATTER OF *TIME* BEFORE WE LEARN WHO HE REALLY *IS!*

HE *CAN'T* GET AWAY FROM US *AGAIN!*

3

I'M--IN *BED*--IN A BARE ROOM--WITH *BARS* ON THE WINDOW!

I'VE BEEN *CAPTURED* --BY THE *POLICE!*

AND, JUDGING BY THE *SNATCHES* OF *CONVERSATION* I'VE OVERHEARD--THEY WON'T TRY TO *UNMASK* ME--*YET!*

THAT MEANS I CAN LIE HERE AND *RELAX*--WHILE MY *STRENGTH* COMES BACK TO ME!

AND THEN--I'LL HAVE TO FIND SOME WAY-- TO *BREAK OUT!*

C'MON, SPIDEY-*STRENGTH*--DON'T PLAY HARD-TO-GET --WHEN I *NEED* YOU!

THEN, AS THE LONG, LONELY HOURS TICK BY--

NO WORD ABOUT *PARKER* YET, DEAR?

WELL, IT MAY BE NOTHING MORE *MOMENTOUS* THAN A *DATE* WITH ANOTHER *GIRL!*

WHAT'S THAT? NO, GWEN--YOU'D BETTER HAVE DINNER *WITHOUT* ME!

I'D LIKE TO *STAY* HERE IN CASE I'M *NEEDED!*

I *READ* YOU, DADDY MINE!

BUT, IF YOU *CHANGE* YOUR *MIND,* I'M *BAKING* THE MOST *DELICIOUS, DELIGHTFUL, DAZZLINGLY DELECTABLE* LITTLE-- *DAD!*

WHAT WAS THAT FUNNY *NOISE* YOU MADE?

--DAD??

GRAB THAT GUY! HE'S JUST WHAT WE *NEED!*

THE ONLY WAY TO BREAK *OUT* OF HERE IS WITH A *HOSTAGE!*

NOT A *SOUND,* POPS--IF YOU WANNA STAY *HEALTHY!*

DAD! WHAT IS IT??

WE'RE *BLOWIN'* THIS JOINT--'N *YOU'RE* OUR TICKET HOME!

5

IT SOUNDS LIKE--SOME SORT OF A *SCUFFLE!*

DAD! ARE YOU ALL RIGHT! WHY DON'T YOU *ANSWER?* DAD!

I *TOLD* YA OUR BEST BET WAS THRU THE *INFIRMARY!*

YEAH, BUT HOW ABOUT THEM *BRASS BUTTONS* WE HADDA PUT TO SLEEP?

THERE WUZ *TWICE* AS MANY AS WE *EXPECTED!*

I DON'T *LIKE* IT! THERE MUST BE SOMETHIN' GOIN' ON!

BRING THAT GUY TO THE *GATE*--SO THE *GUARD* CAN SEE 'IM!

GUARD?? *WHAT* GUARD? THERE AINT *NO ONE* THERE!

AWRIGHT, AWRIGHT! KEEP YER *SHIRT* ON!--LONG AS WE GOT OURSELVES A *HOSTAGE*, WE CAN AFFORD TO *WAIT!*

NOW THAT WE GOT THIS FAR, AINT *NO ONE* STOPPIN' US FROM HERE ON *IN!*

"NO ONE" DID HE SAY? WE KINDA WONDER IF THAT INCLUDES-- SPIDER-MAN--?

DESPITE ALL MY NUTTY HANG-UPS, THERE'S *ONE* THING I'M *LUCKY* ABOUT--

IT DOESN'T TAKE ME LONG TO GET BACK TO *NORMAL* AFTER I'VE BEEN INJURED!

SAY--WHAT'S ALL THAT COMMOTION IN THE *HALL* OUTSIDE?

SINCE WHEN DO THEY HOLD CONVENTIONS IN PRISON INFIRMARIES?

6

A HANDFUL OF CONS-- TRYING A BREAKOUT!

AND THEY'VE GOT GEORGE STACY AS A HOSTAGE!

NINE TIMES OUT OF TEN I COULD HANDLE A CAPER LIKE THIS WITH MY EYES SHUT--

--BUT NOW--??!

STOP SQUIRMIN', MISTER-- OR WE'LL STOP YA PERMANENT!

I'M RECOVERED FROM MY FALL NOW--BUT MY HEAD'S STILL GROGGY--

IF I TRY TO FREE MR. STACY AND FOUL IT UP--IT COULD COST HIM HIS LIFE!

THEN THERE'S MY SHOULDER! --WHAT IF IT ACTS UP AGAIN?

DO I DARE RISK IT--WITH THE LIFE OF GWEN'S DAD AT STAKE--NOT TO MENTION MY OWN?

WHAT'S THE MATTER WITH ME? I'VE GOT TO RISK IT! I HAVEN'T ANY CHOICE!

I ONCE SWORE NEVER TO TURN MY BACK ON ANYONE AGAIN-- AND I'M NOT STARTING NOW!

7

MY BEST BET IS TO *BLUFF* IT OUT-- MAKE THEM THINK I WANNA THROW *IN* WITH THEM!

IS THAT A *PRIVATE* PARTY, BOYS--OR CAN *ANYONE* JOIN IN?

HEY! IT'S *SPIDER-MAN!*

SO *THAT'S* WHY THEY HAD THEM *EXTRA* GUARDS!

HE WAS HURT IN A *FALL!* HE CAN'T STOP *ALL* OF US NOW!

C'MON--LET'S *JUMP* 'IM, WHILE WE *CAN,*

YOU'VE GOT IT ALL *WRONG,* GROUP!

I WANNA *JOIN* YOU-- NOT *STOP* YOU!

HEY! IF HE *MEANS* IT, WE CAN *USE* A GUY LIKE HIM!

I DON'T *LIKE* IT! HE NEVER HELPED ANY OF US ON THE *OUTSIDE*--

WHY SHOULD HE WANNA HELP US *NOW?*

HELP US? I WOULDN'T *BE* IN HERE IF NOT FOR THAT CRUMMY PUNK!

I SAY WE *POLISH* 'IM OFF-- RIGHT *NOW!*

NUTS! HE MUST BE ONE OF THE *DOZENS* OF PETTY HOODS I'VE PUT ON *ICE* IN THE PAST FEW YEARS!

LET'S *GIT* 'IM-- WHILE HE'S STILL *WEAK!*

HEY-- YOU'RE *RIGHT!*

HE JUST *STOOD* THERE AND *TOOK* IT!

8

DO WHAT YOU *WANT* WITH HIM--IT'S NO SKIN OFF *MY* NOSE!

IF THIS DOESN'T *WORK*, I'LL *JUMP* HIM BEFORE GWEN'S DAD CAN BE *HURT*-- BUT I'M BETTING IT'LL DO THE *TRICK*!

HEY! HE *MEANS* IT! HE DON'T *CARE NOTHIN'* ABOUT THIS GUY!

HE'S TRYING TO *BREAK OUT*-- JUST LIKE *US*!

YEAH! WISE UP! LET 'IM *JOIN* US! WE CAN *USE* A GUY LIKE THAT!

WHEW! IT WAS *CLOSE*-- BUT IT *WORKED!*

AWRIGHT, AWRIGHT-- STOP MAKIN' WITH THE *MUSCLE!*

WE PICKED OURSELVES UP A *HOSTAGE*--AND NOW WE GOT *SPIDER-MAN* ON OUR SIDE!

BUT WE STILL AINT *OUTTA* HERE!

OKAY, SPIDEY-- YOU *COOLED* THE SCENE. NOW WHAT'S YOUR *NEXT* MOVE?

LET'S SEE WHAT *HE'S* GOT TO OFFER--!

GO ON, BIG MAN-- START *TALKIN'!*

THIS IS *IT!* I'VE GOT TO THINK *FAST!*

OKAY, GENTLE- MEN--HERE'S WHAT WE'RE GONNA DO--!

MEANWHILE, AT THAT VERY MOMENT, A DEJECTED *HARRY OSBORN* CONTINUES THE SEARCH FOR HIS MISSING *FATHER*--

HE'S *SICK!* HE CAN'T ROAM THE CITY ALONE! HE NEEDS *HELP!* I'VE *GOT* TO FIND HIM!

MAYBE HE CAME BACK *HERE*-- TO HIS *CLUB*--?

10

11

MAN! YOU'RE JUST A BARREL OF LAUGHS!

HOW DID ROWAN AND MARTIN EVER MAKE IT WITHOUT YOU?

WELL, SAY HELLO TO THE OTHER SWINGERS AT THE FUNERAL HOME!

OKAY, INTERRUPTION-TIME'S OVER! SO, BACK TO THE BLUECOATS--

GET THE RIOT GUNS!

THERE'S A BREAK AT THE INFIRMARY!

THAT'S WHERE SPIDER-MAN IS!

YOU'LL HAVE TO HOLD YOUR FIRE IN THERE! THE WORD JUST CAME THRU--THEY'VE TAKEN CAPTAIN STACY AS A HOSTAGE!

THAT MASKED WALL-CRAWLER'S PROBABLY BEHIND THE WHOLE THING!

BUT DON'T WORRY! WE'LL GET 'IM!

AH, BUT WILL THEY? LET'S SEE--

SO LONG AS GWEN'S DAD IS IN DANGER, I CAN'T DO ANYTHING TO JEOPARDIZE HIS LIFE!

AND I'VE GOT TO THINK OF MYSELF, TOO! IF I DON'T BREAK OUT, THEY'RE SURE TO UNMASK ME SOONER OR LATER!

I MUST ACT AS THOUGH I'M SIDING WITH THE CONS!

FOLLOW ME! I CAN GET YOU OUT BY BREAKING THE BARS WITH MY BARE HANDS!

THEN WHAT'RE WE WAITIN' FOR?

LET'S GO!

I KEEP HOPING THEY'LL RELAX THEIR GRIP ON CAPTAIN STACY--SO I CAN TEAR INTO THEM!

AND, NO MATTER HOW FAST I AM--IF I RUSH THEM ALL--ONE OF THEM IS SURE TO HURT HIM!

BUT SO FAR--IT'S NO SOAP!

SO PLAY IT COOL, SPIDEY--AND WAIT FOR AN OPENING!

THERE'S WHAT WE'RE AFTER! THOSE BARS UP AHEAD--!

12

WHAT GOOD'S *THAT* GONNA DO? WE CAN'T GET UP THAT HIGH!

YOU DON'T *HAVE* TO--!

I'LL FIND US AN *ESCAPE ROUTE* IN THE YARD OUTSIDE--

WHILE YOU GET PAST THE *GUARDS* DOWN THERE BY HOLDING *STACY* IN FRONT OF YOU!

I THINK I *KNOW* WHAT I'VE GOT TO *DO*--

BUT, WHETHER I CAN PULL IT *OFF* OR NOT IS *ANOTHER* MATTER!

THE ONLY WAY TO REALLY *SQUASH* THEIR BREAKOUT-- AND FREE CAPTAIN STACY-- IS TO PICK THEM OFF, *ONE* AT A TIME!

AND MY BEST CHANCE OF GETTING *AWAY* WITH IT IS--TO WORK IN THE *DARK!*

WHICH MEANS I'VE GOT TO MAKE IT TO THE *MASTER FUSE BOX!*

--WHILE THE *CONS* WASTE TIME GETTING THRU THE LOCKED *INFIRMARY GATE!*

OPEN UP 'N LET US *OUT* OR STACY GETS IT--*HERE* AND *NOW!*

WE CAN'T RISK THE CAPTAIN'S *LIFE!*

WE'VE *GOT* TO DO AS THEY SAY!

INFIRMARY

THEY'LL NEVER GET *AWAY* WITH IT, ANYHOW!

13

SO, WE WON'T GIT AWAY WITH IT, HUH?

THEN HE DID THROW IN WITH YOU!

WELL, WE GOT US A LITTLE ACE IN THE HOLE-- BY THE NAME OF SPIDER-MAN!

SURE! WHAT DID YA EXPECT?

I NEVER THOUGHT-- THE WEB-SLINGER-- WOULD DO IT!

THERE'S WHAT I'M LOOKING FOR-- INSIDE THAT ROOM!

NO SHOOTING WHILE STACY'S WITH THEM!

GOOD! THEN I CAN DO IT MY WAY!

WHAT ABOUT SPIDER-MAN? THERE'S NO SIGN OF HIM.

FUNNY YOU SHOULD ASK!

LOOK! ON THE CEIL-ING--!

THWIPPP!

IT'S HIM!

YOU'D NEVER BELIEVE ME IF I TOLD YOU I'M ON YOUR SIDE-- SO I WON'T EVEN TRY!

ANYWAY, YOU'LL BE FREE IN A WHILE-- WHEN THE WEBBING WEARS OFF!

AND, WITH LUCK, THE CONS'LL ALL BE BACK IN THEIR BUNKS BY THEN!

NOW, MY NEXT STEP IS-- SAY! THAT PHONE REMINDS ME--

I HAVEN'T CALLED AUNT MAY IN DAYS! SHE'LL BE WORRIED SICK ABOUT ME!

BETTER GIVE HER A JINGLE NOW-- WHILE I HAVE THE CHANCE!

14

MY FACE MUST *STILL BE* SORE FROM THAT FIGHT WITH THE *VULTURE!*

IT EVEN *HURTS* WHEN I JUST *MOVE* MY MASK!

BUT I *HAVE* TO DO IT!

SHE'D WONDER WHY MY VOICE SOUNDS SO *MUFFLED!*

I'M *FINE*-- BUT I'VE BEEN REAL *BUSY!*

AUNT MAY! THIS IS PETER! FIRST CHANCE I'VE HAD TO *CALL* YOU!

I WAS SO *WORRIED!* WHERE *ARE* YOU?

I, EH, CAN'T *TELL* YOU RIGHT NOW!

YOU'VE NEVER *KEPT* THINGS FROM ME BEFORE! THERE'S SOMETHING *WRONG*--I JUST *KNOW* THERE IS!

WHY WON'T YOU *TELL* ME? WHATEVER IT *IS*--I WANT TO *HELP!*

I NEVER SHOULD HAVE *DONE* IT! SHE'S MORE UPSET THAN *EVER* NOW!

THE LONGER I TALK--THE *WORSE* IT'LL BE!

I HAVE TO *HANG UP* NOW, AUNT MAY! BUT I'LL CALL BACK REAL *SOON!*

PLEASE DON'T WORRY! I PROMISE THAT I'M OKAY! *HONEST!*

I WAS A *FOOL!* IT DIDN'T DO A *BIT* OF GOOD!

THERE'S NO TELLING *WHAT* KIND OF TROUBLE SHE'LL THINK I'M IN!

AND, WITH HER *WEAK HEART*-- SHE *MUSTN'T* WORRY!

THIS TIME I'VE *REALLY DONE* IT!

NOW, MORE THAN *EVER*--I HAVE TO FINISH THIS *FAST*--AND EASE HER MIND SOME- HOW!

TH-WIPP! TH-WIPP!

THAT TAKES CARE OF THE *FUSES!*

NOW I'LL HAVE THE *DARKNESS* THAT I NEED!

15

SECONDS LATER--

RIGHT THIS WAY, GENTS!

WHERE'VE YA BEEN? WHY'D THE LIGHTS GO OUT?

I DID IT!

WE'LL BE HARDER TO FIND IN THE DARK!

THE WEB-SLINGER'S MAKIN' SENSE!

C'MON, LET'S GIT MOVIN'!

I'VE GOT TO LET THEM ALL PASS ME--EXCEPT THE LAST TWO--!

YOU'RE GOIN' FIRST, GRAMPS--JUST IN CASE THERE'S A WELCOMING COMMITTEE WAITIN' FOR US UP AHEAD!

THEY WON'T TRY ANY SHOOTIN' IF THEY KNOW THAT YOU'RE GONNA BE THEIR TARGET!

HEY, WHERE'S THE WALL-CRAWLER?

CAN'T MAKE 'IM OUT HERE IN THE DARK!

BE RIGHT WITH YOU, FRIEND!

16

JUST KEEP *GOING,* GANG! I'VE GOT EVERYTHING *MAPPED OUT* FOR US UP AHEAD!

WAIT! WHAT HAPPENED TO *MACK*--AND *GIMPY?*

WHERE'D THEY CUT OUT TO?

I THOUGHT THEY WERE *RIGHT HERE* WITH *US!*

I DON'T *LIKE* IT!

BETTER GO BACK 'N LOOK FOR 'EM!

THIS BLASTED *DARKNESS* IS GIVIN' ALL OF US THE *SHAKES!*

THEN, AFTER A FEW TENSE *MINUTES* PASS BY--

NO USE! THERE AINT A *SIGN* OF 'EM!

WHAT ABOUT *SPIDER-MAN!* HE'S SUPPOSED TO BE *LEADIN'* US!

THERE'S SOMETHIN' *FISHY* GOIN' ON HERE!

AND I'M GONNA FIND OUT WHAT IT *IS!*

HEY! WHAT WAS *THAT?*

JUST TRYING TO ANSWER HIS *QUESTION,* THAT'S ALL!

17

AND, SINCE *YOU* WERE NICE ENOUGH TO ASK--

THE *LEAST* I CAN DO IS *OBLIGE!*

FOUR DOWN-- *TWO* TO *GO!*

FIVE DOWN-- *ONE* TO GO!

THE *TOUGHEST* ONE!

SO LONG AS THE *LIGHTS* STAY OUT, MY *SPIDER SENSE* GIVES *ME* THE ADVANTAGE!

BUT I DON'T WANT CAPTAIN STACY *HURT!*

WHERE IS EVERYONE?

WHAT'S GOIN' ON HERE?

DUKE! RED! THE REST OF YA-- *SAY* SOMETHIN'

PERFECT TIMING! THE AUXILIARY GENERATORS HAVE THE *SPOTLIGHTS* WORKING AGAIN!

THEY'RE ALL *WEBBED-UP!*

SPIDER-MAN *DOUBLE-CROSSED* US!

I'M *WARNIN'* YA! NO ONE'S TAKIN' ME *ALIVE!*

IF I DON'T *MAKE* IT, THEN *NEITHER* DOES *HE!*

SO GIT THEM *GATES* OPEN-- 'CAUSE I'M COMIN' *THRU!*-- OR ELSE WE BOTH GET IT-- *TOGETHER!*

HE'S ALL *WORKED* UP --*DESPERATE*-- ON THE VERGE OF *PANIC!*

IT'S *NOW*-- OR *NEVER!*

THUPPP!

MOVE, CAPTAIN! PITCH YOURSELF FORWARD OUT OF HIS REACH!

ARHHH--!

YOU GRABBED FOR THE WEBBING-- JUST AS I HOPED YOU WOULD!

IT WAS MIGHTY COOPERATIVE OF YOU!

DON'T WORRY, CAPTAIN-- I'LL HAVE YOU UNTIED IN NO TIME!

I'M GRATEFUL TO YOU, SPIDER-MAN! I NEVER REALLY BELIEVED YOU'D THROW IN WITH THEIR KIND!

YOU MAY BE CERTAIN THAT I'LL TESTIFY IN YOUR BEHALF WHEN THE TIME COMES!

IN MY BEHALF? YOU MEAN-- YOU EXPECT ME TO STAY HERE--AS A PRISONER--TILL I COME TO TRIAL?

OF COURSE! YOU'VE DONE NOTHING WRONG--IT'S YOUR CHANCE TO CLEAR YOURSELF!

CAN'T DO IT! THEY MIGHT DECIDE TO UNMASK ME!

WHAT IF THEY DO? IF YOU'RE NOT A CRIMINAL, WHY HIDE YOUR IDENTITY?

BECAUSE OF AUNT MAY,--BUT I CAN'T TELL HIM THAT!

19

LOOK! IT'S ALL OVER!

CAPTAIN STACY! ARE YOU ALL RIGHT?

LUCKILY, I AM! THANKS TO SPIDER-MAN!

SPIDER-MAN? BUT, HE ESCAPED! HE'S A FUGITIVE!

PERHAPS-- BUT THAT DOESN'T ALTER THE FACTS--

BECAUSE OF HIM, THE JAILBREAK WAS FOILED--

--AND I STAND BEFORE YOU-- UNHARMED!

MINUTES LATER, AT THE OFFICE OF THE DEPUTY COMMISSIONER--

SAY IT ISN'T SO! TELL ME IT NEVER HAPPENED!

THAT WEASELLY WALL-CRAWLER DIDN'T GET AWAY AGAIN!?

LET'S JUST SAY YOU CAN'T WIN THEM ALL, JONAH!

HE DID SMASH A JAIL-BREAK, YOU KNOW!

SMASH IT? HE PROBABLY STARTED IT-- JUST TO TAKE THE HEAT OFF HIM!

BUT HE WOULDN'T HAVE ESCAPED IF I HAD BEEN THERE!

THAT SO? HOW WOULD YOU HAVE MANAGED TO STOP HIM?

'CAUSE I'M SMARTER THAN HE IS, THAT'S HOW!

NO MORONIC, MASKED MEATHEAD LIKE SPIDER-MAN CAN GET THE BEST OF J. JONAH JAMESON!

HE COULD NEVER HIDE FROM ME-- AND HE KNOWS IT!

RAVE ON, CHUCKLES! LIFE WOULD BE A BED OF ROSES IF YOU WERE MY ONLY HANG-UP!

NOW, BEFORE IT TOO LATE-- I'VE GOT TO SEE AUNT MAY.

BUT-- WHAT AM I GOING TO SAY TO HER?

NEXT--

MYSTERIO